Foundations and Slopes

An introduction to applications of
critical state soil mechanics

J. H. ATKINSON

*Reader in Soil Mechanics and Head of the Division of Geotechnical Engineering,
The City University, London*

McGRAW-HILL Book Company (UK) Limited

London · New York · St Louis · San Francisco · Auckland · Bogotá · Guatemala
Hamburg · Johannesburg · Lisbon · Madrid · Mexico · Montreal · New Delhi
Panama · Paris · San Juan · São Paulo · Singapore · Sydney · Tokyo · Toronto

Published by

McGRAW–HILL Book Company (UK) Limited

MAIDENHEAD · BERKSHIRE · ENGLAND

00300 8843

British Library Cataloguing in Publication Data

Atkinson, J H
    Foundations and slopes. – (University series in
    civil engineering).
    1. Soil mechanics
    I. Title   II. Series
    624′.1513   TA710   80-40871
    ISBN 0-07-084118-7

12345 AP 84321

Printed and bound in Great Britain by the Alden Press, Oxford.

D
624.1513
ATK

CONTENTS

Consulting editor's foreword ix

Preface xi

A note on units xiii

Glossary of symbols xiv

1. Stress, Strain, Elasticity, and Plasticity

1.1 Introduction 1
1.2 Stress, strain, and effective stress 2
1.3 Analysis of deformation and strain 4
1.4 Analysis of states of stress 11
1.5 Relationships between stress and strain 14
1.6 Elastic and plastic deformations 16
1.7 Yielding, hardening, and plastic flow 17
1.8 Ideal elastic behaviour 22
1.9 Elasto-plastic behaviour 23
1.10 Equilibrium and compatibility 25
1.11 Relationships between stress and strain for plane strain 27
     References 29

2. An Introduction to the Mechanics of Soils

2.1 Introduction 30
2.2 Drained and undrained loading 31
2.3 The state boundary surface 32
2.4 Yielding and hardening 42
2.5 Failure of soil 48
2.6 Elastic stress–strain relationships 53
2.7 Elasto-plastic stress–strain relationships 56
2.8 Failure and plastic flow at the critical state 59
2.9 Residual strength 66
2.10 Anisotropic compression 68
2.11 Summary 70
     References 72
     Worked examples 72

v

3. Natural Soils in Foundations and Slopes

3.1	Introduction	83
3.2	Formation of natural soils	83
3.3	States of stress in the ground	85
3.4	Overconsolidation of natural soils	90
3.5	Profiles of water content and strength for natural soils	91
3.6	Loading of soil in foundations and slopes	95
3.7	Investigations, sampling, and testing	99
3.8	Analysis of soil structures	101
3.9	Selection of strength parameters for design	104
3.10	Factor of safety	105
	References	106
	Worked examples	106

4. Theorems of Plastic Collapse and their Application to Soil Structures

4.1	Introduction	109
4.2	Principle of virtual work	109
4.3	Theorems of plastic collapse	111
4.4	Use of bound theorems for the collapse of a beam	114
4.5	Failure criteria for soils	116
4.6	Mechanisms for plane plastic collapse	118
4.7	Increments of work done during plastic collapse	122
4.8	Displacement diagrams	125
4.9	Slip fans	126
4.10	Discontinuous stress states	130
4.11	Stress fans	135
4.12	α and β discontinuities	141
4.13	Summary	143
	References	145

5. Undrained Stability of Soil Structures

5.1	Introduction	146
5.2	Bound calculations for undrained loading	148
5.3	Undrained stability of cuts and slopes	149
5.4	Undrained stability of a smooth retaining wall	158
5.5	Undrained stability of a foundation	164
5.6	Undrained stability of a rough retaining wall	177
5.7	Effect of external water pressures	180
5.8	Discussion	185
	References	185
	Worked examples	185

6. Drained Stability of Soil Structures

6.1 Introduction 194
6.2 Bound calculations for drained loading 195
6.3 Stability of slopes in dry soil 197
6.4 Drained stability of a smooth wall 202
6.5 Drained stability of a foundation 208
6.6 Bound calculations for saturated soil 225
6.7 Drained stability of a rough retaining wall 232
6.8 Discussion 236
References 237
Worked examples 237

7. Associated Fields and Slip Line Methods

7.1 Introduction 247
7.2 Relationships between stress and strain in a perfectly plastic material
at failure 247
7.3 Stress field calculations for undrained loading 253
7.4 Stress field calculations for drained loading 256
7.5 Displacement field calculations 258
7.6 Associated fields calculations 261
7.7 Slip line sketching for undrained loading 262
7.8 Slip line solutions for undrained loading 264
7.9 Slip line sketching for drained loading 269
7.10 Slip line solutions for drained loading 272
7.11 Discussion 278
References 279
Worked examples 279

8. The Limit Equilibrium Method

8.1 Introduction 286
8.2 The theory of the limit equilibrium method 286
8.3 Limit equilibrium solutions for retaining walls 287
8.4 Graphical methods for limit equilibrium calculations 291
8.5 The slip circle method for undrained loading 297
8.6 The slip circle method for drained loading – the method of slices 301
8.7 General limit equilibrium solutions 307
8.8 Factor of safety 309
8.9 Discussion 310
References 310
Worked examples 311

9. Routine Methods for Stability Calculations

9.1	Introduction	319
9.2	Bearing capacity factors for undrained loading	320
9.3	Stability numbers for undrained loading	322
9.4	Earth pressure coefficients for undrained loading	324
9.5	Bearing capacity factors for drained loading	325
9.6	Stability numbers for drained loading	328
✗ 9.7	Earth pressure coefficients for drained loading	329
9.8	Discussion ✓	331
	References	331
	Worked examples	331

10. Settlement of Foundations

10.1	Introduction	335
10.2	Drained and undrained loading of foundations	335
10.3	States of stress in elastic soil	339
10.4	Standard solutions for foundations on elastic soil	343
10.5	Influence factors for stress and displacement	349
10.6	One-dimensional loading of elastic soil	354
10.7	Consolidation settlements	355
10.8	Rate of consolidation of foundations	359
10.9	Stress path methods	363
	References	365
	Worked examples	366

11. Concluding Remarks   372

Index   375

CONSULTING EDITORS' FOREWORD

McGraw-Hill's *University Series in Civil Engineering* has been planned to make available to students and lecturers a number of textbooks that reflect the philosophy of the Consulting Editors and the Company, namely that the emphasis of engineering degree courses should be on the fundamental principles. Therefore the primary aim of the books in the series is to develop a sound understanding of the subject matters and an ability to apply the relevant scientific principles to the solution of engineering problems. Where familiarity with a Code of Practice or an empirical method is desirable, the technical background is explained, so that the student understands the *why* as well as the *what* and the *how* of the subject.

Dr Atkinson's *Foundations and Slopes* aims to convey a fundamental understanding of the behaviour of soil structures encountered in geotechnical engineering. Emphasizing the underlying principles and the unifying concepts, it welds together the ideas of critical states, elasticity, plasticity, and Mohr–Coulomb and Hvorslev failure criteria. The contents include a clear exposition of the powerful theorems of plastic theory, which provide the engineer with a simple tool for the rapid calculation of a set of numbers, which are the so-called lower-bound and upper-bound solutions. Engineers will in time appreciate the value and relevance of this simple but powerful technique of establishing bounds. *Foundations and Slopes* provides a link between theories and real soils and real problems; it is a useful companion volume to Atkinson and Bransby's *The Mechanics of Soils* published earlier by McGraw-Hill.

The Consulting Editors wish to thank their colleagues in the universities and industry for their valuable advice concerning the development of the series; the initiative and foresight of McGraw-Hill's former Editor Ian Pringle have contributed much to its successful launching. In particular, they wish to record the exemplary care and attention devoted to the Series by McGraw-Hill's Editor John M. W. Smith and his predecessor David Roberts.

F. K. KONG and R. H. EVANS

PREFACE

This book is about the behaviour of slopes, foundations and retaining walls and it deals with the theories behind many routine geotechnical engineering calculations. It develops the ideas of *critical state soil mechanics* to include simple engineering calculations and the work follows on from that covered in *The Mechanics of Soils* by J. H. Atkinson and P. L. Bransby (McGraw-Hill, 1978). The book is aimed primarily at students taking first degree courses in civil engineering in universities and polytechnics, but it may appeal also to postgraduate students and practising engineers wishing for a simple introduction to the common geotechnical engineering calculations and to the applications of critical state soil mechanics theories.

In practice many routine calculations in geotechnical engineering are assisted by the use of charts and tables and by the use of established computer programs. Thus, for the capacity of foundations there are bearing capacity factors and for the stresses in the ground below foundations there are various influence factors, while the finite element method is now widely used in geotechnical engineering. Clearly, care must be taken to see that these tables, charts, and computer programs are correctly applied and to do this the engineer must properly understand the basic theories and methods from which the tables, charts, and computer programs were prepared. Furthermore, if the basic theories and methods are understood they may be used to analyse problems for which tables and charts do not exist. Certainly, knowledge of the basic theories from which tables and charts were prepared illuminates the approximations involved in many of the routine design calculations. All the methods of analysis discussed here are relatively simple and most are amenable to hand calculation. In many cases the solutions obtained are approximate, but since the uncertainties involved are often no worse than those in determining the engineering properties of natural soils they are generally sufficient for practical engineering purposes.

The arrangement of the material differs from that usually found in texts on soil mechanics and foundation engineering. Since the book is concerned with theories and with methods of calculation the chapters are arranged accordingly, so that a chapter on a particular method of analysis will contain calculations for slopes, retaining walls, and foundations. Another departure from conventional texts in this book is that a clear distinction is made between drained loading on the one hand and undrained loading on the other, and different methods of analysis are developed for each kind of loading. Thus analyses in terms of total stresses for undrained loading are discussed quite separately from analyses in terms of effective stresses for drained loading.

Chapters 1 and 2 deal with the mechanical behaviour of soils and these chapters summarize the material covered in *The Mechanics of Soils*. Chapter 3 examines the occurrence of natural soils and the states of stress in the ground. Chapter 4 covers theories of plastic collapse, and in Chapters 5–8 these theories are applied to the stability of slopes, retaining walls, and foundations. Much of the work on associated fields and slip line methods in Chapter 7 is unavoidably mathematical and is beyond the scope of most undergraduate courses in civil engineering. It should, however, appeal to postgraduate students and to engineers who wish for an introduction to some of the more advanced applications of plasticity theory in soil engineering. Chapter 9 covers the use of charts and tables for stability calculations and Chapter 10 deals with methods for estimating the settlement of foundations. The book closes with Chapter 11 which, very briefly, draws together the various methods of analysis.

Much of the material in this book is based on my lectures on soil mechanics and geotechnical engineering to undergraduate and postgraduate students in Civil and Structural Engineering at University College, Cardiff, but I hope it is made clear that most of the ideas and theories discussed are attributable to others. Much of the research which led to the theories of critical state soil mechanics and to the applications of plasticity theory in geotechnical engineering was carried out by others and particularly by the late Professor K. H. Roscoe and his students, colleagues, and successors in the University Engineering Department, Cambridge. I am indebted to all those at Cambridge, at Imperial College, at Cardiff, and elsewhere with whom I have discussed these ideas and who have helped my understanding of the behaviour of soil structures. I am particularly grateful to Dr P. L. Bransby, Dr R. H. G. Parry and Dr N. J. Naylor for reading and criticizing parts of the book and to Moira Owen for typing my manuscript.

March 1980

J. H. Atkinson

The picture on the front cover of this book is a print taken from an X-ray plate of an experimental wall retaining dense sand in a state of passive failure. Dense sand dilates as it shears and the darker regions on the print, representing looser sand, show slip planes and a fan zone. The light discs on the print are due to lead shot embedded in the sand and they are used to measure displacements which occur during an experiment. The original X-ray plate was obtained by Dr R. H. Bassett at Cambridge University, and the print is reproduced here with his kind permission.

A NOTE ON UNITS

The SI system of units is used throughout this book. The basic units of measurements are:

$$\text{length} \quad \text{m} \quad \text{(metre)}$$

$$\text{time} \quad \text{s} \quad \text{(second)}$$

$$\text{force} \quad \text{N} \quad \text{(newton)}$$

Multiples:

$$\text{kilo} = 10^3, \text{e.g. kilonewton, } 1 \text{ kN} = 10^3 \text{ N}$$

$$\text{mega} = 10^6, \text{e.g. meganewton, } 1 \text{ MN} = 10^6 \text{ N}$$

Some useful derived units are:

$$\text{velocity} \quad \text{m s}^{-1}$$

$$\text{acceleration} \quad \text{m s}^{-2}$$

$$\text{stress or pressure} \quad \text{kN m}^{-2}$$

$$\text{unit weight} \quad \text{kN m}^{-3}$$

Unit force (1 N) gives unit mass (1 kg) unit acceleration (1 m s^{-2}). The acceleration due to earth's gravity is $g = 9.81$ m s^{-2}; hence, the force due to a mass of 1 kg at rest on Earth is 9.81 N.

Conversion from imperial units:

$$1 \text{ ft} = 0.3048 \text{ m}$$

$$1 \text{ lbf} = 4.448 \text{ N}$$

$$1 \text{ lbf in}^{-2} = 6.895 \text{ kN m}^{-2}$$

$$1 \text{ lbf ft}^{-3} = 0.157 \text{ kN m}^{-3}$$

GLOSSARY OF SYMBOLS

A	area
A, B	Skempton's pore pressure parameters
B	width or breadth
$[C']$	compliance matrix
E	work done by external forces
E'	Young's modulus for effective stresses
E_u	Young's modulus for undrained loading
F	flow parameter
F	force, foundation load
F_s	factor of safety
G'	shear modulus for effective stresses
G_u	shear modulus for undrained loading
G_s	specific gravity of soil grains
G, J	bearing capacity factors
G, H	hardening parameters
H	height, thickness, depth
H	drainage path
H	slope of constant volume section of Hvorslev surface
K'	bulk modulus for effective stresses
K_u	bulk modulus for undrained loading
K_0	coefficient of earth pressure at rest
K_a	coefficient of active earth pressure
K_p	coefficient of passive earth pressure
I_σ	influence factor for stress
I_ρ	influence factor for settlement
L	length
M, N	bearing capacity factors
$\left.\begin{array}{c} N_c \\ N_\gamma \\ N_q \end{array}\right\}$	bearing capacity factors
N_s	stability number
N	normal force on a retaining wall
P	load on a wall
P_w	force due to free water pressures
R	radius
R_0	overconsolidation ratio for one dimensional compression
R_p	overconsolidation radio for isotropic compression

T_v	time factor
U	upthrust
U	force due to pore pressures
U_t	degree of consolidation
V	velocity
V	volume
V	shear force on retaining wall
V_s	volume occupied by mineral grains
W	weight
W	work done by internal stresses
a	radius or half width of a foundation
a, b	pore pressure parameters
a	(subscript) axial, active, allowable
b	breadth
c_c	compression index
c_s	swelling index
c'	cohesion
c'_h	Hvorslev cohesion
c_u	undrained shear strength
c_{ur}	residual undrained shear strength
c_v	coefficient of consolidation for vertical flow
c_h	coefficient of consolidation for horizontal flow
c	(subscript) triaxial compression
c	(subscript) collapse
c_w	shear stress on retaining wall
d	differential operator
e	(subscript) triaxial extension
e	(superscript) elastic
f	(subscript) failure
h	height of water in a standpipe
h	horizontal displacement
h	(subscript) horizontal
i_s	hydraulic gradient
i	slope angle
k	coefficient of permeability
l	length
l	(subscript) lower bound
ln	natural logarithm
m_v	coefficient of compressibility for 1-D compression
m, n	stability numbers
n	(subscript) normal
n	number of discontinuities
p'	$= \frac{1}{3}(\sigma'_1 + \sigma'_2 + \sigma'_3)$

p_f'	value of p' at failure
p	(superscript) plastic
ps	(subscript) plane strain
p	$= \frac{1}{3}(\sigma_1 + 2\sigma_3)$ ⎫
q	$= (\sigma_1 - \sigma_3)$ ⎬ stress parameters for $\sigma_2 = \sigma_3$
p'	$= \frac{1}{3}(\sigma_1' + 2\sigma_3')$ ⎭
q'	$= (\sigma_1' - \sigma_3')$
q_f'	value of q' at failure
q	bearing pressure of a foundation
r	radius
r	(subscript) residual, radial
r_u	pore pressure parameter
s	length along a flowline
s	$= \frac{1}{2}(\sigma_1 + \sigma_3)$ ⎫
t	$= \frac{1}{2}(\sigma_1 - \sigma_3)$ ⎬ stress parameters for plane strain
s'	$= \frac{1}{2}(\sigma_1' + \sigma_3')$ ⎭
t'	$= \frac{1}{2}(\sigma_1' - \sigma_3')$
t	time
u	displacement
u	pore pressure
u_0	steady state pore pressure
$\bar{u}$	excess pore pressure
u	(subscript) upper bound
u	(subscript) undrained
u_f	value of u at failure
v	vertical displacement
v	(subscript) vertical
v	specific volume
v_f	value of v at failure
v_κ	value of v for overconsolidated soil at $p' = 1.0$ kN/m²
w	water content
w	displacement
x ⎫	
y ⎬	coordinate axes : z vertical
z ⎭	
z	depth below ground surface
$'$	effective stress (e.g. σ')
Γ	specific volume of soil at the critical state with $p' = 1.0$ kN/m²
Δ	large increment of
M	slope of critical state line
N	specific volume of soil compressed isotropically to $p' = 1.0$ kN/m²
P	$= (90° - \delta\theta)$
Σ	sum of

α, β	labels for discontinuities, slip lines and characteristics
α	$= (45° + \frac{1}{2}\phi'_{cs})$ angle defining planes with $\tau'_n = \sigma'_n \tan \phi'_{cs}$
β	$= (45° + \frac{1}{2}\psi)$ angle defining directions of zero strain increment
γ	angle
γ	engineer's shear strain
γ_n	shear strain on plane with $\epsilon_n = 0$
γ	unit weight
γ_w	unit weight of water
∂	partial differential operator
δ	small increment of
ϵ	strain
ϵ_v	$= (\epsilon_1 + \epsilon_2 + \epsilon_3)$ volumetric strain
ϵ_s	$= \frac{2}{3}(\epsilon_1 - \epsilon_3)$ shear strain for $\epsilon_2 = \epsilon_3$
ϵ_γ	$= (\epsilon_1 - \epsilon_3)$ shear strain for plane strain
η	angle defining directions of σ'_1 and $\delta\epsilon_1$
η'	$= q'/p'$
η'_0	value of η' for one-dimensional compression
θ	angle
θ	angle defining direction of a characteristic
θ_f	fan angle
κ	slope of overconsolidation line
λ	slope of normal consolidation line
μ	$= (90° - \psi)$ angle between slip planes
ν'	Poisson's ratio for effective stresses
ν_u	$= 0.5$ Poisson's ratio for undrained loading
ρ'	angle of shearing resistance
ρ	settlement
ρ_i	initial settlement
ρ_c	consolidation settlement
σ	stress
σ_n	normal stress
σ'_s	seepage stress
σ_w	stress due to free water
τ	shear stress
τ_n	shear stress on plane normal to σ_n
τ_w	shear stress on a retaining wall
ϕ'	angle of friction
ϕ'_{cs}	critical state angle of friction
ϕ'_h	Hvorslev friction angle
ϕ'_w	angle of wall friction
ψ	angle of dilation
ψ_p	angle of dilation for plastic strains

ONE

STRESS, STRAIN, ELASTICITY, AND PLASTICITY

1.1 INTRODUCTION

Civil engineering is concerned with the use of engineering materials, such as steel, concrete, soil, and rock, for the provision of structures, services, communications, and power. A branch of civil engineering is *geotechnical engineering*, which deals with the use of natural geological materials (i.e. soil and rock) in civil engineering. Soil may be undisturbed in a foundation or it may be excavated and recompacted into an earth bank; loads may increase as foundations are loaded or decrease as excavations are made but, in any case, engineers must do calculations which demonstrate the safety and serviceability of any new construction.

Calculations such as these require physical theories for the mechanical behaviour of the materials involved, and such a representation of material behaviour is often known as a *model*. It should be understood that use of the word 'model' in this context does not imply a physical representation in the sense of a scale model and a model may be simply a conceptual idea or a number of mathematical equations. Thus the idea of a continuum is a conceptual model, a linear spring is a physical model for uniaxial extension of steel in the elastic range, and Hooke's law is a mathematical model for elastic materials. It will be appreciated at once that such models are, in general, approximations to the true behaviour of materials. Accuracy may often be improved, but usually at the expense of simplicity. A satisfactory model for material behaviour will be a compromise between accuracy and simplicity, but it will need to be useful for engineering purposes.

For engineering calculations, mathematical models for material behaviour will be required and these must include relationships between stresses and strains and changes of stress and strain. Some familiar models for material behaviour are the theories of elasticity, plasticity, viscosity, fracture, and friction and the most suitable model must be chosen for the particular material in question and also for the particular circumstances of the problem. The choice of model may depend on the circumstances; thus for steel, for example, it would be appropriate to use the theory of plasticity for large strain problems of rolling and forming, while the theory of elasticity would be relevant for analysis of the small deflections of structures.

For soils the relevant mathematical models are based on the theories of elasticity, plasticity, and friction and these may be combined into a single framework

1

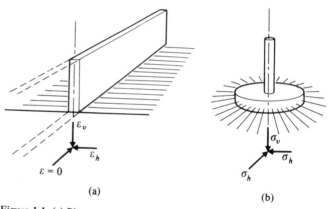

Figure 1.1 (a) Plane strain. (b) Axial symmetry.

known as the *critical state model*. The critical state model is described in detail elsewhere (Schofield and Wroth, 1968; Atkinson and Bransby, 1978) and briefly in Chapter 3 of this book. First, however, in this chapter, we introduce the essential features of the theories of elasticity and plasticity and also define some parameters for stress and strain.

1.2 STRESS, STRAIN, AND EFFECTIVE STRESS

Many problems in geotechnical engineering may be approximated either to *plane strain* or to *axial symmetry* without serious error. Plane strain means that in one direction — usually a horizontal direction — a principal strain is zero. Thus in the case of the foundation of a long wall or a long embankment, strains in the direction of the length of the wall or embankment will approximate to zero, as illustrated in Fig. 1.1(a). Axial symmetry means that all stresses and strains remain constant with rotation about the axis of symmetry, which is usually vertical. Thus in the case of a small circular foundation, all radial stresses and strains at a given radius and depth will be equal as illustrated in Fig. 1.1(b). There is a special case of axial symmetry for which $\sigma'_2 = \sigma'_3$ and $\delta\epsilon_2 = \delta\epsilon_3$ and this is assumed in a solid cylinder, whereas in a hollow cylinder, for example, the states of stress and strain are axially symmetric but, in general, $\sigma'_2 \neq \sigma'_3$ and $\delta\epsilon_2 \neq \delta\epsilon_3$. In this book we will only be concerned with solid cylinders of soil in triaxial tests and below small foundations, and hence we will only be concerned with the special case of axial symmetry for which $\sigma'_2 = \sigma'_3$ and $\delta\epsilon_2 = \delta\epsilon_3$.

Plane strain is a common assumption in geotechnical engineering and it is the case for which many routine solutions apply. For much of this book we will consider the case of plane strain and we will consider the conditions in a slice of soil of unit thickness cut normal to the axis of zero strain.

Figure 1.2 illustrates normal and shear stresses and strains in an element in the

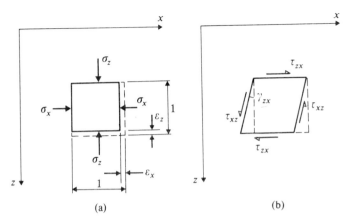

Figure 1.2 Positive stresses and strains. (a) Normal stress and normal strain. (b) Shear stress and shear strain.

$x:z$ plane, where the z axis is positive downwards so that z and σ_z increase with depth. Following the usual conventions for soil mechanics, stress and strain are defined so that compressive stresses and strains are positive quantities. Thus Fig. 1.2(a) illustrates positive normal stress σ and normal strain ϵ and Fig. 1.2(b) illustrates positive shear stress τ and shear strain γ.

Soil consists of an aggregate of mineral grains with a fluid filling the pore spaces. The fluid may be water or gas, usually air, or a combination of air and water. If the pore fluid is air alone then the soil is *dry* and if the pore fluid is water alone then the soil is *saturated* and throughout this book we will consider only dry or saturated soils. The stresses shown in Fig. 1.2 act on the boundaries of the elements, and they are resisted in part by stresses in the mineral grains and in part by pressures in the pore fluid. Such stresses, which act on the boundaries of elements, are known as *total stresses* and the pressures in the pore fluid are known as *pore pressures*.

During loading, both total stresses and pore pressures may change and it is intuitively obvious that the behaviour of a soil will depend on some combination of the total stress σ and the pore pressure u. This special combination of σ and u is known as the *effective stress* and is given the symbol σ'. The way in which the effective stress σ' controls soil behaviour is described by the principle of effective stress.

The principle of effective stress, as stated by Terzaghi (1936), is an essential feature of soil mechanics. The *effective stress* σ' is related to the total stress σ and to the pore pressure u by the simple equation

$$\sigma' = \sigma - u \tag{1.1}$$

and the principle of effective stress states that all measurable *effects* of a change of stress, such as compression, distortion, and a change of shearing resistance, are due exclusively to changes of *effective stress*. This is really all that needs to be said

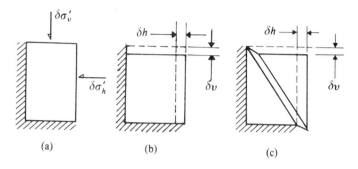

Figure 1.3 Modes of deformation. (a) Stresses on a plane element. (b) Continuous straining. (c) Discontinuous slipping.

about the principle of effective stress, but for a more detailed discussion the reader may refer to Atkinson and Bransby (1978, Chapter 2). The essential point is that, since in geotechnical engineering we are concerned with deformations and failure, we must conduct calculations in terms of effective, not total, stress; consequently, mathematical models for soil behaviour must be written in terms of effective stress.

As water flows into or from an element of soil it swells or compresses as the volume of the element changes, although of course the quantity of soil grains remains the same. In order to describe the volume of a soil sample, it is convenient to define a *specific volume* v as the ratio of the total volume V to the volume V_s occupied by the mineral grains and

$$v = \frac{V}{V_s} \tag{1.2}$$

If the water content of a soil sample is w and its unit weight is γ then

$$v = \frac{1 + w}{1 + w - w(\gamma/\gamma_w)} \tag{1.3}$$

where $\gamma_w = 9.81\,\text{kN/m}^3$ is the unit weight of water. Values for w and γ may be found by simple measurement of soil samples and the specific volume found easily.

1.3 ANALYSIS OF DEFORMATION AND STRAIN

Materials may deform in one of two basic modes; they may deform by *continuous*†
straining or by *discontinuous slipping*. Figure 1.3(a) shows a plane element subjected to increments $\delta\sigma_v'$ and $\delta\sigma_h'$ of vertical and horizontal effective stress which

---

† The word *continuous* here and throughout this book means that strains vary *smoothly* throughout the material and there are no *discontinuities* in the strains. It does not imply continuity with respect to time and the finite increments of displacement δh and δv in Fig. 1.3 may happen instantaneously or during any time interval.

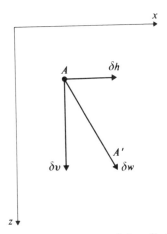

Figure 1.4 Increments of plane displacement.

cause small changes δv and δh of the vertical and horizontal dimensions of the sample. Figure 1.3(b) illustrates continuous straining; there are no discontinuities in the element and the behaviour of each and every part of the element is the same. Figure 1.3(c) illustrates an example of discontinuous slipping on a narrow zone of intense shearing passing through the element; strains in the triangular blocks either side of the narrow slip zone are negligible and all deformations are due to very large strains within the slip zone. In the limit when the narrow zone has zero thickness it becomes a *slip plane*; by convention, any narrow zone of discontinuous slipping is known as a slip plane, although it may have finite thickness. Of course, in practice, continuous strain and discontinuous slipping often occur simultaneously but usually one or other mode of deformation predominates and it is convenient to regard an increment of deformation as being due either to continuous straining or to discontinuous slipping along a narrow slip plane.

Figure 1.4 shows part of a plane section which suffers an increment of strain such that a point initially at A moves through a small distance δw to A' where δw has components δh and δv as shown. Increments of normal strain $\delta \epsilon_x$ and $\delta \epsilon_z$ and of shear strain $\delta \epsilon_{xz} = \delta \epsilon_{zx}$ are given by

$$\delta \epsilon_x = -\frac{\partial (\delta h)}{\partial x} \tag{1.4}$$

$$\delta \epsilon_z = -\frac{\partial (\delta v)}{\partial z} \tag{1.5}$$

$$\delta \epsilon_{xz} = -\frac{1}{2} \left[\frac{\partial (\delta v)}{\partial x} + \frac{\partial (\delta h)}{\partial z} \right] \tag{1.6}$$

In Eq. (1.6) ϵ_{xz} is known as a *shear strain* and is related to the *engineer's shear strain* γ_{xz} by

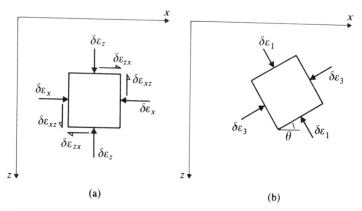

Figure 1.5 Increments of strain.

$$\delta\gamma_{xz} = 2\delta\epsilon_{xz} = -\left[\frac{\partial(\delta v)}{\partial x} + \frac{\partial(\delta h)}{\partial z}\right] \tag{1.7}$$

Thus the engineer's shear strain gives a measure of the change of angle between two initially orthogonal fibres embedded in the plane.

A simple method of analysis for small strains is to make use of the Mohr's circle of strain in the same way that the Mohr's circle of stress is used to analyse a state of stress. Strain analysis must be carried out in terms of the shear strain ϵ_{xz} but it is more convenient, and conventional, to work with engineer's shear strain. Thus, for an increment of strain, the Mohr's circle will be plotted with axes $\frac{1}{2}\delta\gamma$ and $\delta\epsilon$.

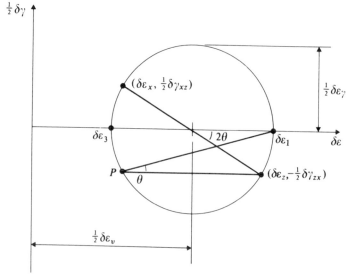

Figure 1.6 Mohr's circle of plane strain corresponding to the increments of strain in Fig. 1.5.

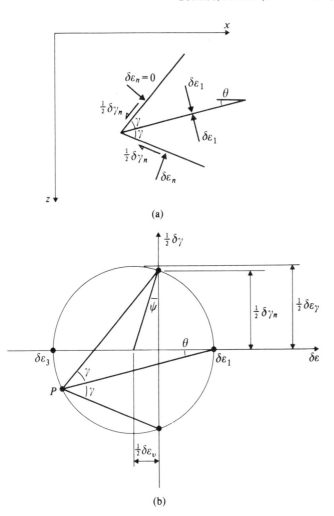

Figure 1.7 Planes of zero strain increment.

Figure 1.5(a) illustrates increments of strain $\delta\epsilon_x$, $\delta\epsilon_z$, and $\delta\epsilon_{xz} = \delta\epsilon_{zx} = \frac{1}{2}\delta\gamma_{xz} = \frac{1}{2}\delta\gamma_{zx}$ in a plane element. For convenience, we consider the case of plane strain where strains normal to the page are zero and, noting the choice of axes, Fig. 1.5(a) shows positive straining. The Mohr's circle of strain corresponding to the state of strain in Fig. 1.5(a) is shown in Fig. 1.6, in which counterclockwise shear strains γ_{xz} are positive. The pole of planes is at P and hence, or otherwise, increments or principal strain $\delta\epsilon_1$ and $\delta\epsilon_3$ occur normal to principal planes, which are the faces of an element rotated through an angle θ, as shown in Fig. 1.5(b). The Mohr's circle in Fig. 1.6 represents an increment of strain in which both major and minor principal strains are positive and compressive. A more usual case is shown in Fig. 1.7, where the increment of minor principal strain is negative and tensile. Furthermore, in Fig. 1.7(b) the value of $\delta\epsilon_3$ is numerically greater than the value of $\delta\epsilon_1$, and the centre of the Mohr's circle lies to the left of the origin of axes.

A Mohr's circle of strain may be defined by two principal strain increments $\delta\epsilon_1$ and $\delta\epsilon_3$ and the relative magnitudes of the normal and shear strains may be represented by an *angle of dilation* ψ, as shown in Fig. 1.7(b), where

$$\sin\psi = -\frac{(\delta\epsilon_1 + \delta\epsilon_3)}{(\delta\epsilon_1 - \delta\epsilon_3)} \tag{1.8}$$

Alternatively, the Mohr's circle may be defined by the parameters $\delta\epsilon_\gamma$ and $\delta\epsilon_v$, as shown in Fig. 1.7(b), where

$$\delta\epsilon_\gamma = \delta\epsilon_1 - \delta\epsilon_3 \tag{1.9}$$

$$\delta\epsilon_v = \delta\epsilon_1 + \delta\epsilon_3 \tag{1.10}$$

Hence,

$$\sin\psi = -\frac{\delta\epsilon_v}{\delta\epsilon_\gamma} \tag{1.11}$$

and, in the limit,

$$\sin\psi = -\frac{d\epsilon_v}{d\epsilon_\gamma} \tag{1.12}$$

For plane strain $\delta\epsilon_2 = 0$ and the parameter ϵ_v is equal to the volumetric strain, while the parameter ϵ_γ is equal to the maximum shear strain in the given state of strain. The value of $\delta\epsilon_\gamma$ is always positive, since $\delta\epsilon_1 > \delta\epsilon_3$ by definition, and hence ψ will be positive for negative (dilational) volumetric strain and negative for positive (compressive) volumetric strain.

For the special case of axial symmetry for which $\delta\epsilon_2 = \delta\epsilon_3$, we choose parameters $\delta\epsilon_s$ and $\delta\epsilon_v$, defined as

$$\delta\epsilon_s = \tfrac{2}{3}(\delta\epsilon_1 - \delta\epsilon_3) \tag{1.13}$$

$$\delta\epsilon_v = (\delta\epsilon_1 + 2\delta\epsilon_3) = -\frac{\delta v}{v} \tag{1.14}$$

where ϵ_v is the volumetric strain and v is the specific volume. The derivation of the parameters ϵ_s, ϵ_γ and ϵ_v and their relationships with the stress parameters t', s' and q', p' are discussed by Atkinson and Bransby (1978, Chapter 4).

In Fig. 1.7(b) the origin of axes lies inside the Mohr's circle and there are two planes at angles $\pm\gamma$ to the major principal plane, for which the increments of normal strain are zero, as shown in Fig. 1.7(a). The increments of shear strain for these planes are $\tfrac{1}{2}\delta\gamma_n$ where, from the geometry of Fig. 1.7(b),

$$\tfrac{1}{2}\delta\gamma_n = \tfrac{1}{2}(\delta\epsilon_1 - \delta\epsilon_3)\cos\psi \tag{1.15}$$

Hence, from Eqs (1.11) and (1.15),

$$\tan\psi = -\frac{\delta\epsilon_v}{\delta\gamma_n} \tag{1.16}$$

and, in the limit,

$$\tan \psi = -\frac{d\epsilon_v}{d\gamma_n} \tag{1.17}$$

where $\delta\gamma_n$ is the increment of shear strain for the plane for which the normal strain is zero. Since the sign of ψ depends on the sign of the increment of volumetric strain $\delta\epsilon_v$, we must always take the positive value of $\delta\gamma_n$ in Eq. (1.17) and so ψ will be positive for negative (dilational) volumetric strain and negative for positive (compressive) volumetric strain. From the geometry of Fig. 1.7(b) the angle γ defining the planes across which the normal strains are zero is given by

$$\gamma = (45° - \tfrac{1}{2}\psi) \tag{1.18}$$

Figure 1.8(a) shows the *directions* of zero strain increment corresponding to the *planes* in Fig. 1.7(a) and Fig. 1.8(b) again shows the Mohr's circle of strain. The broken lines in Fig. 1.8(b) are the *planes*, from Fig. 1.7(b), for which the increments of normal strain are zero and the *directions* of zero strain increment are normal to these planes. From the geometry of Fig. 1.8, the angle β defining the directions of zero strain increment is given by

$$\beta = (45° + \tfrac{1}{2}\psi) \tag{1.19}$$

The increments of shear strain and normal strain for planes parallel with the directions of zero strain increment are $\delta\gamma_n$ and $\delta\epsilon_n$, as shown in Fig. 1.8, and from the geometry of Fig. 1.8(b) $\delta\epsilon_n = \delta\epsilon_v$ and the value of the increment of shear strain $\delta\gamma_n$ is the same for the planes normal to, and parallel with, the directions of zero strain increment.

From the geometry of Fig. 1.8, the tangents to the points on the Mohr's circles for which the strain increments are $\pm\tfrac{1}{2}\delta\gamma_n$, $\delta\epsilon_n$ make an angle ψ with the $\delta\epsilon$ axis. Thus the role played by the angle of dilation ψ for increments of strain corresponds to the role played by the mobilized angle of shearing resistance ρ' for states of stress in Fig. 1.12. For the special case when $\rho' = \psi$, the planes for which the stresses are τ_n', σ_n' are also the planes for which the increments of strain are $\delta\gamma_n$, $\delta\epsilon_n$ and these are also directions of zero strain increment.

Figure 1.9 shows a section of a long slip plane, thickness δy, separating blocks which are assumed to be rigid so that all deformations and strains are contained within the slip plane. During an increment of deformation in which the lower block remains stationary, the soil within the slip plane shears and dilates, so that the upper block suffers a small relative displacement δw with components δm and δn. Since the slip plane is long, increments of strain in the direction of the slip plane are zero and the slip plane coincides with the direction of zero strain shown in Fig. 1.8. In addition, strains normal to the page are zero and hence the increment of normal strain $\delta\epsilon_n$ is equal to the increment of volumetric strain $\delta\epsilon_v$.

The increments of shear and normal strain in the soil within the slip plane are

$$\delta\gamma_n = -\frac{\delta m}{\delta y} \tag{1.20}$$

$$\delta\epsilon_v = -\frac{\delta n}{\delta y} \tag{1.21}$$

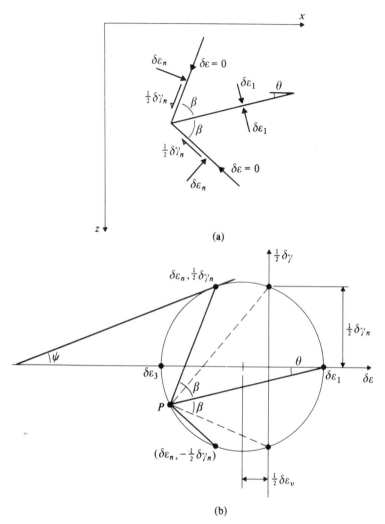

Figure 1.8 Directions of zero strain increment.

and, from Eq. (1.16), taking $\delta\gamma_n$ as positive, we have, in the limit,

$$\tan\psi = \frac{dn}{dm} \tag{1.22}$$

and ψ is negative for compressive volumetric strain and is positive for dilation. Thus, for discontinuous slipping the direction of the relative displacement δw is directed at an angle ψ to the slip plane, as shown in Fig. 1.9.

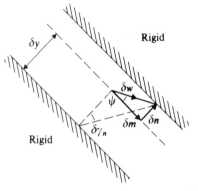

Figure 1.9 Analysis of discontinuous slipping.

1.4 ANALYSIS OF STATES OF STRESS

The simplest method for the analysis of stress is to make use of the Mohr's circle construction. Figure 1.10(a) illustrates effective stresses σ'_x, σ'_z and $\tau'_{xz} = \tau'_{zx}$ on the faces of an element. For convenience we consider only the two-dimensional stress state, neglecting stresses acting on planes parallel with the page and, noting the choice of axes, Fig. 1.10(a) shows positive straining. The Mohr's circle of effective stress corresponding to the state of stress in Fig. 1.10(a) is shown in Fig. 1.11, in which counterclockwise shear stresses τ'_{xz} are positive. The pole of planes is at P and hence (or otherwise) principal stresses σ'_1 and σ'_3 act on principal planes which are the faces of an element rotated through an angle θ as shown in Fig.1.10(b).

A Mohr's circle may be defined by two principal stresses σ'_1 and σ'_3 and the relative magnitudes of the shear and normal stresses may be represented by a mobilized *angle of shearing resistance* ρ' where, from the geometry of Fig. 1.11,

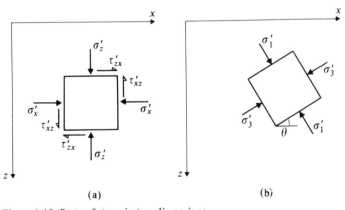

(a)   (b)

Figure 1.10 State of stress in two dimensions.

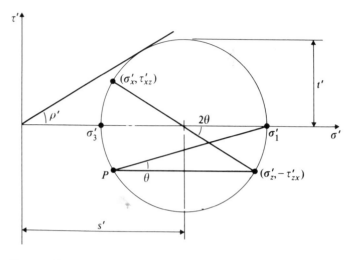

Figure 1.11 Mohr's circle of stress corresponding to the state of stress in Fig. 1.10.

$$\sin \rho' = \frac{\frac{1}{2}(\sigma_1' - \sigma_3')}{\frac{1}{2}(\sigma_1' + \sigma_3')} \tag{1.23}$$

Alternatively, the Mohr's circle may be defined by parameters t' and s', as indicated in Fig. 1.11, where

$$t' = \frac{1}{2}(\sigma_1' - \sigma_3') \tag{1.24}$$

$$s' = \frac{1}{2}(\sigma_1' + \sigma_3') \tag{1.25}$$

and

$$\sin \rho' = \frac{t'}{s'} \tag{1.26}$$

For the special case of axial symmetry for which $\sigma_2' = \sigma_3'$ and stresses on planes parallel with the page cannot be ignored we define parameters q' and p' as

$$q' = (\sigma_1' - \sigma_3') \tag{1.27}$$

$$p' = \frac{1}{3}(\sigma_1' + 2\sigma_3') \tag{1.28}$$

and

$$\eta' = \frac{q'}{p'} \tag{1.29}$$

where the parameter η' is analogous to ρ' and represents the relative magnitudes of the shear and normal stresses. The parameters t', s' and q', p' are convenient as axes for plotting stress paths; axes $t':s'$ may be used for conditions of plane strain where $\epsilon_2 = 0$ and the intermediate principal stress may be ignored, while axes $q':p'$ may be used for conditions of axial symmetry where $\sigma_2' = \sigma_3'$.

Of particular interest for cases of discontinuous slipping are the stresses τ_n' and σ_n' on planes rotated through $\pm \alpha$ from the major principal plane, as shown in Fig. 1.12(a), such that the stresses correspond to the points on the circumference

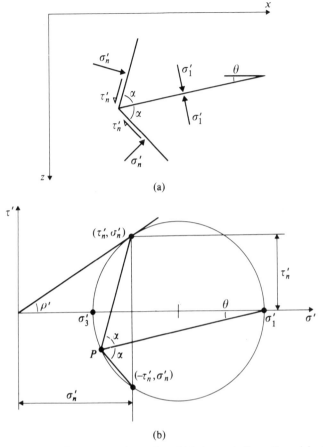

Figure 1.12 Stresses on planes for which tangents from the origin touch the Mohr's circle.

of the Mohr's circle in Fig. 1.12(b), where the tangents from the origin touch the circle. From the geometry of Fig. 1.12

$$\tau'_n = \tfrac{1}{2}(\sigma'_1 - \sigma'_3) \cos \rho' \tag{1.30}$$

$$\sigma'_n = \tfrac{1}{2}(\sigma'_1 + \sigma'_3) \cos^2 \rho' \tag{1.31}$$

and
$$\tan \rho' = \frac{\tau'_n}{\sigma'_n} \tag{1.32}$$

The magnitude of the angle α between the major principal plane and the planes on which τ'_n and σ'_n act is given from the geometry of Fig. 1.12 as

$$\alpha = (45° + \tfrac{1}{2}\rho') \tag{1.33}$$

If the pore pressure in the element in Fig. 1.10(a) is u then $\sigma_1 = \sigma'_1 + u$ and $\sigma_3 = \sigma'_3 + u$ and the Mohr's circle of total stress in Fig. 1.13 is identical to the

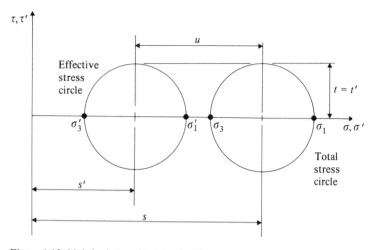

Figure 1.13 Mohr's circles of total and effective stress.

Mohr's circle of effective stress but it is shifted to the right by a distance given by the magnitude of the pore pressure u. From the geometry of Fig. 1.13 or otherwise, the various parameters for total and effective stress are related by

$$\tau_n' = \tau_n \qquad \sigma_n' = \sigma_n - u \qquad (1.34)$$

$$t' = t \qquad s' = s - u \qquad (1.35)$$

$$q' = q \qquad p' = p - u \qquad (1.36)$$

but $\rho' \neq \rho$ and $\eta' \neq \eta$. For soils, in accordance with the principle of effective stress, we are normally required to consider effective, not total, stresses. The Mohr's circle of stress shown for states of stress is equally valid for the analysis of increments of stress, but it is essential always to distinguish carefully between states of stress and increments of stress.

1.5 RELATIONSHIPS BETWEEN STRESS AND STRAIN

So far we have considered states of stress and increments of strain separately and it must not be assumed that the state of stress shown in Fig. 1.10(a) will give rise to the small increment of strain shown in Fig. 1.5(a). We will, however, assume that principal planes of stress and principal planes of strain and strain increment coincide. This coincidence of principal planes is known as the *coaxiality* condition. Coaxiality is not a general theoretical requirement of material behaviour but experiments indicate that in many circumstances the coaxiality condition is a good approximation for material behaviour.

Forces acting on the boundaries of an element do work on the element during an increment of deformation and an increment of energy is transferred to the material. The increment of energy transferred from the external forces is δE per unit volume and of this a part δU is stored and will be recovered on unloading, while a part δW is dissipated in the material. Since energy is conserved, $\delta E = \delta U + \delta W$ and we may make use of this division to distinguish between two classes of material. If no energy is stored, $\delta U = 0$ and the material is known as *dissipative*; if, on the other hand, no energy is dissipated, $\delta W = 0$ and the material is known as *conservative*. Plastic materials are dissipative, while elastic materials are conservative.

For soil, the increment of work done per unit volume by the external forces for an increment of deformation is given by

$$\delta E = \sigma_1' \, \delta\epsilon_1 + \sigma_2' \, \delta\epsilon_2 + \sigma_3' \, \delta\epsilon_3 \tag{1.37}$$

$$\delta E = \sigma_n' \, \delta\epsilon_n + \tau_n' \, \delta\gamma_n \tag{1.38}$$

for continuous strain and for discontinuous slipping, respectively. Equation (1.37) was given by Atkinson and Bransby (1978, pp. 61–62) and Eq. (1.38) is discussed in Section 4.7 of this book for the case of a perfectly plastic soil for which $\delta E = \delta W$.

It is common experience that, if the loading on a structure is changed, deformations will occur† and, consequently, increments of strain will occur as a result of increments of stress. Thus, in general, we may write

$$\{\delta\epsilon\} = [C']\{\delta\sigma'\} \tag{1.39}$$

where $\{\delta\epsilon\}$ is a vector containing the components of the strain increment, $\{\delta\sigma'\}$ is a vector containing the components of the effective stress increment, and $[C']$ is a compliance matrix which contains a number of material parameters. If the determinant of the matrix $[C']$ is non-zero it may be inverted and Eq. (1.39) may be written

$$\{\delta\sigma'\} = [C']^{-1}\{\delta\epsilon\} \tag{1.40}$$

which gives the stress increment in terms of the corresponding strain increment. Equations (1.39) and (1.40) are written for soil in terms of effective stresses, and so the parameters in $[C']$ are those appropriate for effective stresses. An important feature of the matrix $[C']$ is that it is symmetric about the leading diagonal. This is always the case if the material is elastic and it is the case also if the material is plastic with an associated flow rule.

Although, in general, the increments of stress $\{\delta\sigma'\}$ and of strain $\{\delta\epsilon\}$ each contain six independent components (i.e., $\delta\sigma_x'$, $\delta\sigma_y'$, $\delta\sigma_z'$, $\delta\tau_{xy}'$, $\delta\tau_{yz}'$, $\delta\tau_{zx}'$), it is often simplest to consider relationships between invariants, or parameters of stress and strain as discussed by Atkinson and Bransby (1978, Chapter 4). Thus, for axial symmetry, we have

† In fact, since no material and no structure can ever be perfectly rigid, changes of loading must always cause deflections.

$$\begin{Bmatrix} \delta\epsilon_s \\ \delta\epsilon_v \end{Bmatrix} = [C'_{qp}] \begin{Bmatrix} \delta q' \\ \delta p' \end{Bmatrix} \tag{1.41}$$

and for plane strain we have

$$\begin{Bmatrix} \delta\epsilon_\gamma \\ \delta\epsilon_v \end{Bmatrix} = [C'_{ts}] \begin{Bmatrix} \delta t' \\ \delta s' \end{Bmatrix} \tag{1.42}$$

where the components of the matrices $[C'_{qp}]$ and $[C'_{ts}]$ are related to the components of the matrix $[C']$ in Eq. (1.39).

The parameters ϵ_s and ϵ_v correctly correspond with q' and p' and the parameters ϵ_γ and ϵ_v correctly correspond with t' and s', since, as shown by Atkinson and Bransby (1978, pp. 61–62), both sets lead to the same value for δE, the work done by the external loads during an increment of deformation.

Equation (1.39) relates increments of strain to increments of stress and it is known as an *incremental model*. This is the most common and convenient form of mathematical model for engineering calculations but materials do not always behave in this incremental way. For example, during continuous processes like rolling or forming steel and during the collapse of a slope or of a foundation, strain increments occur without change of stress. In these cases the incremental model is inappropriate and an alternative formulation must be found which relates increments of strain to *states*, rather than *increments*, of stress.

1.6 ELASTIC AND PLASTIC DEFORMATIONS

Mathematical models for material behaviour relate states and increments of stress to states and increments of strain. The useful models for soil are based on the theories of elasticity and plasticity and before examining soil behaviour we will consider the essential features of these theories. In order to illustrate the various aspects of material behaviour it is convenient to examine the behaviour of an ideal soil-like material subjected to principal effective stresses σ'_a, σ'_b and σ'_c and which suffers principal strains ϵ_a, ϵ_b and ϵ_c, as discussed by Atkinson and Bransby (1978, pp. 274–278). The material is like soil in that it obeys the principle of effective stress and so strains depend on effective, not total, stresses.

Figure 1.14 shows stress–strain curves for uniaxial compression tests for which $\sigma'_b = \sigma'_c$ and $\epsilon_b = \epsilon_c$ and for which the axial stress σ'_a is plotted against the axial strain ϵ_a. For the range OY the material behaviour is linearly *elastic* and strains caused by increasing the stress are fully recovered if the stress is reduced. For states beyond Y additional irrecoverable *plastic* strains occur but if the stress is reduced from G the material behaviour is again elastic and reversible in the range BG. Points such as Y and G are known as *yield points* and one effect of plastic straining is to change the yield stress from σ'_y to σ'_g. In Fig. 1.14(a) the yield stress increases with plastic strain and the material is said to be *strain hardening*, while in

Fig. 1.14(b) the yield stress decreases with plastic strain and the material is said to be *strain softening*. Strain hardening and strain softening are different aspects of the same kind of behaviour and both occur in soils under different circumstances.

A material at G in Fig. 1.14(a) will move along $G \to F$ suffering elastic and plastic strains if the stress is increased, and it will move along $G \to B$ suffering purely elastic strains if the stress is reduced. It is not immediately apparent, however, which path a strain softening material at G in Fig. 1.14(b) will follow. It turns out that the behaviour of a strain softening material can only be determined by considering the change of *strain* rather than the change of stress. Thus the material at G in Fig, 1.14(b) will move along $G \to F$ suffering elastic and plastic strains if the strain is increased, while it will move along $G \to B$ suffering purely elastic strains if the strain is reduced, but in both cases the stress will diminish.

If either a strain hardening or a strain softening material is strained beyond G it will *fail* at F with very large strains and no further change of stress.

The stress–strain curves shown in Fig. 1.14 correspond to uniaxial compression tests for which $\sigma_b' = \sigma_c' = 0$. If a number of similar tests are carried out in which the samples are loaded in plane strain with $\epsilon_b = 0$ and each with a constant value σ_c' then the stress–strain curves will be similar to those shown in Fig. 1.14, except that the magnitudes of the yield stresses and of the failure stresses, though not the gradients of the linear elastic sections, will depend on the magnitudes of σ_c'.

1.7 YIELDING, HARDENING, AND PLASTIC FLOW

If the various combinations of σ_a' and σ_c' at yield and at failure for a strain hardening material are plotted together as shown in Fig. 1.15(a) then all states of stress at first yield lie on a *yield curve* $Y_a Y_c$ and all states of stress at failure lie on a *failure envelope* $F_a F_c$; thus the material will yield if the particular combination of stresses σ_a' and σ_c' plots on to the yield curve and it will fail if the stresses plot on to the failure envelope. The failure envelope and the yield curve may, or may not, be geometrically similar. The state of stress cannot lie beyond the failure envelope and if the state of stress lies inside the appropriate yield curve then the material behaviour is elastic. If the material is loaded beyond Y to G and then unloaded, on reloading it will yield at G when the new yield stress is σ_g' and there will be a new yield curve $G_a G_c$ in Fig. 1.15(a). The expansion of the yield curve in Fig. 1.15(a) due to plastic straining along YG in Fig. 1.14(a) is due to strain hardening and the relationship between the change of yield curve and the plastic strain from Y to G is known as a *hardening law*.

The complete yielding, hardening, and failure may be represented by a single diagram with axes $\sigma_a' : \sigma_c' : \epsilon^p$, as shown in Fig. 1.15(b). We may find an infinite number of yield curves such as $G_a G_c$, each associated with a particular value of plastic strain ϵ^p, and together these define a surface which we will call a *yield surface*. The state of the material may be on or within the yield surface but cannot lie outside it, so the yield surface represents a boundary for all possible states.

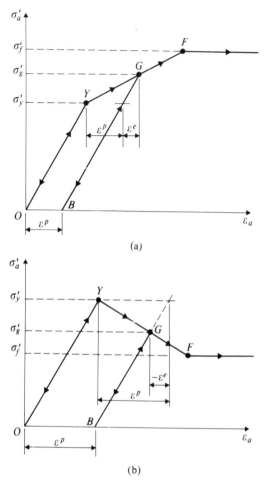

(a)

(b)

Figure 1.14 Stress–strain curves for an ideal soil-like material for uniaxial compression. (a) strain hardening. (b) Strain softening. (*From Atkinson and Bransby, 1978.*)

For a strain softening material the yield surface is similar to that shown in Fig. 1.15(b), except that the yield curves become smaller and the surface contracts with increasing plastic strain.

Figure 1.16(a) shows the yield surface from Fig. 1.15 with the shaded plane $O_g G_a G_c$ vertically below the yield curve $G_a G_c$. A sample brought to a point A on the yield surface may be subjected to a number of loading paths such as $A \rightarrow B$ to $A \rightarrow E$. For the paths $A \rightarrow B$, $A \rightarrow C$, and $A \rightarrow D$ the state traverses the yield surface and plastic strains occur as the state moves from the yield curve $G_a G_c$ towards the failure envelope $F_a F_c$. The path $A \rightarrow E$, on the other hand, cannot traverse the yield surface to E' in Fig. 1.16(b), as this would imply negative, or recoverable,

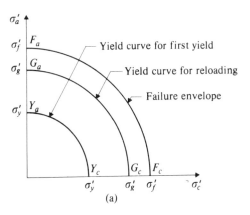

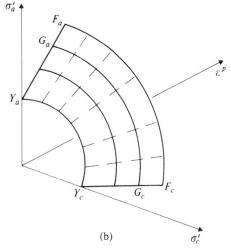

Figure 1.15 Yielding and hardening. (a) Yield curves and failure envelope. (b) Yield surface. (*From Atkinson and Bransby, 1978.*)

plastic strains, which are impossible by definition. Instead, the path $A \to E$ will traverse the shaded plane $O_g G_a G_c$, causing purely elastic strains. Each yield curve such as $G_a G_c$ has associated with it a vertical plane corresponding to zero plastic strain increment and we will call these planes *elastic walls*. All paths inside the yield surface will traverse an elastic wall, causing purely elastic strains.

Figure 1.16(b) shows the yield surface for a strain softening material with an elastic wall $O_g G_a G_c$. A material at A may follow paths such as $A \to B$, $A \to C$, and $A \to D$ which traverse the yield surface if plastic strains increase, but otherwise it will follow the unloading path $A \to E$ which traverses the elastic wall.

In general paths such as $A \to B$ to $A \to E$ in Fig. 1.16 may be due to increasing or decreasing stresses, depending on the shape of the yield surface and on the kind

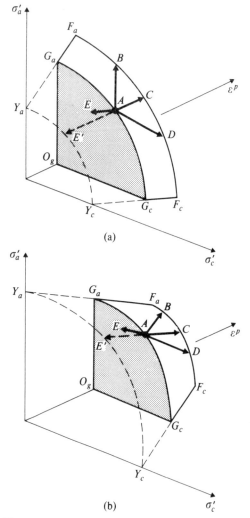

Figure 1.16 Paths for loading and unloading. (a) Hardening material. (b) Softening material.

of loading, but we must distinguish between loading and unloading. For *loading* irrecoverable plastic strains occur (i.e., $\delta\epsilon^p > 0$) as the paths such as $A \to B, A \to C$, or $A \to D$ traverse the yield surface. For an *unloading* path (which would imply impossible recoverable plastic strains if the path such as $A \to E'$ were to traverse the yield surface) plastic strains are zero (i.e., $\delta\epsilon^p = 0$) as the path such as $A \to E$ traverses an elastic wall.

The theory of plasticity relates the *ratio* of increments of plastic strain in an increment of plastic deformation to the *state* of stress causing the plastic deformations. In order to illustrate this idea it is convenient to plot increments of plastic strain on the same diagram as states of stress, provided that parameters chosen for

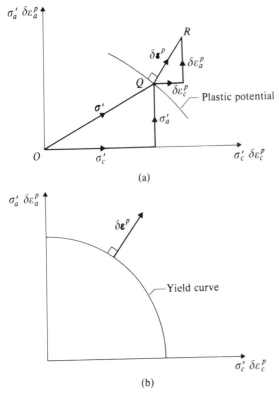

Figure 1.17 Flow rule of plasticity theory. (a) Plastic potential. (b) Normality condition. (*From Atkinson and Bransby, 1978.*)

stress and strain correctly correspond to one another. Thus in Fig. 1.17(a) the axes $\sigma'_a : \sigma'_c$ are superimposed on axes $\delta\epsilon^p_a : \delta\epsilon^p_c$. The state of a sample at Q is represented by the stress vector $\boldsymbol{\sigma}'$ (OQ) made up of components σ'_a and σ'_c and it suffers an increment $\delta\boldsymbol{\epsilon}^p$ (QR) of plastic strain made up of components $\delta\epsilon^p_a$ and $\delta\epsilon^p_c$. Thus, in the theory of plasticity the gradient $d\epsilon^p_a / d\epsilon^p_c$ of the vector of plastic strain is related to the vector of stress $\boldsymbol{\sigma}'$ and is independent of the increment of stress causing the plastic strain. This plastic behaviour contrasts with perfectly elastic behaviour where the gradient of the vector of elastic strain increment depends wholly on the change of stress.

The precise relationship between the vector of plastic strain increment and the vector of stress is known as a *flow rule*. It is convenient to define a plastic potential such that vectors of strain increment are orthogonal to the plastic potential, as shown in Fig. 1.17(a). The part of the plastic potential in Fig. 1.17(a) is similar to the part of the yield curve in Fig. 1.15(a) and the flow rule may be specified as a relationship between the plastic potential and a yield curve. In particular, if the plastic potential and yield curve coincide, the material is said to have an *associated flow rule* and the *normality condition* applies in the sense that vectors of plastic strain increment are normal to the yield curve, as illustrated in Fig. 1.17(b).

1.8 IDEAL ELASTIC BEHAVIOUR

The behaviour of an isotropic elastic material in three dimensions is given by the generalized form of Hooke's law

$$\delta\epsilon_x = (1/E')[\delta\sigma_x' - \nu'\delta\sigma_y' - \nu'\delta\sigma_z']$$
$$\delta\epsilon_y = (1/E')[\delta\sigma_y' - \nu'\delta\sigma_z' - \nu'\delta\sigma_x']$$
$$\delta\epsilon_z = (1/E')[\delta\sigma_z' - \nu'\delta\sigma_x' - \nu'\delta\sigma_y']$$
$$\delta\gamma_{xy} = (2/E')(1 + \nu')\delta\tau_{xy}' \tag{1.43}$$
$$\delta\gamma_{yz} = (2/E')(1 + \nu')\delta\tau_{yz}'$$
$$\delta\gamma_{zx} = (2/E')(1 + \nu')\delta\tau_{zx}'$$

where E' and ν' are the Young's modulus and Poisson's ratio appropriate for effective stresses. If the material is *linear* and elastic values of E' and ν' remain constant. Stress–strain behaviour given by Eqs. (1.43) corresponds to material behaviour below yield in the ranges OY and BG in Fig. 1.14. The behaviour of an *ideal* elastic material is reversible and strains caused by loading are fully recovered on unloading; consequently, ideal elastic materials are conservative and the work done during an increment of deformation is stored as recoverable strain energy.

If the normal stresses and strains in Eqs. (1.43) are principal stresses and strains so that shear stresses and shear strains are zero then we have

$$\delta\epsilon_1 = (1/E')[\delta\sigma_1' - \nu'\delta\sigma_2' - \nu'\delta\sigma_3']$$
$$\delta\epsilon_2 = (1/E')[\delta\sigma_2' - \nu'\delta\sigma_3' - \nu'\delta\sigma_1'] \tag{1.44}$$
$$\delta\epsilon_3 = (1/E')[\delta\sigma_3' - \nu'\delta\sigma_1' - \nu'\delta\sigma_2']$$

For the special case of axial symmetry for which $\delta\epsilon_2 = \delta\epsilon_3$ and $\delta\sigma_2' = \delta\sigma_3'$ we have

$$\delta\epsilon_s = \frac{2(1 + \nu')}{3E'}\delta q' = \frac{1}{3G'}\delta q' \tag{1.45}$$

$$\delta\epsilon_v = \frac{3(1 - 2\nu')}{E'}\delta p' = \frac{1}{K'}\delta p' \tag{1.46}$$

where K' is known as the *bulk modulus*, G' is known as the *shear modulus*, and these are related to Young's modulus and Poisson's ratio by

$$K' = \frac{E'}{3(1 - 2\nu')} \qquad G' = \frac{E'}{2(1 + \nu')} \tag{1.47}$$

For plane strain, putting $\delta\epsilon_2 = 0$ into Eqs. (1.44), we have $\delta\sigma_2' = \nu'(\delta\sigma_1' + \delta\sigma_3')$ and

$$\delta\epsilon_1 = \frac{1+v'}{E'}[(1-v')\delta\sigma_1' - v'\delta\sigma_3'] \tag{1.48}$$

$$\delta\epsilon_3 = \frac{1+v'}{E'}[-v\delta\sigma_1' + (1-v')\delta\sigma_3']$$

or

$$\delta\epsilon_\gamma = \frac{2(1+v')}{E'}\delta t' = \frac{1}{G_{ps}'}\delta t' \tag{1.49}$$

$$\delta\epsilon_v = \frac{2(1+v')(1-2v')}{E'}\delta s' = \frac{1}{K_{ps}'}\delta s' \tag{1.50}$$

where K_{ps}' and G_{ps}' are a bulk modulus and a shear modulus, respectively, appropriate for plane strain, and from Eqs. (1.47), (1.49), and (1.50) we have

$$K_{ps}' = K' + \tfrac{1}{3}G' \qquad G_{ps}' = G' \tag{1.51}$$

Equations (1.45), (1.46), (1.49), and (1.50) demonstrate an important property of an isotropic elastic material. When parameters of strain such as ϵ_s and ϵ_v are correctly associated with parameters of stress, such as p' and q', increments $\delta\epsilon_s$ of shear strain are dependent only on the corresponding increments $\delta q'$ of shear stress and increments $\delta\epsilon_v$ of volumetric strain are dependent only on the corresponding increments $\delta p'$ of normal stress. Similarly, for plane strain, increments $\delta\epsilon_\gamma$ of shear strain are dependent only on the corresponding increments $\delta t'$ of shear stress and increments $\delta\epsilon_v$ of volumetric strain are dependent only on the corresponding increments $\delta s'$ of normal stress. From Eqs. (1.45) and (1.46)

$$\frac{\delta\epsilon_v}{\delta\epsilon_s} = \frac{9(1-2v')}{2(1+v')}\frac{\delta p'}{\delta q'} \tag{1.52}$$

Thus, for an isotropic elastic material the ratio $\delta\epsilon_v/\delta\epsilon_s$ depends on the ratio $\delta p'/\delta q'$ and, moreover, the relationship between the two ratios depends only on the value of Poisson's ratio and is independent of the value of Young's modulus.

1.9 ELASTO-PLASTIC BEHAVIOUR

The ideas of elasticity, yielding, hardening, and plastic flow may be combined into general stress–strain equations for materials which suffer simultaneous elastic and plastic components of strain. The analysis given here follows that given by Atkinson and Bransby (1978, Chapter 13); a more general, but mathematically more difficult, approach is given by Zienkiewicz (1977) and readers may wish to refer there for more details.

For any increment of load and displacement, total strains are simply the sum of their elastic and plastic components

$$\delta\epsilon_s = \delta\epsilon_s^e + \delta\epsilon_s^p \tag{1.53}$$

$$\delta\epsilon_v = \delta\epsilon_v^e + \delta\epsilon_v^p \tag{1.54}$$

where the elastic components are given by Eqs. (1.45) and (1.46) as

$$\delta \epsilon_s^e = \frac{1}{3G'} \delta q' \tag{1.55}$$

$$\delta \epsilon_v^e = \frac{1}{K'} \delta p' \tag{1.56}$$

If the flow rule is associated then the vector of plastic strain increment is normal to the yield curve and in general

$$\frac{\delta \epsilon_s^p}{\delta \epsilon_v^p} = F \tag{1.57}$$

where the flow parameter F depends on the shape of the yield curve and on the state of stress. As the state of stress traverses the yield surface it moves from one yield curve to another and for soil it is convenient to relate the resulting increment of plastic volumetric strain $\delta \epsilon_v^p$ to the stress increments $\delta q'$ and $\delta p'$ by an equation of the form

$$\delta \epsilon_v^p = H \, \delta q' + G \, \delta p' \tag{1.58}$$

where the hardening parameters H and G depend on the shape of the yield surface and on the state of stress. Equation (1.58) can be thought of as a hardening law since it relates an increment of plastic strain to the corresponding changes of stress from one yield curve to another.

From Eqs. (1.57) and (1.58) we have

$$\delta \epsilon_s^p = FH \, \delta p' + FG \, \delta p' \tag{1.59}$$

Hence, making use of Eqs. (1.53) to (1.54), we have

$$\delta \epsilon_s = \left(FH + \frac{1}{3G'} \right) \delta q' + FG \, \delta p' \tag{1.60}$$

$$\delta \epsilon_v = H \, \delta q' + \left(G + \frac{1}{K'} \right) \delta p' \tag{1.61}$$

which are the expanded form of Eq. (1.41). This is essentially the approach taken by Atkinson and Bransby (1978, pp. 283–287) except that, in describing the simple Cam clay model for soil, they took elastic shear strains to be zero following Schofield and Wroth (1968). It may be noted that if the coaxiality condition holds and the flow rule is associated so that the matrix in Eq. (1.41) is symmetric then we have, from Eqs. (1.60) and (1.61),

$$G = H/F \tag{1.62}$$

and Eqs. (1.60) and (1.61) become

$$\delta \epsilon_s = \left(FH + \frac{1}{3G'} \right) \delta q' + H \, \delta p' \tag{1.63}$$

$$\delta \epsilon_v = H \, \delta q' + \left(\frac{H}{F} + \frac{1}{K'} \right) \delta p' \tag{1.64}$$

Equations (1.63) and (1.64), with appropriate values for the material parameters, define the stress–strain behaviour of a soil-like material for conditions of axial symmetry. If the material is unloaded so that its state passes inside the yield surface and traverses an elastic wall then the behaviour is elastic and given by Eqs. (1.45) and (1.46). Thus, with $H = 0$ for states of stress inside the yield surface, Eqs. (1.63) and (1.64) are valid for all loading and unloading paths for axial symmetry; it remains only to determine the elastic constants G' and K' and to specify the shape of the yield surface from which values for the parameters F and H may be calculated.

Similar arguments apply for plane strain, but now we must relate the strain parameters ϵ_γ and ϵ_v to the stress parameters t' and s' as in Eq. (1.42). Thus, by analogy with Eqs. (1.63) and (1.64) we have

$$\delta\epsilon_\gamma = \left(F_{ps}H_{ps} + \frac{1}{G'_{ps}}\right)\delta t' + H_{ps}\,\delta s' \tag{1.65}$$

$$\delta\epsilon_v = H_{ps}\,\delta t' + \left(\frac{H_{ps}}{F_{ps}} + \frac{1}{K'_{ps}}\right)\delta s' \tag{1.66}$$

which are the expanded form of Eq. (1.42). The parameters F_{ps} and H_{ps} are analogous to the parameters F and H in Eqs. (1.63) and (1.64) and they may be obtained from a yield surface appropriate for plane strain, while the elastic shear and bulk moduli G'_{ps} and K'_{ps} are given by Eq. (1.51). If the material is unloaded so that its state passes inside the state boundary surface then the behaviour is elastic and is given by Eqs. (1.49) and (1.50) which may be obtained from Eqs. (1.65) and (1.66) with $H_{ps} = 0$.

1.10 EQUILIBRIUM AND COMPATIBILITY

In order to obtain a complete solution for stresses and displacements of a soil structure, or for any other structure for that matter, it is necessary to satisfy conditions of equilibrium and compatibility, together with the appropriate material properties. In the next chapter we will investigate stress–strain relationships appropriate for soils. For the present we will derive the equilibrium and compatibility conditions and in later chapters we will see how solutions may be obtained. Since much of this later analysis will be restricted to plane strain conditions we will obtain the equilibrium and compatibility conditions here for plane strain only.

Figure 1.18 shows an element in the $x{:}z$ plane with sides δx and δz and with total normal and shear stresses which vary through the element. Resolving vertically and horizontally, for equilibrium,

$$\frac{\partial\sigma_z}{\partial z} + \frac{\partial\tau_{xz}}{\partial x} = \gamma \tag{1.67}$$

$$\frac{\partial\sigma_x}{\partial x} + \frac{\partial\tau_{zx}}{\partial z} = 0 \tag{1.68}$$

where γ is the unit weight of the soil. Equations (1.67) and (1.68) may be written in terms of effective stresses as

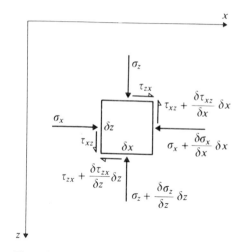

Figure 1.18 Equilibrium state of stress.

$$\frac{\partial \sigma_z'}{\partial z} + \frac{\partial \tau_{xz}'}{\partial x} = \gamma - \frac{\partial u}{\partial z} \tag{1.69}$$

$$\frac{\partial \sigma_x'}{\partial x} + \frac{\partial \tau_{zx}'}{\partial z} = -\frac{\partial u}{\partial x} \tag{1.70}$$

where u is the pore pressure. For saturated soil, where there is no seepage so that pore pressures are hydrostatic, we have

$$\frac{\partial u}{\partial z} = \gamma_w \qquad \frac{\partial u}{\partial x} = 0 \tag{1.71}$$

and hence

$$\frac{\partial \sigma_z'}{\partial z} + \frac{\partial \tau_{xz}'}{\partial x} = (\gamma - \gamma_w) \tag{1.72}†$$

$$\frac{\partial \sigma_x'}{\partial x} + \frac{\partial \tau_{zx}'}{\partial z} = 0 \tag{1.73}$$

Equations (1.67) and (1.68) or (1.69) and (1.70) are the required conditions of equilibrium for total stresses and for effective stresses, respectively.

The compatibility condition follows directly from Eqs. (1.4) to (1.6). Differentiating partially we have

$$\frac{\partial^2 \epsilon_x}{\partial z^2} = -\frac{\partial^3 (\delta h)}{\partial x \, \partial z^2} \tag{1.74}$$

$$\frac{\partial^2 \epsilon_z}{\partial x^2} = -\frac{\partial^3 (\delta v)}{\partial z \, \partial x^2} \tag{1.75}$$

† The term $(\gamma - \gamma_w)$ is often given the symbol γ' and is known as the submerged or buoyant unit weight. Use of γ' can lead to difficulties in some instances and to avoid confusion we will always write $(\gamma - \gamma_w)$.

$$\frac{\partial \gamma_{xz}}{\partial x \, \partial z} = -\frac{\partial^3(\delta v)}{\partial z \, \partial x^2} - \frac{\partial^3(\delta h)}{\partial x \, \partial z^2} \tag{1.76}$$

and hence

$$\frac{\partial^2 \epsilon_x}{\partial z^2} + \frac{\partial^2 \epsilon_z}{\partial x^2} - \frac{\partial \gamma_{xz}}{\partial x \, \partial z} = 0 \tag{1.77}$$

Equation (1.77) is a compatibility equation and it specifies the relationship beween shear and normal strains for a permissible deformation. It is valid for drained and for undrained loading noting that for undrained loading volumetric strains are zero.

1.11 RELATIONSHIPS BETWEEN STRESS AND STRAIN FOR PLANE STRAIN

The equilibrium equations for plane strain, Eqs. (1.69) and (1.70), contain the three components of stress, σ'_x, σ'_z, and τ'_{xz}, and the compatibility equation (1.77) contains the three components of strain, ϵ_x, ϵ_z, and γ_{xz}. However, the stress–strain relationship for plane strain given by Eqs. (1.65) and (1.66) is written in terms of the parameters for stress t' and s' and the parameters for strain ϵ_γ and ϵ_v and in order to obtain solutions these must be rewritten in terms of the components of stress and of strain as

$$\begin{Bmatrix} \delta\epsilon_x \\ \delta\epsilon_z \\ \delta\gamma_{xz} \end{Bmatrix} = [C'_{ps}] \begin{Bmatrix} \delta\sigma'_x \\ \delta\sigma'_z \\ \delta\tau'_{xz} \end{Bmatrix} \tag{1.78}$$

where $[C'_{ps}]$ is a 3×3 compliance matrix. The general analysis for elasto-plastic behaviour given by Zienkiewicz (1977) leads to stress–strain relationships in the form of Eq. (1.78) or, alternatively, the compliance matrix $[C'_{ps}]$ may be obtained from the matrix $[C'_{ts}]$ in Eq. (1.42). The analysis given here follows that of Naylor (1978).

From Eqs. (1.65) and (1.66), separating the elastic and plastic components of the strain increment, we have

$$\begin{Bmatrix} \delta\epsilon^p_\gamma \\ \delta\epsilon^p_v \end{Bmatrix} = \begin{bmatrix} (F_{ps}H_{ps})\, H_{ps} & H_{ps} \\ H_{ps} & \dfrac{H_{ps}}{F_{ps}} \end{bmatrix} \begin{Bmatrix} \delta t' \\ \delta s' \end{Bmatrix} = [C'^p_{ts}] \begin{Bmatrix} \delta t' \\ \delta s' \end{Bmatrix}^\dagger \tag{1.79}$$

From the geometry of Fig. 1.11 we have

$$t'^2 = \tfrac{1}{4}(\sigma'_z + \sigma'_x)^2 + \tau'^2_{xz} \tag{1.80}$$

$$s' = \tfrac{1}{2}(\sigma'_z + \sigma'_x) \tag{1.81}$$

and hence, differentiating,

---

† The superscripts p denote plastic strains while the subscripts ps in Eq. (1.78) and elsewhere denote plane strain.

$$2t'\delta t' = \tfrac{1}{2}(\sigma'_z - \sigma'_x)(\delta\sigma'_z - \delta\sigma'_x) + 2\tau'_{xz}\,\delta\tau'_{xz} \tag{1.82}$$

$$\delta s' = \tfrac{1}{2}(\delta\sigma'_z + \delta\sigma'_x) \tag{1.83}$$

If θ is the angle between the major principal plane of stress and the x axis as shown in Fig. 1.10 we have, from Fig. 1.11,

$$\text{yti} = \tfrac{1}{2}(\delta\sigma'_z - \delta\sigma'_x)\cos 2\theta + \delta\tau'_{xz}\sin 2\theta \tag{1.84}$$

where

$$\tan 2\theta = \frac{2\tau'_{xz}}{\sigma'_z - \sigma'_x} \tag{1.85}$$

Equations (1.83) and (1.84) may be written

$$\begin{Bmatrix} \delta t' \\ \delta s' \end{Bmatrix} = \begin{bmatrix} (-\tfrac{1}{2}\cos 2\theta)(\tfrac{1}{2}\cos 2\theta)(\sin 2\theta) \\ \tfrac{1}{2} \quad \tfrac{1}{2} \quad 0 \end{bmatrix} \begin{Bmatrix} \delta\sigma'_x \\ \delta\sigma'_z \\ \delta\tau'_{xz} \end{Bmatrix} \tag{1.86}$$

From the geometry of Fig. 1.6 we have, for plastic strain increments,

$$\delta\epsilon^p_x = -\tfrac{1}{2}\delta\epsilon^p_\gamma \cos 2\theta + \tfrac{1}{2}\delta\epsilon^p_v \tag{1.87}$$

$$\delta\epsilon^p_z = \tfrac{1}{2}\delta\epsilon^p_\gamma \cos 2\theta + \tfrac{1}{2}\delta\epsilon^p_v \tag{1.88}$$

$$\delta\gamma^p_{xz} = \delta\epsilon^p_\gamma \sin 2\theta \tag{1.89}$$

where θ is the angle between the major principal plane of strain increment and the x axis as shown in Fig. 1.5 and, if the coaxiality condition holds, the angles θ in Figs 1.5 and 1.10 are the same. From Eqs. (1.87) to (1.89),

$$\begin{Bmatrix} \delta\epsilon^p_x \\ \delta\epsilon^p_z \\ \delta\gamma^p_{xz} \end{Bmatrix} = \begin{bmatrix} (-\tfrac{1}{2}\cos 2\theta)\tfrac{1}{2} \\ (\tfrac{1}{2}\cos 2\theta)\ \tfrac{1}{2} \\ (\sin 2\theta)\ \ 0 \end{bmatrix} \begin{Bmatrix} \delta\epsilon^p_\gamma \\ \delta\epsilon^p_v \end{Bmatrix} \tag{1.90}$$

Hence, from Eqs. (1.79), (1.86), and (1.90) we have

$$\begin{Bmatrix} \delta\epsilon^p_x \\ \delta\epsilon^p_z \\ \delta\gamma^p_{xz} \end{Bmatrix} = \begin{bmatrix} (-\tfrac{1}{2}\cos 2\theta)\tfrac{1}{2} \\ (\tfrac{1}{2}\cos 2\theta)\ \tfrac{1}{2} \\ (\sin 2\theta)\ \ 0 \end{bmatrix} \begin{bmatrix} (F_{ps}H_{ps})\ H_{ps} \\ H_{ps}\ \dfrac{H_{ps}}{F_{ps}} \end{bmatrix} \begin{bmatrix} (-\tfrac{1}{2}\cos 2\theta)(\tfrac{1}{2}\cos 2\theta)(\sin 2\theta) \\ \tfrac{1}{2} \quad \tfrac{1}{2} \quad 0 \end{bmatrix} \begin{Bmatrix} \delta\sigma'_x \\ \delta\sigma'_z \\ \delta\tau'_{xz} \end{Bmatrix} \tag{1.91}$$

and the compliance matrix for plastic strains for plane strain is given by

$$[C'^p_{ps}] = [R]^T [C'^p_{ts}] [R] \tag{1.92}$$

where the transformation matrix $[R]$ is given by

$$[R] = \begin{bmatrix} (-\tfrac{1}{2}\cos 2\theta)(\tfrac{1}{2}\cos 2\theta)(\sin 2\theta) \\ \tfrac{1}{2} \quad \tfrac{1}{2} \quad 0 \end{bmatrix} \tag{1.93}$$

and the angle θ is given by Eq. (1.85).

The elastic components of the strain increment for plane strain may be found from Eqs. (1.43) with $\delta\epsilon_y^e = 0$ and $\delta\gamma_{xy}^e = \delta\gamma_{yz}^e = 0$ as

$$\delta\epsilon_x^e = (1/E')[\delta\sigma_x'(1 - \nu'^2) - \delta\sigma_z'\nu'(1 + \nu')] \tag{1.94}$$

$$\delta\epsilon_z^e = (1/E')[\delta\sigma_z'(1 - \nu'^2) - \delta\sigma_x'\nu'(1 + \nu')] \tag{1.95}$$

$$\delta\gamma_{xz}^e = (1/E')[2(1 + \nu')\delta\tau_{xz}' \tag{1.96}$$

$$\begin{Bmatrix} \delta\epsilon_x^e \\ \delta\epsilon_z^e \\ \delta\gamma_{xz}^e \end{Bmatrix} = \frac{1 + \nu'}{E'} \begin{bmatrix} (1 - \nu') & -\nu' & 0 \\ -\nu' & (1 - \nu') & 0 \\ 0 & 0 & 2 \end{bmatrix} \begin{Bmatrix} \delta\sigma_x' \\ \delta\sigma_z' \\ \delta\tau_{xz}' \end{Bmatrix} \tag{1.97}$$

and the compliance matrix for elastic strains for plane strain is given by

$$[C_{ps}'^e] = \frac{1 + \nu'}{E'} \begin{bmatrix} (1 - \nu') & -\nu' & 0 \\ -\nu' & (1 - \nu') & 0 \\ 0 & 0 & 2 \end{bmatrix} \tag{1.98}$$

Finally, since total strain increments are simply the sum of their elastic and plastic components, the plane strain compliance matrix in Eq. (1.78) is given by

$$[C_{ps}'] = [C_{ps}'^p] + [C_{ps}'^e] \tag{1.99}$$

where $[C_{ps}'^p]$ and $[C_{ps}'^e]$ are given by Eqs. (1.92) and (1.98).

The stress–strain relationships for plane strain given by Eqs. (1.78) are in the form required for the finite element method. The compliance matrix $[C_{ps}']$ given by Eq. (1.99) contains the elastic moduli E' and ν' and the parameters F_{ps} and H_{ps}, which may be obtained from the yield surface for plane strain in the same way that the parameters F and H in Eqs. (1.63) and (1.64) were obtained from the yield surface for axial symmetry. In this book we will not discuss the use of the finite element method but we will, in Chapter 2, examine values for the parameters F and H and F_{ps} and H_{ps} for soil.

REFERENCES

Atkinson, J. H. and P. L. Bransby (1978), *The Mechanics of Soils*, McGraw-Hill, London.

Naylor, D. J. (1978), 'Stress–strain laws for Soil', in *Developments in Soil Mechanics*, C. R. Scott (ed.), Applied Science Publishers, London, pp. 39–68.

Schofield, A. N. and C. P. Wroth (1968), *Critical State Soil Mechanics*, McGraw-Hill, London.

Terzaghi, J. (1936). 'The shearing resistance of saturated soil and the angle between the planes of shear', *Proc. 1st Int. Conf. Soil Mech. and Foundn Engng*, **1**, pp. 54–56, Harvard, Mass.

Zienkiewicz, O. C. (1977), The Finite Element Method, 3rd edn., McGraw-Hill, London.

AN INTRODUCTION TO THE MECHANICS OF SOILS

2.1 INTRODUCTION

An important aspect of geotechnical engineering is the mechanical behaviour of small elements of soil, and for engineering calculations we will require mathematical models for soil behaviour. There are a number of ways in which a mathematical model for soil can be constructed but the essential requirement is for a stress–strain relationship which is valid for all cases of loading and unloading. A relatively simple model for soil behaviour is based on the idea that loaded soil will ultimately reach a critical state and that a state boundary surface can be found which separates elastic from plastic behaviour. Thus the state boundary surface idea provides a conceptual model and this is known as the *critical state model.* The state boundary surface may also be taken to be a yield surface and thus, using the theories described in Chapter 1, a mathematical model may be constructed. In this chapter we will describe, in an essentially qualitative way, the essential features of the critical state model and, from it, develop the mathematical model. The material covered in this chapter is dealt with at greater length by Atkinson and Bransby (1978) and readers may wish to refer there for a more detailed treatment.

Soils are particulate materials consisting of assemblies of mineral grains, with water filling the pore spaces of saturated soils, but it is conventional to approximate the behaviour of soil to that of an equivalent ideal *continuum.* In a continuum all elements merge continuously into their neighbouring elements and infinitesimal elements have the same properties as the mass; there can be no such thing as a real soil continuum, which is simply an imaginary material having the same bulk behaviour as the real particulate soil it represents. The pressure in the pore water is known as the *pore pressure u* and it gives rise to effective stresses, as described in Sec. 1.2. Clearly, if the soil is dry, pore pressures are zero and total and effective stresses are equal. In this book we will only consider soils which are either saturated or dry.

Soils are classified for engineering purposes according to their nature and state. The nature of a soil is described by the distribution of grain sizes and the mineralogy of the grains and the state of a soil is described by the *specific volume v* together with the current effective stresses. One of the most important differences between fine grained clay soils and coarse grained sand soils is that the value of the coefficient of permeability for clays is approximately six orders of magnitude less than that for sands. Thus, for the same conditions water will seep through, and out of, sand soils approximately 10^6 times faster than for clay soils.

Pore pressures in soil may occur as one of two cases. First, if the pore pressures do not change with time then the conditions are known as *steady state* and the water is either stationary or flowing with a velocity which does not change with time. If there is no flow then the pore pressures are hydrostatic in the ground and are taken to be uniform in small samples, while if there is steady flow the pore pressures may be determined by constructing a *flownet*. In either case of steady state conditions it is relatively simple to calculate pore pressures. Second, during *transient* seepage pore pressures and effective stresses vary with time and, as a consequence of the principle of effective stress, soil deformations occur. These complex interrelationships between pore pressures, seepage, and deformations are known as *consolidation*. Transient seepage phenomena are governed by *excess pore pressures* $\bar{u}$ which occur over and above the *steady state pore pressures* u_0. It is not usually possible to calculate simply the excess pore pressures and effective stresses which occur during consolidation.

2.2. DRAINED AND UNDRAINED LOADING

As soil is loaded or unloaded, the pore pressure responds to the changes of total stress and there will be excess pore pressures in the soil. These excess pore pressures will give rise to consolidation and, as time passes, the soil will compress and distort as the effective stresses change as a result of the changes both of total stress and of pore pressure. Thus, during loading of soil there are complex relationships between stress, distortion, seepage, and volume change which depend on, among other things, the rate of loading compared with the rate of consolidation. Such will be the case whether the soil is loaded as a small sample in a laboratory test or as a large body in a foundation or a slope. Soil loading may be relatively quick or it may be relatively slow; the important point is the speed of loading compared with the speed at which excess pore pressures set up by the loading can dissipate owing to consolidation.

There are two limiting cases for the rate of loading of soil. On the one hand, the loading may be so quick that there is no time for any dissipation of pore pressure or for any water to flow from the soil; loading of this kind is known as *undrained*. Since no water flows from the soil there can be no volume change during undrained loading of saturated soil. On the other hand, the loading may be so slow that all excess pore pressures dissipate during the loading; loading of this kind is known as *drained*. Since all excess pore pressures dissipate, the pore pressure remains constant during drained loading.

The rate at which excess pore pressures dissipate owing to consolidation depends to a great extent on the permeability of the soil; excess pore pressures dissipate very rapidly in coarse grained sands and gravels but very slowly in fine grained clays. Thus, for most practical purposes, for construction involving sands and gravels the loading may usually be assumed to be drained, while for construction involving clays the loading may be assumed to be undrained. It must be appreciated however, that for the very quick loadings that may occur during explosive shocks, granular soils may suffer undrained loading while, for the very slow loadings that occur during geological processes clay soils may suffer drained loading. There are, in addition, cases such as construction of an earthfill dam with internal drainage, where the loading is neither drained nor undrained; but for most practical purposes it is sufficient to assume that the loading of clay in the ground is undrained while the loading of a granular soil in the ground is drained.

2.3 THE STATE BOUNDARY SURFACE

Soil behavior may be understood in a qualitative way with reference to a *state boundary surface*. Thus the state boundary surface provides a conceptual model for soil behaviour and this is known as the *critical state model*. The state boundary surface may be expressed mathematically and so, making use of the theories of elasticity and plasticity discussed in Chapter 1, the critical state model may be extended to provide a complete mathematical model for soil behaviour.

A view of the state boundary surface for soil in triaxial compression is sketched with axes q' : p' : v in Fig 2.1. The importance of the state boundary surface is that it represents a boundary to all possible states of shear stress q', normal stress p', and specific volume v in the same way that the yield surface shown in Fig. 1.15(b) represented a boundary to all possible states of σ_a', σ_c', and ϵ^p for the ideal soil-like material described in Sec. 1.6. It is assumed that the behaviour of samples of soil whose states are inside the state boundary surface is purely elastic and that plastic strains occur as the state of a sample traverses the state boundary surface.

The complete state boundary surface shown in Fig. 2.1 is made up of a number of features. The line *AB* is the *critical state line* and represents all possible states of ultimate failure. The line *GH* is the *normal consolidation line* and represents the states of soil samples during isotropic (i.e., $q' = 0$) normal compression. The curved surface *ABHG* joining the critical state line and the normal consolidation line is known as the *Roscoe surface* and it represents states of yielding normally consolidated soil. The plane *CDFE* represents a condition of zero tensile stress which is assumed to be a requirement for all soils; clearly, if tensile forces between individual grains can exist in a particular soil owing to cementing or some other reason, the precise position of the plane *CDFE* must be modified for that soil. The surface *ABCD*, between the critical state line and an intersection with the no-tension cutoff, is known as the *Hvorslev surface* and represents the states of yielding heavily overconsolidated soil.

The state boundary surface represents relationships between q', p', and v for yielding soil, but it is important to note that it may not represent the states of

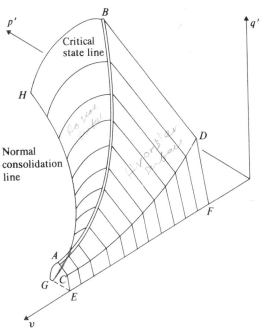

Figure 2.1 State boundary surface. (*From Atkinson and Bransby, 1978.*)

samples suffering discontinuous slipping. If there are slip planes, measurements of stress and, particularly, of strain made at the boundaries of samples may not represent the states of small elements of soil in the slip planes. In addition, because of the very large shear strains which occur in very thin slip planes, the structure of the soil in the slip planes may alter, perhaps as particles become preferentially aligned and the ultimate state may fall below the critical state towards a residual state, as discussed in Sec. 2.9.

The behaviour of an overconsolidated sample whose state lies inside the state boundary surface is assumed to be elastic, and so its behaviour is governed by Eqs. (1.45) and (1.46). Since volumetric strains are independent of changes $\delta q'$ of shear stress, the state of a sample inside the state boundary surface must remain in the vertical plane above a particular unloading–reloading line. A vertical plane *JLMK* above an isotropic swelling line like that shown in Fig. 2.2 is known as an *elastic wall*; there are of course an infinite number of elastic walls, each associated with a particular swelling line. Thus we have very strong restrictions on the possible state paths for soils. The state of a soil can only traverse the state boundary surface or an elastic wall; if the path traverses an elastic wall then the strains are purely elastic and if the path traverses the state boundary surface then some plastic strains occur.

Figure 2.3 shows projections of the state boundary surface onto the $v : p'$ plane and onto the $q' : p'$ plane. Thus Fig. 2.3(a) is a view of the state boundary surface seen by looking back along the q' axis towards the origin and Fig. 2.3(c)

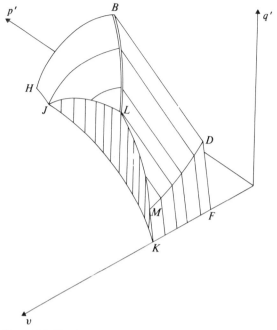

Figure 2.2 Elastic wall. (*After Atkinson and Bransby, 1978.*)

is a view seen by looking back towards the origin from the negative v axis; Fig. 2.3(b) is simply Fig. 2.3(a) replotted with axes $v : \ln p'$. The line GH is the part of the state boundary surface corresponding to $q' = 0$ and is the isotropic normal consolidation line given by

$$v = N - \lambda \ln p' \tag{2.1}$$

where N and λ are soil parameters; N is the specific volume of a soil sample isotropically normally consolidated to $p' = 1.0$ and hence its value depends on the units chosen for p'. The line KJ is the projection of a vertical elastic wall and so corresponds to the unloading–reloading line KJ for isotropic overconsolidation given by

$$v = v_\kappa - \kappa \ln p' \tag{2.2}$$

where v_κ is the specific volume on the line KJ corresponding to $p' = 1.0$ and the value of v_κ like that of N, depends on the units chosen for p'. The line AB is the projection of the critical state line; it is parallel with the isotropic normal consolidation line and it is given by

$$v_f = \Gamma - \lambda \ln p_f' \tag{2.3}$$

where Γ is a soil parameter whose value, like that of N, depends on the units chosen

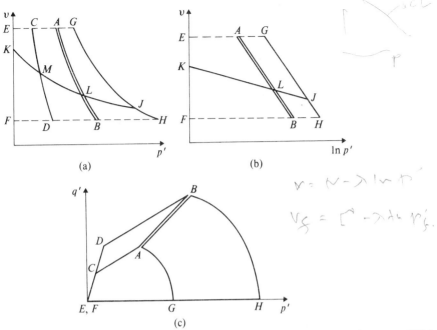

Figure 2.3 Projections of the state boundary surface (*After Atkinson and Bransby, 1978.*)

for p'. In Fig. 2.3(c) the line AB is the projection of the critical state line on to the $q' : p'$ plane and is given by

$$q'_f = M p'_f \tag{2.4}$$

where M is a soil parameter. Equation (2.4) states that when soil fails at its critical state the shearing resistance q'_f is linearly proportional to the mean stress p'_f and so the strength of soil is regarded as being frictional. The lines EC and FD in Figs. 2.1 and 2.3 lie in the plane representing the condition of no tension. For no tension $\sigma'_3 \geqslant 0$ and, taking the limiting case of $\sigma'_3 = 0$, the lines EC and FD are given by

$$q' = 3p' \tag{2.5}$$

The lines CA and DB lie in the Hvorslev surface and the lines BH and AG lie in the Roscoe surface. These lines are constant volume sections of the state boundary surface and they represent the paths followed by soil samples during undrained (i.e. constant volume) loading. The parameters λ, κ, M, N, Γ, and v_κ required to define the critical state line, an elastic wall, and the normal consolidation lines are shown in Fig. 2.4.

The precise shapes of the Roscoe and Hvorslev surfaces depend on a number of factors and various authorities have proposed slightly different shapes. For example, Schofield and Wroth (1968, Chapter 6) defined the Roscoe surface by

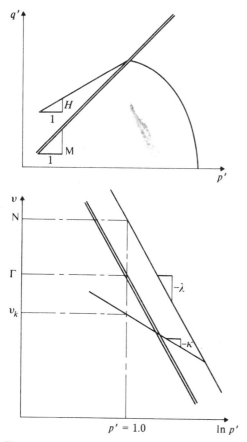

Figure 2.4 Definitions of the state boundary surface parameters.

$$\frac{q'}{Mp'} + \left(\frac{\lambda}{\lambda - \kappa}\right) \ln p' - \left(\frac{\Gamma - v}{\lambda - \kappa}\right) = 1 \qquad (2.6)$$

and the soil model based on Eq. (2.6) is usually known as *Cam clay*, while Atkinson and Bransby (1978, Chapters 10 and 11) defined the Hvorslev surface by

$$\frac{q'}{Hp'} - \left(\frac{M - H}{Hp'}\right) \exp\left(\frac{\Gamma - v}{\lambda}\right) = 1 \qquad (2.7)$$

where H is a soil parameter equal to the slope of a constant volume section of the Hvorslev surface, as shown in Fig. 2.4.

So far we have examined the state boundary surface and the behaviour of soil samples for triaxial compression for which $\sigma'_a = \sigma'_1$ and $\sigma'_r = \sigma'_2 = \sigma'_3$, where σ'_a and σ'_r are the axial and radial stresses on a cylindrical sample. For triaxial extension $\sigma'_a = \sigma'_3$ and $\sigma'_r = \sigma'_1 = \sigma'_2$, and it is convenient to redefine parameters for stress and strain as

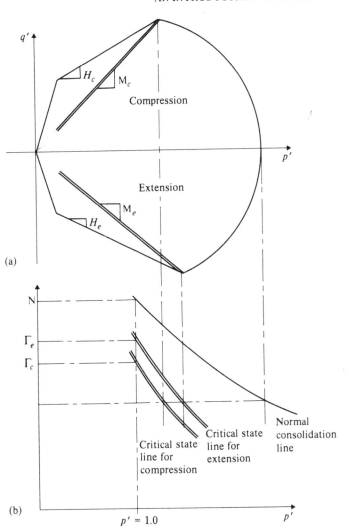

Figure 2.5 State boundary surface for triaxial compression and extension.

$$q' = (\sigma'_a - \sigma'_r) \qquad p' = \tfrac{1}{3}(\sigma'_a + 2\sigma'_r) \qquad (2.8)$$

$$\epsilon_s = \tfrac{2}{3}(\epsilon_a - \epsilon_r) \qquad \epsilon_v = (\epsilon_a + 2\epsilon_r) \qquad (2.9)$$

Thus, for triaxial compression q' is positive while for triaxial extension q' is negative and we expect the state boundary surface shown in Fig. 2.1 to extend *below* the $v : p'$ plane. A constant volume section of this 'complete' state boundary surface is shown in Fig. 2.5. The parts for triaxial compression and triaxial extension each have the same features but the one may not be a precise mirror image of the other. Experimental results from laboratory tests indicate that the Roscoe surface may be taken to be symmetric about the p' axis, except perhaps near the critical state line, but the slope of the critical state line for triaxial compression M_c is not the same as the slope M_e for triaxial extension. Thus, for triaxial extension the critical state line is given by

$$q'_f = M_e \, p'_f \tag{2.10}$$

$$v_f = \Gamma_e - \lambda \ln p'_f \tag{2.11}$$

and the Hvorslev surface is given by

$$\frac{q'}{H_e p'} - \left(\frac{M_e - H_e}{H_e p'}\right) \exp\left(\frac{\Gamma_e - v}{\lambda}\right) = 1 \tag{2.12}$$

Clearly, since the isotropic consolidation and swelling lines are the same for both parts of the state boundary surface the parameters N, λ, and κ, may be regarded as soil constants but Γ, M, and H depend on the state of stress and require subscripts c for compression and e for extension.

For plane strain it is convenient to define parameters for stress and strain

$$t' = \tfrac{1}{2}(\sigma'_v - \sigma'_h) \qquad s' = \tfrac{1}{2}(\sigma'_v + \sigma'_h) \tag{2.13}$$

$$\epsilon_\gamma = (\epsilon_v - \epsilon_h) \qquad \epsilon_v = (\epsilon_v + \epsilon_h) \tag{2.14}$$

where σ'_v and σ'_h are vertical and horizontal stresses respectively. Thus, for plane strain compression t' is positive, while for plane strain extension t' is negative.

We may adopt parameters $t' : s' : v$ as axes for plotting states of soils for plane strain and we will assume that the general features of the state boundary surface for triaxial tests shown in Figs. 2.1 and 2.5 apply also for plane strain. Since for isotropic soil plane strain compression is the same as plane strain extension, the state boundary surface will be symmetric about the $v : s'$ plane. Figure 2.6 shows a constant volume section of the state boundary surface for plane strain. Although isotropic compression is impossible at the same time as plane strain, we may consider normal consolidation and welling lines for $\sigma'_v = \sigma'_h$ and $t' = 0$ given by

$$v = N_{ps} - \lambda \ln s' \tag{2.15}$$

$$v = v_\kappa - \kappa \ln s' \tag{2.16}$$

and it may be assumed that λ and κ are soil constants. Equation 2.16 also defines an elastic wall.

Figure 2.7 shows the Mohr's circle of effective stress for an element of soil which is at ultimate failure at the critical state in plane strain. The state of stress may be characterized by the *critical state angle of friction* ϕ'_{cs} shown in Fig. 2.7, where

$$t' = s' \sin \phi'_{cs} \tag{2.17}$$

Comparing Fig. 2.7 with Fig. 1.12(b), ϕ'_{cs} is the same as ρ', the angle of shearing resistance, for states corresponding to the critical state. The relationships between ϕ'_{cs} and the triaxial friction parameters M_c and M_e were discussed by Atkinson and

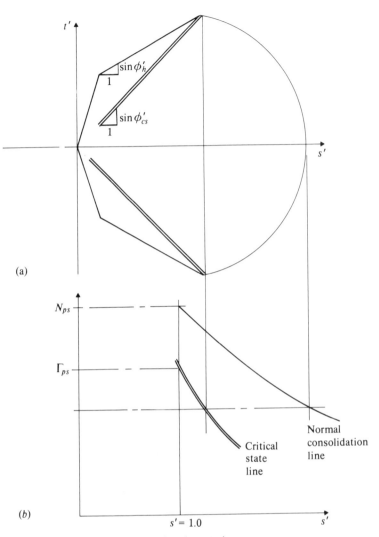

Figure 2.6 State boundary surface for plane strain.

Bransby (1978, pp. 310–312). Laboratory experiments (Bishop, 1972) show that the value of ϕ'_{cs} for plane strain is approximately the same as that for triaxial extension and both are only slightly greater than the value of ϕ'_{cs} for triaxial compression, and for most practical purposes ϕ'_{cs} may be taken as a soil constant.

Thus, for plane strain the critical state line is given by

$$t'_f = s'_f \sin \phi'_{cs} \tag{2.18}$$

$$v_f = \Gamma_{ps} - \lambda \ln s'_f \tag{2.19}$$

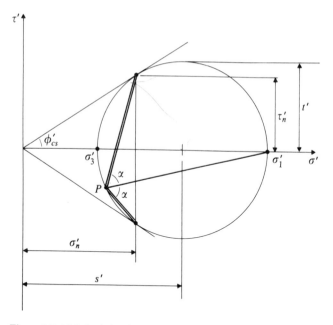

Figure 2.7 Mohr's circle of stress for ultimate failure at the critical state.

By analogy with Eqs. (2.6) and (2.7), the Roscoe and Hvorslev surfaces for plane strain may be written respectively as

$$\frac{t'}{s' \sin \phi'_{cs}} + \left(\frac{\lambda}{\lambda - \kappa}\right) \ln s' - \left(\frac{\Gamma_{ps} - v}{\lambda - \kappa}\right) = 1 \tag{2.20}$$

$$\frac{t'}{s' \sin \phi'_h} - \left(\frac{\sin \phi'_{cs} - \sin \phi'_h}{s' \sin \phi'_h}\right) \exp\left(\frac{\Gamma_{ps} - v}{\lambda}\right) = 1 \tag{2.21}$$

where $\sin \phi'_h$ and $\sin \phi'_{cs}$ give the slopes of the Hvorslev surface and critical state line respectively, as shown in Fig. 2.6.

From Fig. 2.7 the stresses τ'_n and σ'_n at the points at which the Mohr's circle just touches the limiting lines are related by

$$\tau'_n = \sigma'_n \tan \phi'_{cs} \tag{2.22}$$

and these stresses occur on planes angled at $\pm \alpha$ to the major principal plane, where

$$\alpha = (45° + \tfrac{1}{2}\phi'_{cs}) \tag{2.23}$$

For the special case when the angle of dilation $\psi = \phi'_{cs}$ these planes are also planes of zero strain and of discontinuous slipping, as discussed in Secs 1.3 and 1.4. It is not appropriate to construct a complete state boundary surface for discontinuous slipping but the critical state line may be written

$$\tau'_{nf} = \sigma'_{nf} \tan \phi'_{cs} \tag{2.24}$$

$$v_f = \Gamma_n - \lambda \ln \sigma'_{nf} \tag{2.25}$$

and by analogy with Eq. (2.7) the Hvorslev surface is given by

$$\frac{\tau'_n}{\sigma'_n \tan \phi'_h} - \left(\frac{\tan \phi'_{cs} - \tan \phi'_h}{\sigma'_n \tan \phi'_h} \right) \exp \left(\frac{\Gamma_n - v}{\lambda} \right) = 1 \tag{2.26}$$

Here ϕ'_{cs} is the slope of the critical state line and ϕ'_h is the slope of a constant volume section of the Hvorslev surface.

It is convenient to distinguish between samples whose states lie on one side of the vertical plane below the critical state line and those whose states lie on the other side. Samples whose states project into the area $ABHG$ to the right of the projection AB of the critical state line in Fig. 2.3(b) are known as *wet of critical* for they exist at states with higher specific volumes (i.e., with higher water contents or wetter) than those samples on the critical state line at the same value of p'; samples on the wet side of critical are normally consolidated if their states lie on the Roscoe surface and are lightly overconsolidated if their states lie below the Roscoe surface in areas such as bhb' in Fig. 2.8(a). Samples whose states project into the area to the left of the projection AB of the critical state line in Fig. 2.8(b) are known as *dry of critical* for they exist at states with lower specific volumes

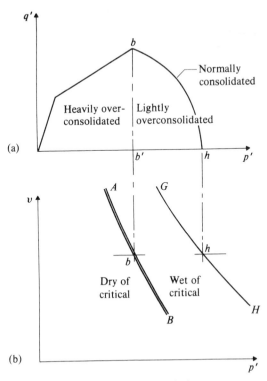

Figure 2.8 States wet and dry of critical.

(i.e., with lower water contents or drier) than those samples on the critical state line at the same value of p'; samples on the dry side of critical are heavily over-consolidated.

The state boundary surface model may be used in a qualitative way to understand the behaviour of soil during loading. The general shape of the state boundary surface shown in Fig. 2.1 shows marked similarities with a boundary surface developed by Schofield and Wroth (1968) from purely theoretical considerations of material behaviour. It must be appreciated that the state boundary surface idea and the critical state model are idealizations for soil behaviour; they correctly represent a number of the important features of the mechanical behaviour of remoulded soil and also of many natural soils but, of course, there may be particular natural soils which, perhaps because of cementing of the grains or for other reasons, may behave differently.

2.4 YIELDING AND HARDENING

It is assumed that soils yield when their states lie on the state boundary surface, which therefore serves as a yield surface. A soil whose state is inside the state boundary surface lies on an elastic wall (Fig. 2.2) above a swelling line and its state can move only on that elastic wall, causing purely elastic strains. Plastic strains can occur only when the state of the soil moves on the state boundary surface, which then serves as a yield surface similar to that shown in Fig. 1.15(b). Hence yield curves, similar to those shown in Fig. 1.15(a), are given by the intersections of elastic walls (on which only elastic strains occur) with the state boundary surface. Thus in Fig. 2.9 the top $JLMK$ of an elastic wall projects on to the $q':p'$ plane to give a yield curve $J'L'M'K'$ for all samples on that elastic wall and the projection of the yield curve on to the $v:p'$ plane is clearly the unloading–reloading line JK. Hence a yield curve is associated with a particular elastic wall.

Figure 2.10 shows the projections of a particular yield curve on to the $q':p'$ and $v:p'$ planes. If the flow rule for soil is taken to be associated then the yield curve $J'L'M'K'$ in Fig. 2.10(a) is also a plastic potential and vectors of plastic strain increment $\delta\varepsilon^p$ are normal to it as shown. For a particular increment of loading the state of the sample will move to another adjacent yield curve and a hardening law may be obtained if the states of stress before and after the increment are known. In order to illustrate these ideas more fully we will examine arbitrary loading paths $Q \rightarrow R$ and $S \rightarrow T$ in Fig. 2.11, which both move on the state boundary surface and so cause plastic strains; the path $Q \rightarrow R$ remains on the Roscoe surface on the wet side of critical and the path $S \rightarrow T$ remains on the Hvorslev surface on the dry side of critical.

Figure 2.12 shows the loading path $Q \rightarrow R$ and the appropriate yield curves and elastic walls projected on to the $q':p'$ and $v:p'$ planes. The path $Q \rightarrow R$ in Fig. 2.12(c) consists of a component QP which represents a change of state from the elastic wall $K_1M_1L_1J_1$ to the elastic wall $K_2M_2L_2J_2$ plus a component PR

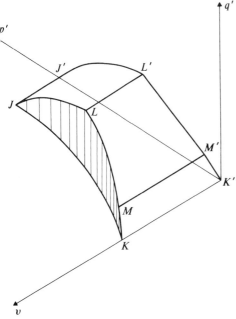

Figure 2.9 Yield curve for soil. (*After Atkinson and Bransby, 1978*).

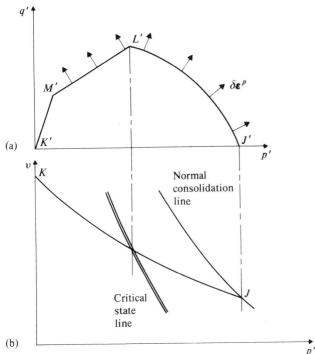

Figure 2.10 Projections of a yield curve.

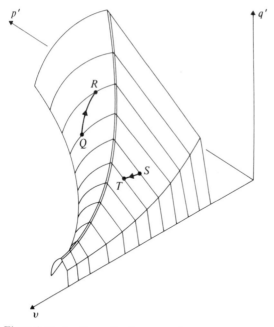

Figure 2.11 Loading paths for states of samples which remain on the state boundary surface.

which represents a change of state on the elastic wall $K_2M_2L_2J_2$. The component QP gives rise to purely plastic strains $\delta\epsilon_s^p$ and $\delta\epsilon_v^p$, while the component PR gives rise to purely elastic strains $\delta\epsilon_s^e$ and $\delta\epsilon_v^e$, corresponding to the increments of stress $\delta q'$ and $\delta p'$ in Fig. 2.12(b). The elastic components $\delta\epsilon_s^e$ and $\delta\epsilon_v^e$ are given from Eqs. (1.45) and (1.46) by

$$\delta\epsilon_s^e = \frac{1}{3G'}\,\delta q' \tag{2.27}$$

$$\delta\epsilon_v^e = \frac{1}{K'}\,\delta p' \tag{2.28}$$

where G' and K' are elastic parameters corresponding to the component PR on the elastic wall $K_2M_2L_2J_2$. The elastic and plastic volumetric strains are given in terms of the changes of specific volume δv^e and δv^p in Fig. 2.12(c) by

$$\delta\epsilon_v^e = -\frac{\delta v^e}{v} \tag{2.29}$$

$$\delta\epsilon_v^p = -\frac{\delta v^p}{v} \tag{2.30}$$

The point Q lies on the yield curve $K_1M_1L_1J_1$, which is also a plastic potential and hence the direction of the plastic strain increment vector $\delta\boldsymbol{\epsilon}^p$ is given by

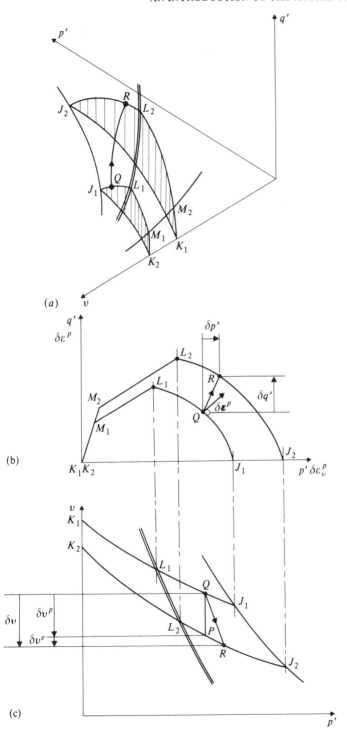

Fig. 2.12 Plastic straining of soil on the wet side of critical (*After Atkinson and Bransby 1978*).

the normal to the curve $L_1 J_1$ in Fig. 2.12(b). The flow rule is given by Eq. (1.57
as

$$\frac{\delta \epsilon_s^p}{\delta \epsilon_v^p} = F \tag{2.31}$$

where the parameter F depends on the state of stress at Q and on the equation
for the yield curve $L_1 J_1$. The point R, representing the end of the increment of
loading from Q, lies on the yield curve $K_2 M_2 L_2 J_2$, and since this yield curve is
larger than $K_1 M_1 L_1 J_1$, the soil has strain hardened from Q to R. Since the path
$Q \to R$ remains on the yield surface, so long as plastic strains occur, a hardening
law may be written in terms of the plastic volumetric strain increment as

$$\delta \epsilon_v^p = H \delta q' + G \delta p' = -\frac{\delta v^p}{v} \tag{2.32}$$

where H and G are parameters which depend on the equation of the state boundary
surface and on the state of stress at Q and δv^p is the plastic change of specific vol
ume for the loading path QR. Thus, given equations for the state boundary surface
we may calculate values for the parameters F and H in Eqs. (1.63) and (1.64) and
this is done later, in Sec. 2.7. These arguments are equally valid for the loading path
$S \to T$ in Fig. 2.13, which moves on the Hvorslev surface except that the yield curve
$K_3 M_3 L_3 J_3$ is smaller than $K_1 M_1 L_1 J_1$ and the soil has *strain softened* from S to
T, although the vector $\delta \boldsymbol{\epsilon}^p$ of the plastic strain increment must still be directed
outwards and normal to the yield curve $M_1 L_1$. The analysis is valid also for the
undrained loading paths $U \to V$ and $W \to X$ in Fig. 2.14, but note that for undrained
loading of saturated soil $\delta v = 0$, and hence the elastic component of the volumetric
strain is equal and opposite to the plastic component and

$$\delta \epsilon_v^p = -\delta \epsilon_v^e \tag{2.33}$$

Since there is no total volume change for undrained loading, the state of an
undrained sample must remain in a constant volume plane and hence the paths
$U \to V$ and $W \to X$ are given by the intersection of a constant volume plane and
the state boundary surface, as shown in Fig. 2.14. If the state is below the state
boundary surface and on an elastic wall it can only move on that elastic wall until
it reaches the state boundary surface. For undrained loading, the paths $Y \to U$ and
$Z \to X$ in Fig. 2.14 are vertical, as they are the intersections of vertical elastic walls
with a vertical constant volume plane. For any total stress path for undrained loading, the pore pressure will adjust itself to give the required effective stress path
$Y \to U \to V$ on the wet side of critical or $Z \to W \to X$ on the dry side. Thus, making
use of Eq. 1.36,

$$q' = q \qquad p' = p - u \tag{2.34}$$

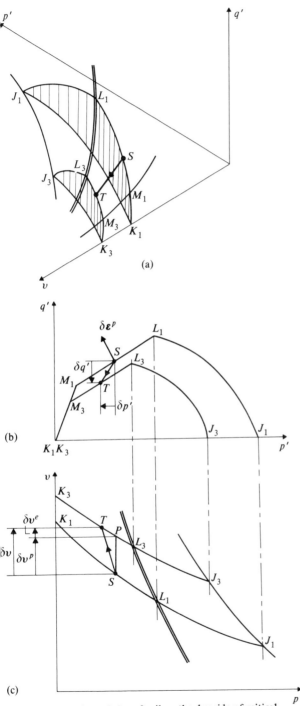

Figure 2.13 Plastic straining of soil on the dry side of critical.

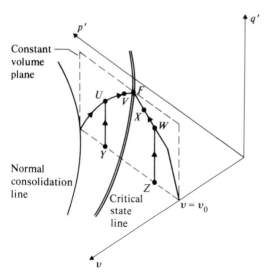

Figure 2.14 State paths for undrained loading.

the pore pressure for undrained loading is given by the horizontal distance between the total stress path and the effective stress path.

2.5 FAILURE OF SOIL

Soils reach a state of ultimate failure at the critical state when (and if) their states reach the critical state line in Fig. 2.1. For triaxial loading, for plane strain loading, and for discontinuous slipping, respectively, the critical state line is given by

$$q' = Mp' \qquad v = \Gamma - \lambda \ln p' \tag{2.35}$$

$$t' = s' \sin \phi'_{cs} \qquad v = \Gamma_{ps} - \lambda \ln s' \tag{2.36}$$

$$\tau'_n = \sigma'_n \tan \phi'_{cs} \qquad v = \Gamma_n - \lambda \text{ in } \sigma'_n \tag{2.37}$$

where ϕ'_{cs} and λ may be assumed to be soil constants but M and Γ depend on the loading conditions. Alternatively, soils may be taken as having failed when (and if) their states first reach the Hvorslev surface. For triaxial loading, for plane strain loading, and for discontinuous slipping, respectively, the Hvorslev surface is given by

$$q' = (M - H) \exp\left(\frac{\Gamma - v}{\lambda}\right) + Hp' \tag{2.38}$$

$$t' = (\sin \phi'_{cs} - \sin \phi'_h) \exp \left(\frac{\Gamma_{ps} - v}{\lambda} \right) + s' \sin \phi'_h \tag{2.39}$$

$$\tau'_n = (\tan \phi'_{cs} - \tan \phi'_h) \exp \left(\frac{\Gamma_n - v}{\lambda} \right) + \sigma'_n \tan \phi'_h \tag{2.40}$$

where ϕ'_h may be assumed to be a soil constant but H depends on the loading conditions. Failure on the Hvorslev surface is appropriate for the peak strength of soils on the dry side of critical for drained loading.

Equations (2.35) to (2.40) are all criteria of failure and they specify relationships between stresses and specific volume for ultimate failure at the critical state and for peak failure on the Hvorslev surface for different loading conditions.

Alternatively, the failure of soil is often written

$$\tau'_n = c' + \sigma'_n \tan \phi' \tag{2.41}$$

where ϕ' is known as the *angle of friction* and c' is known as the *cohesion*. Equation (2.41) is the *Mohr–Coulomb* failure criterion and it expresses the strength of soil as the sum of a cohesion component and a frictional component.

Since τ'_n may be positive or negative, Eq. (2.41) plots as two straight lines AB and AB' in Fig. 2.15(a) and these are known as *failure envelopes*. The Mohr–Coulomb failure criterion relates the shear and normal stresses on particular planes for soil which is failing, and hence the Mohr's circle of effective stress for failing soil must just touch the failure envelopes as shown in Fig. 2.15(b). If the pole of the Mohr's circle is placed at some arbitrary point such as P in Fig. 2.15(b) then, from the geometry of the figure, the *failure planes* for which the circle just touches the failure envelope are at angles $\pm \alpha = (45° + \frac{1}{2}\phi')$ to the major principal plane. The Mohr–Coulomb failure criterion given by Eq. (2.41) is convenient for examining the stability of a soil structure which may collapse by sliding along particular slip planes.

For ultimate failure at the critical state, comparing Eqs. (2.37) and (2.41) we have

$$c' = 0 \qquad \phi' = \phi'_{cs} \tag{2.42}$$

and for peak failure on the Hvorslev surface, comparing Eqs. (2.40) and (2.41) we have

$$c' = (\tan \phi'_{cs} - \tan \phi'_h) \exp \left(\frac{\Gamma_n - v}{\lambda} \right) \qquad \phi' = \phi'_h \tag{2.43}$$

Thus, from Eq. (2.43), the Hvorslev cohesion term is a function of the specific volume and c' decreases exponentially as the specific volume increases. It is important to note here that the Hvorslev surface shown in Fig. 2.1 is limited on one side by the critical state line and on the other side by the no-tension cutoff surface. Hence values for c' and ϕ' given by Eqs. (2.43) which describe the Hvorslev surface in terms of the Mohr–Coulomb criterion are applicable only over a limited range

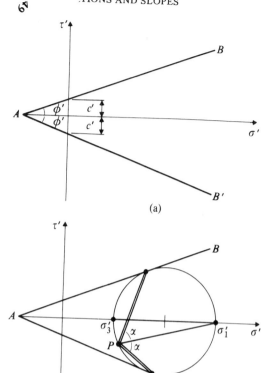

Figure 2.15 The Mohr–Coulomb failure criterion.

of states. In particular, it is incorrect to interpret c' as the strength of soil for drained loading with $\sigma'_n = 0$, since the Hvorslev surface cannot be extended beyond the no-tension cutoff surface.

It is common to attribute cohesion in soils, such as that shown by Eq. (2.41), to forces bonding or cementing individual soil grains together, but the test results from which the Hvorslev surface was constructed were obtained from tests on remoulded samples of clay. For this material the projection of the critical state line passes through the origin of the $q' : p'$ plane and hence interparticle bonding forces can be assumed to be negligible. The Hvorslev cohesion term given by Eq. (2.40) is purely a consequence of overconsolidation of the remoulded samples. In nature, however, soils remain essentially undisturbed for very long periods, perhaps many millions of years, and some bonding forces may develop. We will not enquire here into the nature of these bonding forces and will simply remark that they will appear as a cohesion term over and above that given by Eqs. (2.42). Thus, for heavily overconsolidated natural soils the cohesion term consists of two components; one, given by Eqs. (2.43) is a consequence of overconsolidation and the ther is a consequence of interparticle forces developed in the ground over long periods of time.

For the special case of undrained loading of saturated soil all samples with the same specific volume ultimately reach the critical state line at the same point, such as F in Fig. 2.14, and consequently they all have the same strength, irrespective of the total stress path. This *undrained shear strength* is given the symbol c_u and is given by

$$c_u = \tfrac{1}{2}(\sigma_1' - \sigma_3')_f = \tfrac{1}{2}q_f' = t_f' = \tau_{nf}' \tag{2.44}$$

For undrained loading the specific volume remains a constant and the specific volume at failure is the same as the specific volume at any stage of loading; thus, from Eqs. (2.35) to (2.37) with Eq. (2.44) we have

$$c_u = \tfrac{1}{2}M \exp\left(\frac{\Gamma - v}{\lambda}\right) = \sin\phi_{cs}' \exp\left(\frac{\Gamma_{ps} - v}{\lambda}\right) = \tan\phi_{cs}' \exp\left(\frac{\Gamma_n - v}{\lambda}\right) \tag{2.45}$$

From Eq. (2.45) the undrained shear strength c_u depends only on the specific volume v and on some soil parameters and is independent of the total normal stresses p, s, and σ_n.

For undrained loading of saturated soil, the Mohr–Coulomb failure criterion may be written in terms of total, rather than effective, stresses as

$$\tau_n = c_u + \sigma_n \tan\phi_u \tag{2.46}$$

where the subscripts u indicate that c_u and ϕ_u are appropriate for undrained loading. From Eq. (2.44), noting that $\tau_n' = \tau_n$, we have

$$\tau_n = c_u \tag{2.47}$$

and $\phi_u = 0$. Equation (2.47) is often known as the $\phi_u = 0$ failure criterion for undrained loading; it is valid only for saturated soil, for which there is no volume change during undrained loading.

The failure criterion given by Eq. (2.47) is shown plotted as a failure envelope in Fig. 2.16(a), with axes of total stress $\tau : \sigma$, and Mohr's circles of total stress for failure of a number of samples each with the same specific volume all just touch the undrained failure envelope. For a typical Mohr's circle the pole is at P and the planes for which the circle touches the failure envelope are at $\alpha = \pm 45°$ to the major principal plane.

The single Mohr's circle of effective stress corresponding to *all* the total stress circles is shown in Fig. 2.16(b) and the effective stress circle just touches the critical state failure envelope given by Eq. (2.37) in terms of effective stress. The pole of the circle is at P and the planes for which the Mohr's circle touches the critical state failure envelope are at $\alpha = \pm(45° + \tfrac{1}{2}\phi_{cs}')$ to the major principal plane. The total stress circles in Fig. 2.16(a) are related to the single effective stress circle in Fig. 2.16(b) by the magnitudes of the pore pressures at failure, as shown in Fig.

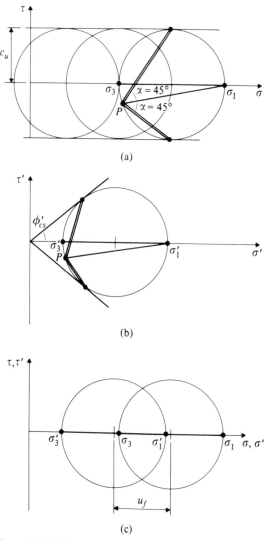

Figure 2.16 Mohr's circles of total and effective stress for undrained failure.

2.16(c), where a total stress circle from Fig. 2.16(a) and the effective stress circle from Fig. 2.16(b) are plotted together.

The technique of describing the failure of soil by its undrained shear strength c_u is attractively simple, but we must be clear about what is involved. The conditions of failure are still dependent on the effective stresses, but these are controlled by the requirement that the soil maintains its volume constant. Thus, by working with total stresses we avoid the need to calculate pore pressures. It must, however, be properly understood that the total stress technique taking $\phi_u = 0$ is alid *only* for the special case of undrained loading of saturated soil where volumetric trains are zero; in all other cases the total stress analysis is not valid and calculations hould proceed in terms of effective stress.

2.6 ELASTIC STRESS–STRAIN RELATIONSHIPS

So long as the state of a sample is inside the state boundary surface, its behaviour is purely elastic, as the state remains on an elastic wall and the stress–strain relationships are given by Eqs. (1.45) and (1.46) as

$$\delta \epsilon_s = \frac{1}{3G'} \delta q' \tag{2.48}$$

$$\delta \epsilon_v = \frac{1}{K'} \delta p' \tag{2.49}$$

where G' and K' are, respectively, the elastic shear and bulk moduli and these are related to Young's modulus and Poisson's ratio by

$$G' = \frac{E'}{2(1+v')} \qquad K' = \frac{E'}{3(1-2v')} \tag{2.50}$$

Now, as the state of a sample remains on an elastic wall, the change of specific volume is given by

$$\delta v = -\kappa \, \delta(\ln p') = -\kappa \frac{\delta p'}{p'} \tag{2.51}$$

or

$$\delta \epsilon_v = \frac{\kappa}{vp'} \delta p' \tag{2.52}$$

Hence, from Eqs. (2.49), (2.50) and (2.52) the elastic moduli are given by

$$K' = \frac{vp'}{\kappa} \tag{2.53}$$

$$G' = \frac{vp'}{\kappa} \frac{3(1-2v')}{2(1+v')} \tag{2.54}$$

$$E' = \frac{3vp'}{\kappa}(1-2v') \tag{2.55}$$

In this treatment of elastic behaviour in soils the elastic moduli depend on the current values of v and p' as well as on the values of κ and v'. It is usual to take v' as a constant and we may obtain a normalized Young's modulus E'_n given by

$$E'_n = \frac{E'}{vp'} = \frac{3}{\kappa}(1-2v') \tag{2.56}$$

which, in theory, may be taken as a constant. For drained triaxial compression where $\delta\sigma_2' = \delta\sigma_3' = 0$ we have

$$\delta\epsilon_1 = \frac{1}{E'}\delta\sigma_1' \qquad \text{and} \qquad \delta\epsilon_2 = \delta\epsilon_3 = -\frac{\nu'}{E'}\delta\sigma_1' \qquad (2.57)$$

and hence, in the limit,

$$E' = \frac{d\sigma_1'}{d\epsilon_1} = \frac{dq'}{d\epsilon_1} \qquad (2.58)$$

$$\nu' = -\frac{d\epsilon_3}{d\epsilon_1} = \frac{1}{2}\left(1 - \frac{d\epsilon_v}{d\epsilon_1}\right) \qquad (2.59)$$

Thus values for Young's modulus and Poisson's ratio may be found directly from the slopes of the deviator stress–axial strain curve and the volumetric strain–axial strain curve obtained from the results of a drained triaxial test.

For undrained loading of saturated soil the effective stress path follows the intersection of an elastic wall and a constant volume plane, as shown in Fig. 2.14. For undrained loading $\delta\epsilon_v = 0$ and hence, from Eq. (2.49), we have $\delta p' = 0$ and the path is vertical as shown. Since $\delta p' = \delta\epsilon_v = 0$ for undrained loading, the elastic parameters given by Eqs. (2.53) to (2.55) remain constants and hence, in theory, stress–strain curves for undrained loading of elastic soil will be linear. It is often helpful to calculate changes of pore pressure for undrained loading in terms of the changes of total stress, by writing

$$\delta u = b[\delta p + a\,\delta q] \qquad (2.60)$$

where a and b are pore pressure parameters; for saturated soil $b = 1$ and for isotropic elastic soil $a = 0$. Equation (2.60) is conventionally expressed, following Skempton (1957), as

$$\delta u = B[\delta\sigma_3 + A(\delta\sigma_1 - \delta\sigma_3)] \qquad (2.61)$$

where for saturated soil $B = 1$ and for isotropic elastic soil $A = \frac{1}{3}$.

So far, in accordance with the principle of effective stress, we have quite properly related strains to *effective* stresses, but for undrained loading of saturated soil it is often convenient to relate strains to total stresses. Thus, in terms of total stress we have

$$\delta\epsilon_s = \frac{1}{3G_u}\delta q \qquad (2.62)$$

$$\delta\epsilon_v = \frac{1}{K_u}\delta p \qquad (2.63)$$

where

$$G_u = \frac{E_u}{2(1 + \nu_u)} \qquad K_u = \frac{E_u}{3(1 - 2\nu_u)} \qquad (2.64)$$

nd the subscripts u indicate that the elastic parameters are appropriate for un-drained loading. Since for undrained loading of saturated soil $\delta \epsilon_v = 0$, we have $K_u = \infty$ and

$$\nu_u = \tfrac{1}{2} \quad \text{and} \quad G_u = \tfrac{1}{3}E_u \tag{2.65}$$

In addition, since $\delta q = \delta q'$ and since for isotropic elastic soil $\delta \epsilon_s$ is independent of δp and $\delta p'$, we have

$$G_u = G' = \frac{\nu p'}{\kappa} \frac{3(1-2\nu')}{2(1+\nu')} \tag{2.66}$$

and

$$E_u = \frac{\nu p'}{\kappa} \frac{9(1-2\nu')}{2(1+\nu')} \tag{2.67}$$

For undrained triaxial compression with $\delta \sigma_2 = \delta \sigma_3 = 0$ we have

$$E_u = \frac{dq}{d\epsilon_1} \tag{2.68}$$

and a value for the undrained Young's modulus may be found directly from the slope of the deviator stress–axial strain curve obtained from the results of an undrained triaxial compression test.

The technique for expressing elastic deformations of soil in terms of total stress is similar to that used for the undrained shear strength c_u discussed earlier. Both are applicable *only* for the special case of undrained loading of saturated soil for which volume changes are zero; for all other cases, it is essential to adopt effective stress analyses. Thus, for calculating elastic deformations of soils it is necessary to determine whether or not the loading is undrained and then to choose between the effective stress parameters E' and ν' and the total stress parameters E_u and $\nu_u = \tfrac{1}{2}$

For plane strain, stresses and strains are related by

$$\delta \epsilon_\gamma = \frac{1}{G'_{ps}} \delta t' \tag{2.69}$$

$$\delta \epsilon_v = \frac{1}{K'_{ps}} \delta s' \tag{2.70}$$

where G'_{ps} and K'_{ps} are elastic moduli appropriate for plane strain and are given by

$$G'_{ps} = G' = \frac{E'}{2(1+\nu')} \qquad K'_{ps} = K' + \tfrac{1}{3}G' = \frac{E'}{2(1-2\nu')(1+\nu')} \tag{2.71}$$

Now, as the state of a sample remains on an elastic wall, the change of specific volume is given by Eq. (2.16) as

$$\delta v = -\kappa \, \delta(\ln s') = -\kappa \frac{\delta s'}{s'} \tag{2.72}$$

or

$$\delta\epsilon_v = \frac{\kappa}{vs'}\,\delta s' \tag{2.73}$$

and, from Eqs. (2.70), (2.71), and (2.73) we have

$$K'_{ps} = \frac{vs'}{\kappa} \tag{2.74}$$

$$G'_{ps} = \frac{vs'}{\kappa}(1 - 2v') \tag{2.75}$$

For undrained loading of saturated soil in plane strain, Eqs. (2.69) and (2.70) are written in terms of total stresses as

$$\delta\epsilon_\gamma = \frac{1}{G_{ups}}\,\delta t \tag{2.76}$$

$$\delta\epsilon_v = \frac{1}{K_{ups}}\,\delta s \tag{2.77}$$

where $K_{ups} = \infty$ since $\delta\epsilon_v = 0$ and $G_{ups} = G'_{ps}$ since $\delta t = \delta t'$ and $\delta\epsilon_s$ is independent of δs and $\delta s'$.

2.7 ELASTO-PLASTIC STRESS–STRAIN RELATIONSHIPS

The stress–strain behaviour of an isotropic elasto-plastic material for axially symmetric loading is given by Eqs. (1.63) and (1.64) as

$$\delta\epsilon_s = \left(FH + \frac{1}{3G'}\right)\delta q' + H\,\delta p' \tag{2.78}$$

$$\delta\epsilon_v = H\,\delta q' + \left(\frac{H}{F} + \frac{1}{K'}\right)\delta p' \tag{2.79}$$

where G' and K' are the elastic shear and bulk moduli respectively and F and H are parameters which depend on the current state and on the shape of the yield surface. A similar pair of equations, Eqs. (1.65) and (1.66), apply for plane strain loading. In Sec. 2.4 we examined, in a qualitative way, how the state boundary surface described in Sec. 2.3 can be adopted as a yield surface for soil and it now remains to show how values for the parameters F and H are obtained from the state boundary surface equations. The analysis given here is relatively simple and follows the approach given by Atkinson and Bransby (1978, Chapter 13). A similar analysis but for plane strain was given by Naylor (1978) and a more general approach was given by Zienkiewicz and Naylor (1972).

The Cam clay equation for the Roscoe surface is

$$\frac{q'}{Mp'} + \left(\frac{\lambda}{\lambda - \kappa}\right) \ln p' - \left(\frac{\Gamma - v}{\lambda - \kappa}\right) = 1 \qquad [2.6]$$

and it intersects the $v : p'$ plane along the normal consolidation line where $q' = 0$ and $v = N - \lambda \ln p'$. Hence we have

$$N - \Gamma = \lambda - \kappa \qquad (2.80)$$

Equation (2.80), which reduces the number of independent soil parameters, is only valid however for Cam clay and it may not hold for other equations for the Roscoe surface. A yield curve is the intersection of an elastic wall given by

$$v = v_\kappa - \kappa \ln p' \qquad [2.2]$$

with the state boundary surface. At failure on the critical state line,

$$v_f = v_\kappa - \kappa \ln p'_f = \Gamma - \lambda \ln p'_f \qquad (2.81)$$

and hence, eliminating v and v_κ, a yield curve is given by

$$\frac{q'}{Mp'} + \ln\left(\frac{p'}{p'_f}\right) = 1 \qquad (2.82)$$

where p'_f is the value of p' at the intersection of the yield curve and the critical state line and serves to locate a particular yield curve.

From the normality condition, the vector of plastic strain increment is normal to the yield curve and, differentiating Eq. (2.82), we have

$$-1 \bigg/ \frac{d\epsilon^p_s}{d\epsilon^p_v} = \frac{dq'}{dp'} = \frac{q'}{p'} - M \qquad (2.83)$$

and, from Eq. (1.57)

$$\frac{1}{F} = M - \eta' \qquad (2.84)$$

where $\eta' = q'/p'$ from Eq. (1.29). Equation (2.6) may be written

$$v = \Gamma + \lambda - \kappa - \lambda \ln p' - \frac{(\lambda - \kappa)q'}{Mp'} \qquad (2.85)$$

Hence, differentiating, dividing by v, and making use of Eq. (1.14) we have

$$\delta\epsilon_v = -\frac{\delta v}{v} = \left[\frac{\lambda - \kappa}{vMp'}\right]\delta q' - \left[\frac{(\lambda - \kappa)\eta'}{vMp'} - \frac{\lambda}{vp'}\right]\delta p' \qquad (2.86)$$

and, subtracting the elastic volumetric strains given by Eq. (2.52), we have

$$\delta\epsilon^p_v = \left[\frac{\lambda - \kappa}{vMp'}\right][\delta q' + (M - \eta')\delta p'] \qquad (2.87)$$

Thus, comparing Eqs. (1.58) and (2.87), we have

$$H = \frac{\lambda - \kappa}{vMp'} \, ^\dagger$$

(2.88)

Thus, for samples whose states remain on the Roscoe surface on the wet side of critical, we have obtained expressions for the parameters F and H in Eqs. (2.78) and (2.79) in terms of the critical state parameters M, λ, and κ. Making use of Eqs (2.84) and (2.88), Eqs. (2.78) and (2.79) written in full, become

$$\delta\epsilon_s = \left[\frac{\lambda - \kappa}{(M - \eta')vMp'} + \frac{1}{3G'} \right] \delta q' + \frac{\lambda - \kappa}{vMp'} \, \delta p'$$

(2.89)

$$\delta\epsilon_v = \frac{\lambda - \kappa}{vMp'} \, \delta q' + \left[(M - \eta')\frac{\lambda - \kappa}{vMp'} + \frac{1}{K'} \right] \delta p'$$

(2.90)

where G' and K' are the elastic shear and bulk moduli, respectively.

Equations (2.89) and (2.90) are valid for samples whose states remain on the Roscoe surface and for axisymmetric loading. For samples whose states are inside the state boundary surface and whose stress–strain behaviour is elastic, we put $H = 0$, as discussed in Sec. 1.9, in Eqs. (2.89) and (2.90) and recover Eqs. (2.48) and (2.49). The criteria by which a state is on the state boundary surface or on an elastic wall were discussed in Sec. 1.7. A path will move on the state boundary surface if irrecoverable plastic strains occur. If, however, a path traversing the state boundary surface implies recoverable plastic strains this is clearly impossible and the path will instead move on an elastic wall with zero plastic strain.

The equation for the Hvorslev surface is

$$\frac{q'}{Hp'} - \left(\frac{M - H}{Hp'} \right) \exp\left(\frac{\Gamma - v}{\lambda} \right) = 1$$

[2.7]

and, making use of Eqs. (2.2) and (2.81), the equation for a yield curve on the dry side of critical is

$$\frac{q'}{Hp'} - \left(\frac{M - H}{Hp'} \right) \left(\frac{p_f'}{p'} \right)^{1 - \kappa/\lambda} = 1$$

(2.91)

Thus, proceeding as before, we have

$$\delta\epsilon_s = \left[\frac{1}{3G'} - \frac{\lambda}{vp'(\eta' - H)\{(\kappa/\lambda)(\eta' - H) + H\}} \right] \delta q' + \frac{\lambda}{vp'(\eta' - H)} \delta p'$$

(2.92)

$$\delta\epsilon_v = \frac{\lambda}{vp'(\eta' - H)} \delta q' + \left[\frac{1}{K'} - \frac{\lambda}{vp'(\eta' - H)} \left\{ \frac{\kappa}{\lambda}(\eta' - H) + H \right\} \right] \delta p'$$

(2.93)

For plane strain the behaviour of an isotropic elasto-plastic material is given by Eqs. (1.65) and (1.66) as

---

†Comparing Eqs. (1.58) and (2.87), we have $G = (M - \eta')H$ and from Eq. (2.84) we have $G = H/F$, which verifies Eq. (1.62) for Cam clay.

$$\delta\epsilon_\gamma = \left(F_{ps}H_{ps} + \frac{1}{G'_{ps}}\right)\delta t' + H_{ps}\,\delta s' \tag{2.94}$$

$$\delta\epsilon_v = H_{ps}\delta t' + \left(\frac{H_{ps}}{F_{ps}} + \frac{1}{K'_{ps}}\right)\delta s' \tag{2.95}$$

where G'_{ps} and K'_{ps} are the elastic shear and bulk moduli respectively, given by Eqs. (2.74) and (2.75), and F_{ps} and H_{ps} are parameters which depend on the state of stress and on the shape of the state boundary surface for plane strain, given by Eqs. (2.20) and (2.21) for the Roscoe and Hvorslev surfaces, respectively. Proceeding as before, for states on the Roscoe surface on the wet side of the critical state we have

$$\frac{1}{F_{ps}} = (\sin\phi'_{cs} - \sin\rho') \tag{2.96}$$

$$H_{ps} = \frac{\lambda - \kappa}{vs'\sin\phi'_{cs}} \tag{2.97}$$

where ρ' is the mobilized angle of shearing resistance given by Eq. (1.26); while for states on the Hvorslev surface on the dry side of the critical state we have

$$\frac{1}{F_{ps}} = -\left[\frac{\kappa}{\lambda}(\sin\rho' - \sin\phi'_h) + \sin\phi'_h\right] \tag{2.98}$$

$$H_{ps} = \frac{\lambda}{vs'(\sin\rho' - \sin\phi'_h)} \tag{2.99}$$

2.8 FAILURE AND PLASTIC FLOW AT THE CRITICAL STATE

The state of an element of soil which is at ultimate failure will usually remain at a single point on the critical state line. If the element is part of a triaxial sample then at failure its state will remain at a single point on the critical state line and it will continue to suffer shear strains without further change of effective stress or volume. These conditions, of course, define a sample at ultimate failure at the critical state. Similarly, if the element forms part of a structure, such as a foundation or slope, which itself is failing, its state will remain at a single point on the critical state line, since the external loads on the structure cannot be increased and so neither can the stresses on the element. For both cases, at ultimate failure we have

$$\delta q' = \delta p' = \delta\epsilon_v = 0 \tag{2.100}$$

and shear strains $\delta\epsilon_s$ are indeterminate. There will then be no possibility of our obtaining an incremental stress–strain relationship of the kind given in Eqs. (1.63) and (1.64) and we will have to seek a quite different mathematical model for soil at ultimate failure.

If, however, a soil element which is at ultimate failure is part of a large structure, such as a slope or a foundation which is itself stable, then additional loading or unloading which does not cause the structure to collapse may alter the state of stress in the element and so cause finite increments of strain. As discussed in Sec. 1.7, a path will traverse the state boundary surface if irrecoverable plastic strains occur. If, however, a path which traverses the state boundary surface implies recoverable plastic strains then the path is impossible and instead the state will traverse an elastic wall with zero plastic strain.

Figure 2.17 shows a state at A on the critical state line and on the elastic wall $JLMK$ and a number of stress paths. For any path between $A \to B$ and $A \to C$ the state remains on the Roscoe surface and increments of stress and strain may be related by Eqs. (2.89) and (2.90). Any path below $A \to C$ is inside the state boundary surface and on the elastic wall $JLMK$ and increments of stress and of strain are related by Eqs. (2.48) and (2.49). For any path between $A \to D$ and $A \to E$ the state remains on the Hvorslev surface if there are irrecoverable plastic strains, but the path will move across the elastic wall $JLMK$ following a path such as $A \to D'$ if the plastic strains are zero. Thus in Fig. 2.17 there are two possible paths $A \to D$ and $A \to D'$ for the same change of stress. For any path below $A \to D$ the state is inside the state boundary surface and on the elastic wall $JLMK$ and increments of stress and of strain are related by Eqs. (2.48) and (2.49).

For the paths $A \to B$ and $A \to D$ which move along the critical state line we have, from Eqs. (2.3) and (2.4),

$$\delta q' = M \, \delta p' \qquad (2.101)$$

$$\delta \epsilon_v = \frac{\lambda}{vp'} \, \delta p' \qquad (2.102)$$

Thus, comparing Eqs. (2.78) and (2.79) with Eqs. (2.101) and (2.102) and making use of Eqs. (2.50), we have

$$H = 0 \qquad K'_{cs} = \frac{vp'}{\lambda} \qquad G'_{cs} = \frac{vp'}{\lambda} \frac{3(1 - 2v')}{2(1 + v')} \qquad (2.103)$$

where K'_{cs} and G'_{cs} are values of the bulk and shear moduli appropriate for failure at the critical state and Eqs. (2.78) and (2.79) become

$$\delta \epsilon_s = \frac{\lambda}{vp'} \frac{2(1 + v')}{9(1 - 2v')} \delta q' \qquad (2.104)$$

$$\delta \epsilon_v = \frac{\lambda}{vp'} \, \delta p' \qquad (2.105)$$

Equations (2.104) and (2.105) are incremental stress–strain relationships for soil at the critical state, but they are applicable only for non-zero stress increments related by Eq. (2.101).

For the case of ultimate failure at the critical state when the state does not

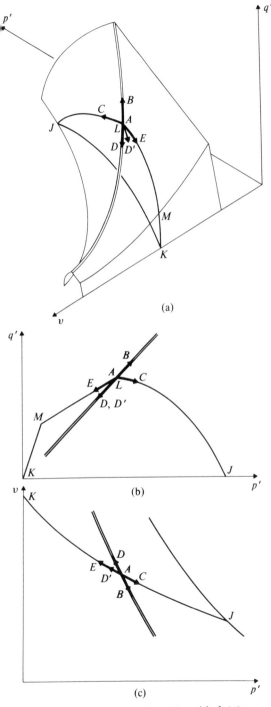

Figure 2.17 Loading of samples at the critical state.

change, an *incremental* stress–strain relationship is inappropriate and we must reconsider the correct form for a mathematical model. Since the state remains constant all elastic components of strain are zero and hence increments of total strain and of plastic strain are equal. From Eq. (1.57), noting that elastic strains are zero, we have

$$\frac{\delta \epsilon_s}{\delta \epsilon_v} = F \qquad (2.106)$$

where, as before, the parameter F depends on the shape of the yield curve and the state of stress. Thus, for ultimate failure at the critical state, when the state does not change, we expect a stress–strain relationship which relates a *strain increment ratio to a state of stress*. In Fig. 1.15 we showed a failure envelope $F_a F_c$ for an ideal material which was geometrically similar to the yield curves such as $G_a G_c$ and limited the yield surface. For soil, however, there is no limit to the state boundary surface in Fig. 2.1, which may continue to increase or decrease in size as the specific volume reduces or increases respectively. Instead, for soil, the envelope for ultimate failure is the critical state line and, if the flow rule is associated and the normality condition is appropriate, this may be taken as a plastic potential from which the parameter F in Eq. (2.106) may be evaluated.

Figure 2.18 shows a section of the state boundary surface as a broken line and the critical state line given by

$$q' = Mp' \qquad [2.4]$$

Thus, if Eq. (2.4) serves as a plastic potential then the direction of the plastic strain increment vector LN in Fig. 2.18 is given by

$$\frac{\delta \epsilon_v^p}{\delta \epsilon_s^p} = -M \qquad (2.107)$$

But we have already seen (Eq. (2.100)) that, at the critical state, $\delta \epsilon_v = 0$, and, since the stresses remain constant, $\delta \epsilon_v^e = 0$ also. Hence $\delta \epsilon_v^p = 0$ and the actual vector of plastic strain increment, LS in Fig. 2.18, is vertical. Consequently, the critical state line given by Eq. (2.4) does *not* serve as a plastic potential for drained loading; the flow rule is *not* associated and the normality condition is *not* satisfied.

For undrained loading of saturated soil the failure criterion in terms of total stress is given by

$$q = 2 c_u \qquad [2.44]$$

where the undrained shear strength c_u is given by Eq. (2.45) and the corresponding failure envelope is shown in Fig. 2.19. If Eq. (2.44) serves as a plastic potential then the direction of the plastic strain increment vector is given by

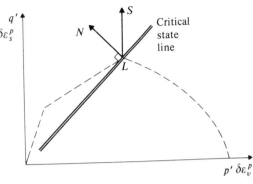

Figure 2.18 The critical state line as a plastic potential.

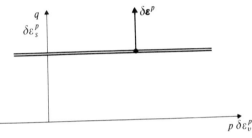

Figure 2.19 Normality for undrained loading of soil in terms of total stress for triaxial compression.

$$\frac{\delta \epsilon_v^p}{\delta \epsilon_s^p} = 0 \tag{2.108}$$

As before, at the critical state when the stresses remain constant, $\delta \epsilon_v = 0$ and $\delta \epsilon_v^e = 0$ and hence $\delta \epsilon_v^p = 0$. Thus the vector of plastic strain increment is vertical in Fig. 2.19 and is normal to the undrained failure envelope given by Eq. (2.44), which serves as a plastic potential. Hence, for undrained loading, for which the failure criterion is written in terms of total stresses, the normality condition for soil is satisfied and the flow rule is associated.

At failure, however, many soils suffer discontinuous slipping as slip planes occur through the soil. Particular planes of failure may exist before any additional loads are applied, as when rocks contain clay-filled joints, when soils contain residual slip planes,[†] or when slip planes develop during loading. When slip planes first occur, they coincide with directions of zero extension angled at $\pm \beta = (45° + \frac{1}{2} \psi)$ to the major principal plane, as shown in Fig. 1.8. For a perfectly plastic

---

[†] If soil is once loaded so that slip planes develop, but is then unloaded, the slip planes will remain as structural features in the soil for any subsequent loading. Such slip planes left over from a previous loading are known as *residual slip planes* and the appropriate shear strength may have fallen to the residual shear strength, as described in Sec. 2.9.

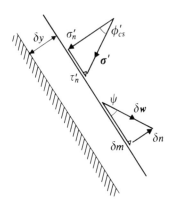

Figure 2.20 Stresses and increments of displacements across a narrow zone of discontinuous slipping.

material with an associated flow rule for which, at failure, $\psi = \psi_p = \phi'_{cs}$ (see below), we have $\alpha = \beta$ and slip planes coincide with the planes for which the Mohr's circle of effective stress at ultimate failure just touches the critical state line, as shown in Fig. 1.11.

Figure 2.20 shows part of a long slip plane and is similar to Fig. 1.9. At ulti-

$$\tan \phi'_{cs} = \frac{\tau'_n}{\sigma'_n} \qquad (2.109)$$

and the vector of effective stress $\boldsymbol{\sigma}'$ makes an angle ϕ'_{cs} with the normal to the slip plane, as shown. For an increment of displacement $\delta\mathbf{w}$ with components δn and δm we have, from Eq. (1.22),

$$\tan \psi = \frac{\delta n}{\delta m} \qquad (2.110)$$

and the vector of displacement $\delta\mathbf{w}$ makes an angle ψ with the slip plane as shown. It may be noted that if $\psi = \phi'_{cs}$ then the vectors of effective stress and displacement are orthogonal.

For discontinuous slipping the critical state line is given by

$$\tau'_n = \sigma'_n \tan \phi'_{cs} \qquad [2.22]$$

as shown in Fig. 2.21. If Eq. (2.22) serves as a plastic potential then the direction of the plastic strain increment vector, LN in Fig. 2.21, is given by

$$\frac{\delta\epsilon_v^p}{\delta\gamma_n^p} = -\tan \phi'_{cs} \qquad (2.111)$$

But, arguing as before, at the critical state, $\delta\epsilon_v = 0$ and $\delta\epsilon_v^e = 0$ and hence $\delta\epsilon_v^p = 0$ also and the actual vector of plastic strain increment, LS in Fig. 2.21, is vertical. Consequently, the critical state line given by Eq. (2.22) does *not* serve as a plastic

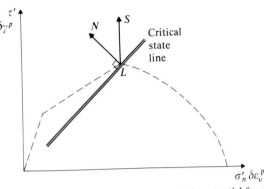

Figure 2.21 The critical state line as a plastic potential for discontinuous slipping.

potential for drained loading, the flow rule is *not* associated, and the normality condition is *not* satisfied. It is convenient to define an angle of dilation for plastic strains as

$$\frac{d\epsilon_v^p}{d\gamma_n^p} = - \tan \psi_p \tag{2.112}$$

similar to the angle of dilation defined by Eq. (1.17). Thus, for a material for which the critical state line serves as a plastic potential the associated flow rule may be written $\phi_{cs}' = \psi_p$. For undrained loading for which $\delta\epsilon_v = 0$ we have $\psi = 0$ and the slip planes for first loading are angled at $\beta = 45°$ to the major principal plane. The undrained failure criterion for a particular plane is given by

$$\tau_n = c_u \tag{2.47}$$

and the corresponding failure envelope is shown in Fig. 2.22. Arguing as before, at the critical state when the stresses remain constant, $\delta\epsilon_v = 0$ and $\delta\epsilon_v^e = 0$. Hence $\delta\epsilon_v^p = 0$ and the actual vector of plastic strain increment at failure is vertical, as shown in Fig. 2.22. Consequently, in terms of total stresses the Mohr–Coulomb failure criterion with $\phi_u = 0$ given by Eq. (2.47) serves as a plastic potential for

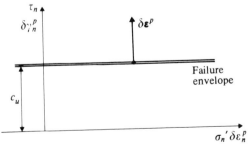

Figure 2.22 Normality for undrained loading in terms of total stresses for discontinuous slipping.

discontinuous slipping and the flow rule is associated and the normality condition satisfied.

2.9 RESIDUAL STRENGTH

It is found that if a sample of soil is subjected to continuing shear in a ring shear apparatus[†] then the strength continues to fall below the ultimate strength associated with the critical state line and the sample only reaches a state at which it suffers no further reduction in strength after very large displacements, perhaps of the order of several metres. Figure 2.23 shows typical results of a drained ring shear test with constant effective normal stress on a sample of heavily overconsolidated clay, where the effective stress ratio τ'_n/σ'_n is plotted against the relative displacement δ across the two halves of the ring shear sample. For relatively small shear displacements in the range OB in Fig. 2.23, the stress–displacement curve is similar to the stress–strain curve for a drained triaxial test on overconsolidated clay, but in the ring shear test the shear stress continues to fall, reaching a constant value at C only after very large shear displacement.

When viewing these results we must note that for states beyond the peak the deformations are not continuous, but are discontinuous, as slip planes develop through the triaxial sample and between the two halves of the ring shear sample. It is clear that measurements of stress and particularly of strain made at the boundaries of such samples do not represent the states of those elements of soil contained within the slip planes and which suffer very large distortions. Thus we must be careful in interpreting the results of the ring shear test and the triaxial test beyond their peaks.

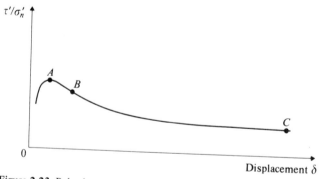

Figure 2.23 Behaviour of heavily overconsolidated clay in a drained ring shear test.

[†] The ring shear apparatus is described briefly by Atkinson and Bransby (1978). The sample is a square section ring loaded so that the top half of the ring shears around its circumference. The essential feature of the test is that very large shear displacements may be applied to the sample.

Both the stress–strain curve for a drained triaxial test on overconsolidated clay and the stress–displacement curve for a drained ring shear test have a peak; both peak strengths are the same and are associated with states on the Hvorslev surface. In both tests elements of soil within slip planes may be assumed to *approach* their critical states after modest strains but in neither test is the ultimate strength measured accurately. In Fig. 2.23 there is a point B on the stress–displacement curve at a strength equal to the ultimate strength inferred from a triaxial test, which may be associated with the point at which elements of soil in the slip plane in the ring shear sample reach their critical state. This point B is not well defined and the ring shear test is not an appropriate test for measuring the ultimate, or critical state, strength of soils. The final strength of the soil in the ring shear test which occurs at C in Fig. 2.23 is known as the *residual strength* and is associated with realignment of soil particles in preferred directions in slip planes due to large relative displacements. For granular soils for which there is little opportunity for regular shaped particles to become aligned in preferred directions, the residual strength is approximately the same as the ultimate strength; for clay soils, however, for which thin platey particles can easily become aligned, the residual strength may be substantially less than the estimated ultimate strength but the residual strength will not be reached until very large displacements have occured.

The relationship between the residual strength of a soil for discontinuous slipping and the normal effective stress on the slip plane is given by the Mohr–Coulomb criterion with parameters c'_r and ϕ'_r (Skempton, 1964), where the subscripts r are added to denote that the cohesion and angle of friction, respectively, are appropriate for the residual strength. It is found that the residual cohesion is often close to zero and thus we have, at the residual state,

$$\tau'_n = \sigma'_n \tan \phi'_r \qquad (2.113)$$

which is similar to Eq. (2.22) for the ultimate, or critical state strength, while for failure at the peak for which the state is on the Hvorslev surface we have Eq. (2.40).

For undrained loading, the undrained shear strength c_u corresponds to a state of effective stress on the critical state line and, for large deformations, it is appropriate to define a residual undrained shear strength c_{ur} corresponding to a state of effective stress at the residual state. It may be noted that for undrained loading of overconsolidated soil, for which the state is on the dry side of critical, the 'peak' shear stress at which the state first reaches the Hvorslev surface (such as at W in Fig. 2.14) is always lower than the undrained shear strength c_u at which the state reaches the critical state line (at F in Fig. 2.14) and hence it is not appropriate to consider the 'peak' or Hvorslev strength for undrained loading.

Thus we have identified three strengths, the peak, the ultimate, and the residual, and each is appropriate for different strains or displacements. The peak strength is appropriate only for very small strains while the residual is for very large displacements of slip planes. The question of which of these strengths should be chosen for design calculations will be discussed in Sec. 3.9.

2.10 ANISOTROPIC COMPRESSION

In anisotropic compression the ratio σ_1'/σ_3' is held constant as the principal stresses σ_1' and σ_3' are raised and lowered and so the ratio $q'/p' = \eta'$ remains constant. For isotropic compression $\sigma_1' = \sigma_3'$, $q' = 0$, and hence $\eta' = 0$, while if $\eta' = M$ the soil compresses and fails simultaneously on the critical state line. Thus, during anisotropic compression $q' = \eta'p'$, and the state of the sample must remain in a constant η' plane through the v axis angled at η' to the $v:p'$ plane, as illustrated in Fig. 2.24. Thus the state path for isotropic compression when $\eta' = 0$ is simply the intersection GJ of the state boundary surface with the $v:p'$ plane and, for unloading, the state path is the intersection JR of the elastic wall through J with the $v:p'$ plane. These are of course simply isotropic normal consolidation and unloading lines like those shown in Fig. 2.3 and given by Eqs. (2.1) and (2.2). For anisotropic compression when η' has some value $0 < \eta' < M$, the state path for loading $P \to Q$ in Fig. 2.24 is the intersection of the η' plane with the Roscoe surface and the state path for unloading $Q \to T$ is the intersection of the η' plane with the elastic wall through Q. Similarly, when $\eta' = M$, the state path follows the intersection AL of the η' plane with the state boundary surface, which is of course the critical state line, and for unloading the state path $L \to S$ is the intersection of the η' plane with the elastic wall through L. The strains for any of these paths may be calculated using the methods described in Secs. 2.6 to 2.8. Projections of the

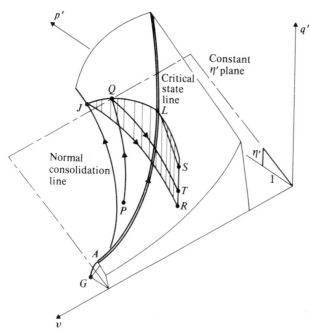

Figure 2.24 State paths for isotropic and anisotropic compression.

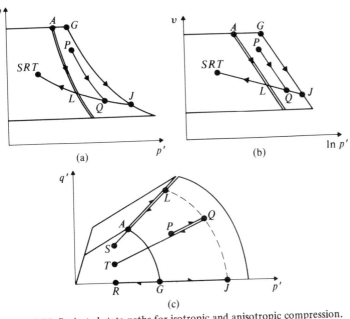

Figure 2.25 Projected state paths for isotropic and anisotropic compression.

state paths $G \to J \to R$ for $\eta' = 0$, $P \to Q \to T$ for $0 < \eta' < M$, and $A \to L \to S$ for $\eta' = M$ on to the $v : p'$ and $q' : p'$ planes are shown in Fig. 2.25. In Fig. 2.25(b) the paths are shown projected on to the $v : \ln p'$ plane and the path $P \to Q$ for anisotropic compression is parallel to the normal consolidation line and to the critical state line; thus the path $P \to Q$ is given by

$$v = N_\eta - \lambda \ln p' \tag{2.114}$$

where the parameter N_η depends on the value of η' for the particular state path.

There is a special case of anisotropic compression for which the stresses are changed so that there is no lateral strain and $\epsilon_2 = \epsilon_3 = 0$. To maintain the condition of zero lateral strain, $\sigma_3' = K_0 \sigma_1'$ where K_0 is known as the *coefficient of earth pressure at rest* and

$$\frac{q'}{p'} = \frac{3(1 - K_0)}{(1 + 2K_0)} = \eta_0' \tag{2.115}$$

For one-dimensional loading it turns out that the value of K_0 may be assumed to be a constant and hence η_0' may be assumed to be constant also. Thus the state path for one-dimensional loading is given by

$$v = N_0 - \lambda \ln p' \tag{2.116}$$

where N_0 is the specific volume of a sample compressed one-dimensionally to $p' = 1.0$. For unloading, however, the state path remains on an elastic wall and the behaviour of the sample is elastic. For one-dimensional strain $\delta\epsilon_2 = \delta\epsilon_3 = 0$, hence shear and volumetric strain increments from Eqs. (1.13) and (1.14) are $\delta\epsilon_s = \frac{2}{3}\delta\epsilon_1$ and $\delta\epsilon_v = \delta\epsilon_1$. Thus, from Eqs. (2.48) and (2.49), assuming that the soil remains isotropic and elastic, the path for one-dimensional unloading is given by

$$\frac{dq'}{dp'} = \frac{2G'}{K'} = \frac{3(1-2\nu')}{(1+\nu')} \tag{2.117}$$

where ν' is the value of Poisson's ratio for the soil in terms of effective stress.

For a sample of soil compressed isotropically to p'_m and then unloaded to p' the overconsolidation ratio R_p is defined by $R_p = p'_m/p'$. For one-dimensional compression and unloading the overconsolidation ratio is $R_0 = \sigma'_{vm}/\sigma'_v$ where σ'_v is the vertical effective stress and σ'_{vm} is the value of σ'_v at the start of unloading. Both p'_m and σ'_{vm} represent the maximum past stresses experienced by a sample; hence for a normally consolidated sample $R_p = R_0 = 1.0$ and the overconsolidation ratio cannot be less than 1.0.

2.11 SUMMARY

1. For soils it is important to distinguish between drained loading for which there are no excess pore pressures and undrained loading where, for saturated soil, there are no volume changes. For drained loading pore pressures can be found and effective stresses calculated; for undrained loading pore pressures cannot be calculated simply but, for saturated soil, some analyses may be carried out in terms of total stresses.

2. The state boundary surface for triaxial compression consists of

critical state line $q' = Mp'$ $\quad v = \Gamma - \lambda \ln p'$ [2.4, 2.3]

normal consolidation line $v = N - \lambda \ln p'$ [2.1]

elastic walls $v = v_\kappa - \kappa \ln p'$ [2.2]

Roscoe surface $\dfrac{q'}{Mp'} + \left(\dfrac{\lambda}{\lambda - \kappa}\right) \ln p' - \left(\dfrac{\Gamma - v}{\lambda - \kappa}\right) = 1$ [2.6]

Hvorslev surface $\dfrac{q'}{Hp'} - \left(\dfrac{M - H}{Hp'}\right) \exp\left(\dfrac{\Gamma - v}{\lambda}\right) = 1$ [2.7]

tension cutoff $q' = 3p'$ [2.5]

Similar state boundary surfaces may be developed for triaxial extension and for plane strain.

3. The state boundary surface may be taken as a yield surface.
4. The Mohr–Coulomb strength criterion gives
(a) for ultimate failure at the critical state

$$\tau'_n = \sigma'_n \tan \phi'_{cs} \qquad [2.37]$$

(b) for peak strength on the Hvorslev surface

$$\tau'_n = (\tan \phi'_{cs} - \tan \phi'_h) \exp\left(\frac{\Gamma_n - v}{\lambda}\right) + \sigma'_n \tan \phi'_h \qquad [2.40]$$

(c) for residual strength

$$\tau'_n = \sigma'_n \tan \phi'_r \qquad [2.113]$$

(d) for undrained failure of saturated soil at the critical state

$$\tau_n = c_u \qquad [2.47]$$

5. For states on an elastic wall inside the state boundary surface, elastic behaviour is given by

$$\delta\epsilon_s = \frac{1}{3G'}\delta q' \qquad \delta\epsilon_v = \frac{1}{K'}\delta p' \qquad [2.48, 2.49]$$

where

$$K' = \frac{vp'}{\kappa} \qquad G' = \frac{vp'}{\kappa}\frac{3(1-2v')}{2(1+v')} \qquad [2.53, 2.54]$$

For undrained loading of saturated soil $\delta\epsilon_v = 0$ and

$$\delta\epsilon_s = \frac{1}{3G_u}\delta q \qquad [2.62]$$

where

$$G_u = G' \qquad \text{and} \qquad v_u = \tfrac{1}{2} \qquad [2.66, 2.65]$$

Similar expressions are applicable for plane strain loading.

6. For isotropic elasto-plastic soil the behaviour is given by

$$\delta\epsilon_s = \left(FH + \frac{1}{3G'}\right)\delta q' + H\,\delta p' \qquad [2.78]$$

$$\delta\epsilon_v = H\,\delta q' + \left(\frac{H}{F} + \frac{1}{K'}\right)\delta p' \qquad [2.79]$$

For the Cam clay equation for the Roscoe surface,

$$1/F = M - \eta' \qquad H = \frac{\lambda - \kappa}{vMp'} \qquad [2.84, 2.88]$$

7. At ultimate failure at the critical state $\psi = \psi_p = 0$. For drained loading in terms of effective stresses $\phi'_{cs} > 0$ and the flow rule is not associated. For undrained loading in terms of total stresses $\phi_u = 0$ and the flow rule is associated.

8. After very large distortions soil strength falls below the critical state strength towards a residual strength given by

$$\tau'_n = \sigma'_n \tan \phi'_r \qquad\qquad [2.113]$$

REFERENCES

Atkinson, J. H. and P. L. Bransby (1978), *The Mechanics of Soils*, McGraw-Hill, London.
Bishop, A. W. (1972), 'Shear strength parameters for undisturbed and remoulded soil samples', *Proc. Roscoe Mem. Symp.*, R. H. G. Parry (ed.), Foulis, Henley-on-Thames, pp. 3–58.
Naylor, D. J. (1978), 'Stress–strain laws for soil' in *Developments in Soil Mechanics*, C. R. Scott (ed.), Applied Science Publishers, London, pp. 39–68.
Schofield, A. N. and C. P. Wroth (1968), *Critical State Soil Mechanics*, McGraw-Hill, London.
Skempton, A. W. (1957), 'Discussion on planning and design of the new Hong Kong Airport', *Proc. Instn Civil Engrs*, 7, 306.
Skempton, A. W. (1964), 'Long term stability of clay slopes', *Geotechnique*, 14, 77–101.
Zienkiewicz, O. C. (1977), *The Finite Element Method*, 3rd edn, McGraw-Hill, London.
———— and D. J. Naylor (1972), 'The adaption of the critical state soil mechanics theory for use in finite elements', *Proc. Roscoe Mem. Symp.*, R. H. G. Parry (ed.), Foulis, Henley-on-Thames, pp. 537–547.

WORKED EXAMPLES

E2.1 Failure of Normally Consolidated Samples

A soil has $\lambda = 0.20$, $\kappa = 0.05$, $N = 3.25$, $\Gamma = 3.16$, and $M = 0.94$ and samples A and C were prepared by isotropic compression to $p = p' = 400 \text{ kN/m}^2$ and $v = 2.05$. Both samples were loaded in triaxial compression tests with constant cell pressure; sample A was drained with zero pore pressure and sample C was undrained. Calculate the effective stresses q'_f and p'_f, the specific volume v_f, and the pore pressures u_f in each sample at ultimate failure and sketch the loading paths.

Both samples were normally consolidated and their initial states were $p'_0 = 400 \text{ kN/m}^2$, $v_0 = 2.05$, and $q'_0 = 0$.

Sample A: For drained triaxial compression $\Delta\sigma_3 = 0$ and $u = 0$ and $dq/dp = dq'/dp' = 3$. Hence we have

$$q'_f - q'_0 = 3(p'_f - p'_0)$$

and, at ultimate failure, the state is given by Eqs. (2.3) and (2.4) as

$$q'_f = Mp'_f$$

$$v_f = \Gamma - \lambda \ln p'_f$$

Hence

$$q'_f = \frac{3Mp'_0}{3-M} = \frac{3 \times 0.94 \times 400}{3 - 0.94}$$

$$\therefore q'_f = 548 \text{ kN/m}^2$$

and

$$p'_f = \frac{q'_f}{M} = \frac{548}{0.94}$$

$$\therefore p'_f = 583 \text{ kN/m}^2$$

and

$$v_f = \Gamma - \lambda \ln p'_f = 3.16 - 0.20 \ln 583$$

$$\therefore v_f = 1.89$$

Sample C: For undrained loading $v_f = v_0 = 2.05$. Hence, at ultimate failure we have

$$v_f = v_0 = \Gamma - \lambda \ln p'_f = 2.05$$

and

$$p'_f = \exp\left(\frac{\Gamma - v_0}{\lambda}\right) = \exp\left(\frac{3.16 - 2.05}{0.20}\right)$$

$$\therefore p'_f = 257 \text{ kN/m}^2$$

and

$$q'_f = Mp'_f = 0.94 \times 257$$

$$\therefore q'_f = 242 \text{ kN/m}^2$$

The initial state was $p_0 = p'_0 = 400 \text{ kN/m}^2$ and for triaxial compression $dq/dp = 3$. Hence we have

$$q_f - q_0 = 3(p_f - p_0)$$

$$\therefore q_f = 3(p_f - p_0) = q'_f$$

and

$$p_f = \tfrac{1}{3}q'_f + p_0 = (\tfrac{1}{3} \times 242) + 400$$

$$p_f = 481 \text{ kN/m}^2$$

Hence

$$u_f = p_f - p'_f = 481 - 257$$

$$\therefore u_f = 224 \text{ kN/m}^2$$

The state paths $A_0 A_f$ and $C_0 C_f$ are shown sketched in Fig. E2.1. Only the start and finish points have been calculated but the paths could be found by making use of an expression for the Roscoe surface such as that given by Eq. (2.6).

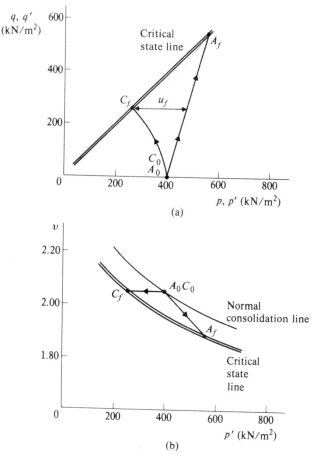

Figure E2.1.

E2.2 Peak States of Overconsolidated Samples

The soil in Example E2.1 has $H = 0.68$. Samples B and D were prepared by isotropic compression and swelling to $p = p' = 120 \text{ kN/m}^2$ and $v = 2.05$ at an overconsolidation ratio of $R_p = 5$. Both samples were loaded in triaxial compression tests with constant cell pressure; sample B was drained with zero pore pressure and sample C was undrained. Calculate the effective stresses q'_p and p'_p, the specific volumes v_p, and the pore pressures u_p for each sample when their states first reach the Hvorslev surface.

The initial states of the samples were $p_0 = p'_0 = 120 \text{ kN/m}^2$, $v_0 = 2.05$, and $q'_0 = 0$. At the maximum consolidation pressure $p'_m = 5 \times 120 = 600 \text{ kN/m}^2$.

$$v = N - \lambda \ln p'_m = v_\kappa - \kappa \ln p'_m$$
$$\therefore v_\kappa = N - \lambda \ln p'_m + \kappa \ln p'_m$$
$$v_\kappa = 2.29$$

Sample B: For drained triaxial compression $\Delta\sigma_3 = 0$ and $u = 0$ and $dq/dp = dq'/dp' = 3$. Hence we have

$$q'_p - q'_0 = 3(p'_p - p'_0)$$
$$\therefore q'_p = 3p'_p - 360$$

The peak state lies at the intersection of an elastic wall and the Hvorslev surface given by Eqs. (2.2) and (2.7) as

$$v_p = v_\kappa - \kappa \ln p'_p = 2.29 - 0.05 \ln p'_p$$
$$q'_p = (M - H) \exp\left(\frac{\Gamma - v_p}{\lambda}\right) + Hp'_p = 0.26 \exp\left(\frac{3.16 - v_p}{0.20}\right) + 0.68\, p'_p$$

Solving the simultaneous equations by trial and error, or otherwise,

$$\underline{q'_p = 203 \text{ kN/m}^2}$$

$$\underline{p'_p = 188 \text{ kN/m}^2}$$

$$\underline{v_p = 2.03}$$

As the sample moves from B_0 to B_p the state is inside the state boundary surface; hence the soil is assumed to be elastic and strains may be calculated from elastic theory.

Sample D: For loading from D_0 to D_p, the state is inside the state boundary surface and the behaviour is elastic. For undrained loading $v_p = v_0 = 2.05$; hence $\delta v = 0$ and for elastic soil $\delta p' = 0$ and we have

$$p'_p = p'_0$$
$$\underline{p'_p = 120 \text{ kN/m}^2}$$

$$q'_p = (M - H) \exp\left(\frac{\Gamma - v_p}{\lambda}\right) + Hp'_p = 0.26 \exp\left(\frac{3.16 - 2.05}{0.20}\right) + 0.68 \times 120$$

$$\underline{q'_p = 149 \text{ kN/m}^2}$$

The initial state was $p_0 = p'_0 = 120$ kN/m² and for triaxial compression $dq/dp = 3$. Hence we have

$$q_p - q_0 = 3(p_p - p_0)$$

and

$$q_p = 3(p_p - p_0) = q_p'$$
$$p_p = \tfrac{1}{3}q_p' + p_0 = (\tfrac{1}{3} \times 149) + 120$$

Hence

$$p_p = 170 \text{ kN/m}^2$$
$$u_p = p_p - p_p' = 170 - 120$$
$$u_p = 50 \text{ kN/m}^2$$

E2.3 Failure of Overconsolidated Samples

For the overconsolidated soil and for the drained and undrained triaxial compression tests in Example E2.2, calculate the effective stresses q_f' and p_f', the specifi volumes v_f, and the pore pressures u_f at ultimate failure at the critical state. Sketc the complete loading paths for both tests.

The initial states of samples B and D were $p_0 = p_0' = 120 \text{ kN/m}^2$, $v_0 = 2.0$ and $q_0' = 0$.

Sample B: For drained triaxial compression $u = 0$ and $\Delta\sigma_3 = 0$ and $dq/dp = dq'/dp' = 3$. Hence we have

$$q_f' - q_0' = 3(p_f' - p_0')$$

and, at ultimate failure, the state is given by Eqs. (2.3) and (2.4) as

$$q_f' = Mp_f'$$

Hence,

$$v_f = \Gamma - \lambda \ln p_f'$$

$$q_f' = \frac{3Mp_0'}{3 - M} = \frac{3 \times 0.94 \times 120}{3 - 0.94}$$

$$q_f' = 164 \text{ kN/m}^2$$

$$p_f' = \frac{q_f'}{M} = \frac{164}{0.94}$$

$$p_f' = 175 \text{ kN/m}^2$$

and

$$v_f = \Gamma - \lambda \ln p_f' = 3.16 - 0.20 \ln 175$$

$$v_f = 2.13$$

Sample D: For undrained loading $v_f = v_0 = 2.05$. Hence at ultimate failur we have

$$v_f = v_0 = \Gamma - \lambda \ln p_f' = 2.05$$

and

$$p'_f = \exp\left(\frac{\Gamma - v_0}{\lambda}\right) = \exp\left(\frac{3.16 - 2.05}{0.20}\right)$$

$$p'_f = 257 \text{ kN/m}^2$$

$$q'_f = Mp'_f = 0.94 \times 257 \text{ kN/m}^2$$

$$q'_f = 242 \text{ kN/m}^2$$

note that the undrained shear strengths of samples C and D with the same specific volume are equal).

The initial state was $p_0 = p'_0 = 120 \text{ kN/m}^2$ and for triaxial compression dq/dp 3. Hence we have

$$q_f - q_0 = 3(p_f - p_0)$$

$$q_f = 3(p_f - p_0) = q'_f$$

$$p_f = \tfrac{1}{3}q'_f + p_0 = (\tfrac{1}{3} \times 242) + 120$$

$$p_f = 201 \text{ kN/m}^2$$

$$u_f = p_f - p'_f = 201 - 257$$

$$u_f = -56 \text{ kN/m}^2$$

The state paths $B_0B_pB_f$ and $D_0D_pD_f$ are shown sketched in Fig. E2.2, where only the initial and final points and one intermediate point have been calculated. The paths B_0B_p and D_0D_p are inside the state boundary surface and correspond to elastic behaviour; the paths B_pB_f and D_pD_f traverse the Hvorslev surface and may be found from an expression for the Hvorslev surface such as that given by Eq. (2.7).

2.4 Calculation of Elastic Strains

soil has $\lambda = 0.20$, $\kappa = 0.05$, $\Gamma = 3.16$, $N = 3.25$, $M = 0.94$, $H = 0.68$, and $v' =$ .25. Samples were prepared with $q'_0 = 60 \text{ kN/m}^2$, $p'_0 = 120 \text{ kN/m}^2$, $u = 0$, and) = 2.05 and the samples were given increments of total stress $\Delta q = 10 \text{ kN/m}^2$ nd $\Delta p = 5 \text{ kN/m}^2$; sample A was drained and sample B was undrained. Calculate the increments of shear strain and volumetric strain and the changes of pore pressure or each sample.

First it is required to locate the initial state with respect to the state boundary urface. For $p' = 120 \text{ kN/m}^2$ the value of v corresponding to the critical state line given by Eq. (2.3) as

$$v_f = \Gamma - \lambda \ln p'_f = 3.16 - 0.20 \ln 120 = 2.20$$

Now $v_0 = 2.05$ is less than the value of v_f on the critical state line and the sample was on the dry side of critical; hence its state must lie on or below the Hvorslev

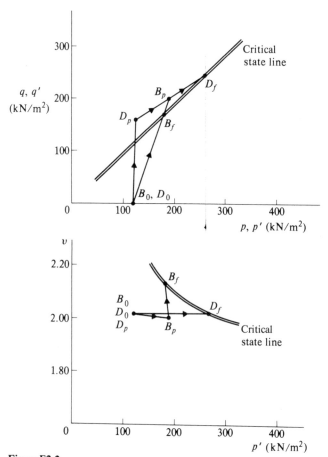

Figure E2.2

surface. For $p' = 120$ kN/m² and $v = 2.05$ the value of q' on the Hvorslev surface is given by Eq. (2.7)

$$q' = (M - H) \exp\left(\frac{\Gamma - v}{\lambda}\right) + Hp'$$

$$= (0.94 - 0.68) \exp\left(\frac{3.16 - 2.05}{0.20}\right) + 0.68 \times 120$$

$$q' = 148 \text{ kN/m}^2$$

Now $q'_0 = 60$ kN/m² is less than the value of q' on the Hvorslev surface; hence the state of the soil was inside the state boundary surface and its behaviour was elastic.

Sample A: For drained loading $\Delta u = 0$ and the total and effective stresses are equal. Hence, elastic strains are given by Eqs. (2.48) and (2.49) as

$$\delta \epsilon_s = \frac{1}{3G'} \delta q'$$

$$\delta \epsilon_v = \frac{1}{K'} \delta p'$$

where from Eqs. (2.53) and (2.54)

$$K' = \frac{vp'}{\kappa} \qquad G' = \frac{vp'}{\kappa} \frac{3(1 - 2v')}{2(1 + v')}$$

Hence, taking v and p' as constants for the whole increment we have

$$\Delta \epsilon_s = \frac{\kappa}{vp'} \frac{2(1 + v')}{9(1 - 2v')} \Delta q'$$

$$= \frac{0.05}{2.05 \times 120} \times \frac{2 \times 1.25}{9 \times 0.5} \times 10$$

$$\underline{\Delta \epsilon_s = 0.00113}$$

and

$$\Delta \epsilon_v = \frac{\kappa}{vp'} \Delta p'$$

$$= \frac{0.05}{2.05 \times 120} \times 5$$

$$\underline{\Delta \epsilon_v = 0.00102}$$

Sample B: For undrained loading $\underline{\Delta \epsilon_v = 0}$ and hence $\Delta p' = 0$

$$\therefore \quad \underline{\Delta u = \Delta p = 5 \text{ kN/m}^2}$$

Elastic shear strains are given by Eq. (2.62) as

$$\delta \epsilon_s = \frac{1}{3G_u} \delta q$$

where from Eq. (2.66)

$$G_u = G' = \frac{vp'}{\kappa} \frac{3(1 - 2v')}{2(1 + v')}$$

Hence, since v and p' are constants for undrained loading, we have

$$\Delta \epsilon_s = \frac{\kappa}{vp'} \frac{2(1 + v')}{9(1 - 2v')} \Delta q$$

$$= \frac{0.05}{2.05 \times 120} \times \frac{2 \times 1.25}{9 \times 0.5} \times 10$$

$$\Delta\epsilon_s = 0.00113$$

E2.5 Calculation of Elasto-plastic Strains for Normally Consolidated soil

A soil has the properties given in Example E2.4 and a sample was brought to a state on the Roscoe surface at $p' = 400$ kN/m², $q' = 150$ kN/m², and $u = 0$. The sample was given increments of total stress $\Delta q = 10$ kN/m² and $\Delta p = 5$ kN/m² and the loading was drained. Calculate the increments of shear strain and volumetric strain and the changes of pore pressure, assuming that the simple Cam clay equation defines the Roscoe surface.

For $p' = 400$ kN/m² and $q' = 150$ kN/m² states on the Roscoe surface are given by Eq. (2.6) as

$$\frac{q'}{Mp'} + \frac{\lambda}{\lambda - \kappa} \ln p' - \frac{\Gamma - v}{\lambda - \kappa} = 1$$

$$\frac{150}{0.94 \times 400} + \frac{0.20}{0.15} \ln 400 - \frac{3.16 - v}{0.15} = 1$$

hence

$$v = 2.05$$

and

$$\eta' = \frac{q'}{p'} = \frac{150}{400} = 0.375$$

For states on the Roscoe surface strain increments are given by Eqs. (2.89) and (2.90) as

$$\delta\epsilon_s = \left[\frac{\lambda - \kappa}{(M - \eta')vMp'} + \frac{1}{3G'} \right] \delta q' + \frac{\lambda - \kappa}{vMp'} \delta p'$$

$$\delta\epsilon_v = \frac{\lambda - \kappa}{vMp'} \delta q' + \left[(M - \eta') \frac{\lambda - \kappa}{vMp'} + \frac{1}{K'} \right] \delta p'$$

where, from Eqs. (2.53) and (2.54),

$$\frac{1}{K'} = \frac{\kappa}{vp'}$$

$$\frac{1}{3G'} = \frac{\kappa}{vp'} \frac{2(1 + v')}{9(1 - 2v')}$$

For drained loading $\Delta u = 0$ and total and effective stresses are equal. Hence, taking v, p', and η' as constants for the whole increment we have

$$\Delta\epsilon_s = \frac{\lambda - \kappa}{vMp'}\left[\left\{\frac{1}{M-\eta'} + \frac{2M\kappa\,(1+v')}{9(\lambda-\kappa)(1-2v')}\right\}\Delta q' + \Delta p'\right]$$

$$= \frac{0.15}{2.05 \times 0.94 \times 400}\left[\left\{\frac{1}{0.56} + \frac{2 \times 0.94 \times 0.05 \times 1.25}{9 \times 0.15 \times 0.5}\right\}10 + 5\right]$$

$$\underline{\Delta\epsilon_s = 0.0048}$$

and

$$\Delta\epsilon_v = \frac{\lambda - \kappa}{vMp'}\left[\Delta q' + \left\{(M-\eta') + \frac{M\kappa}{\lambda-\kappa}\right\}\Delta p'\right]$$

$$= \frac{0.15}{2.05 \times 0.94 \times 400}\left[10 + \left\{0.56 + \frac{0.94 \times 0.05}{0.15}\right\}5\right]$$

$$\therefore \underline{\Delta\epsilon_v = 0.0028}$$

E2.6 Calculation of Elasto-plastic Strains for Heavily Overconsolidated Soil

A soil has the properties given in Example E2.4 and a sample was brought to a state on the Hvorslev surface at $p' = 120$ kN/m^2, $q' = 150$ kN/m^2, and $u = 0$. The sample was given an increment of total stress $\Delta q = -10$ kN/m^2 and $\Delta p = -5$ kN/m^2; the sample was drained and its state remained on the Hvorslev surface during the increment (note that for drained loading the loading path will move *down* the Hvorslev surface towards the critical state line). Calculate the increments of shear strain and volumetric strain.

For $p' = 120$ kN/m^2 and $q' = 150$ kN/m^2 states on the Hvorslev surface are given by Eq. (2.7)

$$q'_p = (M-H)\exp\left(\frac{\Gamma - v_p}{\lambda}\right) + Hp'_p$$

$$150 = (0.94 - 0.68)\exp\left(\frac{3.16 - v}{0.20}\right) + 0.68 \times 120$$

hence

$$v = 2.05$$

and

$$\eta' = \frac{q'}{p'} = \frac{150}{120} = 1.25$$

For states on the Hvorslev surface, strain increments are given by Eqs. (2.92) and (2.93) as

$$\delta\epsilon_s = \left[\frac{1}{3G'} - \frac{\lambda}{vp'(\eta' - H)\{(\kappa/\lambda)(\eta' - H) + H\}}\right]\delta q' + \frac{\lambda}{vp'(\eta' - H)}\,\delta p'$$

$$\delta\epsilon_v = \frac{\lambda}{vp'(\eta' - H)}\,\delta q' + \left[\frac{1}{K'} - \frac{\lambda}{vp'(\eta' - H)}\left\{\frac{\kappa}{\lambda}(\eta' - H) + H\right\}\right]\delta p'$$

where K' and G' are given by Eqs. (2.53) and (2.54).

For drained loading $\underline{\Delta u = 0}$ and total and effective stresses are equal. Hence taking v, p', and η' as constants for the whole increment we have

$$\Delta\epsilon_s = \frac{\lambda}{vp'(\eta' - H)}\left[\left\{\frac{-1}{(\kappa/\lambda)(\eta' - H) + H} + \frac{2(\eta' - H)\kappa(1 + v')}{9\lambda(1 - 2v')}\right\}\Delta q' + \Delta p\right.$$

$$= \frac{0.2}{2.05 \times 120 \times 0.57}\left[\left\{\frac{1}{(0.25 \times 0.57) + 0.68}\right.\right.$$

$$\left.\left. - \frac{2 \times 0.57 \times 0.05 \times 1.25}{9 \times 0.2 \times 0.5}\right\}10 - 5\right]$$

$$\underline{\Delta\epsilon_s = 0.0091}$$

and

$$\Delta\epsilon_v = \frac{\lambda}{vp'(\eta' - H)}[\Delta q' - H\Delta p']$$

$$= \frac{0.20}{2.05 \times 120 \times 0.57}[-10 + (0.68 \times 5)]$$

$$\underline{\Delta\epsilon_v = -0.0094}$$

THREE

NATURAL SOILS IN FOUNDATIONS AND SLOPES

3.1 INTRODUCTION

In the previous chapter we examined the behaviour of small samples of soil in triaxial or plane strain laboratory test and in thin zones of discontinuous slipping and we assumed that soil is *saturated, isotropic,* and *homogeneous.* In a saturated soil the pore spaces are completely filled with water. For an isotropic material the behaviour of a sample is independent of the original orientation of the sample in the material, and for a homogeneous material the behaviour of a sample is independent of its original position in the material. Thus for an isotropic and homogeneous material the properties of any element are the same as the properties of the whole mass, irrespective of the sampling location and the orientation of the element. Most natural soils, however, are neither isotropic nor homogeneous.

In nature, soils in foundations and slopes are usually saturated, at least in temperate climates, and we will not consider construction involving unsaturated soils. States of stress in foundations and slopes can often be assumed to correspond closely to either plane strain or triaxial conditons and, at failure, thin shear zones of discontinuous slipping occur.

3.2 FORMATION OF NATURAL SOILS

With few exceptions, all soils of engineering importance are formed as *residual soils,* were *deposited* from water, air, or ice, or were *compacted* by man in the course of engineering construction. Residual soils are formed by natural weathering processes which change rocks to soils *in situ;* soils and weathered rocks may be eroded and transported by water, wind, or ice and deposited in another place. Residual or deposited soils may by freshly eroded and deposited again and they may also be further weathered *in situ.* Soils may also be excavated by man and compacted or dumped as fill in embankments and tips.

The process of weathering of rocks to soil *in situ* occurs most rapidly at the ground surface where the soil and rock are exposed to the weather and a *soil profile* develops as soils grade into rock with depth. Thus the properties of residual soils

83

with depth. The depth to which a soil profile is developed will depend o
nsity of the weathering processes and the duration of weathering as well
on the nature of the parent rock. It may be noted also that the type of residual so
developed by weathering depends as much on the local climate and drainage as o
the parent rock; processes of weathering and development of residual soils ar
covered in texts on physical geology (e.g. Holmes, 1965). The important poir
about residual soils is that there has been no mass movement of material, althoug
the weathering process may involve vertical movement of certain elements withi
the soil profile.

Deposited soils, however, have suffered mass movement, sometimes over ver
large distances, as they were transported by ice, water, or wind. Transported soi
are deposited when the transporting agent can no longer move the material; thu
soils are deposited as ice melts, as rivers flow into lakes and seas, and as winds die
The maximum size of particle transported by wind or water depends on the
velocity of the wind or river but all particle sizes are carried equally well by ice
Therefore soils deposited from ice contain a large variety of particle sizes but, a
wind or water velocities diminish, progressively smaller particle sizes are deposited
Thus wind and water *sort* soils into different sizes, so gravels are deposited from
relatively fast flowing streams, while silts and clays are deposited in lakes and sea
where the flow is negligible; ice, on the other hand, does not sort soil and so
boulder clays and other varieties of glacial drift may contain particle sizes from
boulders to clay.

So long as the effective stresses increase, as they will when deposition continues or when pore pressures drop, the current state of stress is the maximum
experienced by the soil which is *normally consolidated*. However, if effective
stresses reduce, as they may when material is removed by erosion or if pore
pressures rise, the current stresses are not the largest experienced by the soil, which
is then *overconsolidated*. It is important to appreciate, though, that natural soils
may become lightly overconsolidated solely because of changes of pore pressure,
without erosion occurring. Residual soils behave in general as though they were
heavily overconsolidated and on the dry side of critical, even when no erosion has
occurred.

During deposition, conditions often change slightly for one reason or another,
with the result that the particle sizes deposited at a particular location change with
time, and hence with depth. Thus deposited sediments tend to be layered, each
layer representing a particular phase of deposition. If conditions change rapidly or
if deposition is slow then individual layers will be relatively thin, but if conditions
change slowly or if deposition is rapid then individual layers will be relatively thick.
In either case, however, the soil will not be homogeneous, as the properties of
individual layers will be different. In the case of residual soils where the degree of
weathering decreases with depth the soil properties will vary with depth and again
the soil will not be homogeneous.

As successive layers of soil are deposited the vertical stresses on a particular
element increase as the depth of deposited soil increases. In general, soils will be

posited over quite large areas so that there is no horizontal strain and, as dis-
ussed in Sec. 3.3, horizontal and vertical effective stresses are related by K_0, the
oefficient of earth pressure at rest. Continuing deposition increases the vertical
fective stress and so vertical strains occur as the soil consolidates one-dimensionally.
nce soils are deposited one-dimensionally (i.e. the depositing grains generally fall
rtically) and are consolidated one-dimensonally it is to be expected that natural
ils will be anisotropic but with an axis of symmetry placed vertically in the
ound.

In temperate climates most natural soils are saturated except for a relatively
in surface crust, which may be unsaturated but which is usually sufficiently thin
) be disregarded for engineering purposes. In many cases the thin layer of *topsoil*
hich supports plant life is stripped from the ground before engineering works
egin; the topsoil is often stored and reused during reinstatement works. In tropical
limates the layer of unsaturated soil may be relatively deep and in cold climates
ne pore water may exist as ice in permafrost soils. In this book we consider only
aturated soils whose pores are completely filled with water.

.3 STATES OF STRESS IN THE GROUND

igure 3.1(a) shows vertical and horizontal stresses σ_v and σ_h at a depth z below a
orizontal ground surface in an isotropic and homogeneous soil with unit weight γ;
: is assumed that there is no seepage. The total vertical stress is given by

$$\sigma_v = \gamma z \tag{3.1}$$

nd σ_v increases linearly with depth as shown in Fig. 3.1(c). Water rises in an open
nded standpipe as shown in Fig. 3.1(b) and the pore pressure at a depth z is given by

$$u = \gamma_w h \tag{3.2}$$

vhere γ_w is the unit weight of water and h is the height of water in the standpipe.
:hus the pore pressure increases linearly with depth, as shown in Fig. 3.1(c). The
vater in the standpipe rises to a level which may be above, below, or at ground level;

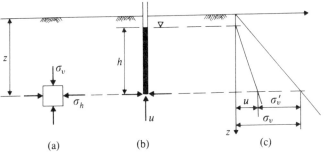

Figure 3.1 Stresses and pore pressures in the ground.

the water level will be above ground level when land is submerged by lakes or sea
If the water level in the standpipe is below ground level pore pressures above the
water level will be negative and the soil may well become unsaturated. In tempera
climates the depth of unsaturated soil is usually negligible for engineering purpos
but in hot, dry climates the depth of unsaturated soil may be an important featu
of the soil profile.

From Eq. (1.1) the vertical effective stress is given by

$$\sigma'_v = \sigma_v - u \tag{3.}$$

and the increase of σ'_v with depth is illustrated in Fig. 3.1(c), which shows the ca
where the soil is dry and pore pressures are zero above the water level. The horizont
effective stress is given by

$$\sigma'_h = K\sigma'_v \tag{3.}$$

where K is known as the *coefficient of earth pressure* and from Eq. (1.1), th
horizontal total stress is given by

$$\sigma_h = \sigma'_h + u \tag{3.}$$

For soil below a horizontal ground surface shear stresses on horizontal and vertic
planes are zero and σ'_v and σ'_h are principal stresses; thus Eqs. (3.1) to (3.5) describ
completely the state of stress in the ground. It should be noted that there is n
simple relation between vertical and horizontal total stresses σ_v and σ_h, sinc
K, the coefficient of earth pressure, is defined in terms of effective stresses σ'_v an
σ'_h by Eq. (3.4).

The value of K for a particular soil depends on a number of factors, bu
principally on any horizontal strains and on the degree of overconsolidation. Fo
naturally deposited soils, horizontal strains may be assumed to be zero durin
deposition, and also during any subsequent erosion, and the value of K has th
special value K_0 where K_0 is known as the *coefficient of earth pressure at rest* and i
given by Eq. (2.115) as

$$\frac{q'}{p'} = \frac{3(1 - K_0)}{(1 + 2K_0)} \tag{3.6}$$

The changing state of stress in an element of soil in the ground during depo
sition and erosion of overlying soil is the same as that experienced by a sample o
soil during compression and unloading with zero lateral strain. Thus in Fig. 3.2, th
path $U \to V$ is the path for soil during deposition and the path $V \to W$ is the patl
for erosion. The path $U \to V$ traverses the Roscoe surface while the path $V \to W$ i
inside the state boundary surface and so lies on an elastic wall; thus normall
consolidated soils compress plastically during deposition, while overconsolidate
soils swell elastically during erosion.

If the reduction in effective stress due to erosion, or due to some other cause
is relatively modest then the state of the soil will remain on the wet side of critica
and the soil is *lightly overconsolidated* but if the effective stresses are reduced stil

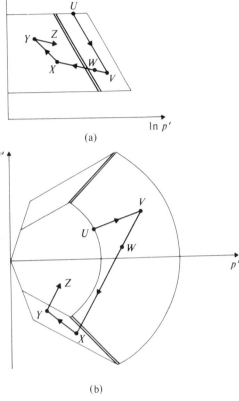

Figure 3.2 State of soil during one-dimensional compression and swelling.

further the state will pass to the dry side of critical and the soil becomes *heavily overconsolidated*. From the geometry of the state boundary surface the state moves from the wet side of critical to the dry side at an overconsolidation ratio of approximately two, although the precise value depends on properties of the particular soil. For heavily overconsolidated soil the horizontal effective stress σ_h' may exceed the vertical effective stress σ_v' and hence, defining q' and p' as

$$q' = (\sigma_v' - \sigma_h') \tag{3.7}$$

$$p' = \tfrac{1}{3}(\sigma_v' + 2\sigma_h') \tag{3.8}$$

q' may become negative as shown in Fig. 3.2. The overconsolidation ratio at which q' becomes negative is approximately two, corresponding roughly to the point at which the state passes from the wet side to the dry side of critical, although again the precise value depends on the properties of the particular soil.

If the effective stresses are reduced still further then, in theory, the state path meets the Hvorslev surface corresponding to negative values of q' at a point such as

X in Fig. 3.2. Thereafter, in theory, the state traverses the Hvorslev surface alo: the path $X \to Y$ and the soil yields plastically as its state traverses the state boun ary surface. Should stresses increase owing to renewed deposition, or due to a other cause, the state will move back inside the state boundary surface and t state path $Y \to Z$ will traverse an elastic wall. As heavily overconsolidated soil yiel plastically as its state moves across the Hvorslev surface, it may suffer discontinuo slipping as the yield stress reduces along the path $X \to Y$; heavily overconsolidate soils are known to contain fissures, joints, and other similar discontinuous feature

For convenience we may redefine $\delta \epsilon_s$ and $\delta \epsilon_v$ from Eqs. (1.13) and (1.14) as

$$\delta \epsilon_s = \tfrac{2}{3}(\delta \epsilon_v - \delta \epsilon_h) \tag{3.!}$$

$$\delta \epsilon_v = (\delta \epsilon_v + 2\delta \epsilon_h) \tag{3.1(}$$

where $\delta \epsilon_v$ and $\delta \epsilon_h$ are increments of vertical and horizontal strain in the groun For one-dimensional compression or swelling $\delta \epsilon_h = 0$ and hence

$$\frac{\delta \epsilon_s}{\delta \epsilon_v} = \frac{2}{3} \tag{3.1:}$$

The stress–strain behaviour of an isotropic elastoplastic soil for axially symmetr loading is given by Eqs. (2.78) and (2.79) and, with Eq. (3.11) for one-dimension compression, and in the limit, we have

$$\frac{dq'}{dp'} = \frac{3H - 2H/F - 2/K'}{2H - 3HF - 1/G'} \tag{3.12}$$

where G' and K' are the elastic shear and bulk moduli respectively and H and F a parameters which depend on the state of stress and on the equations for the stat boundary surface, as discussed in Sec. 2.7. For soil whose state lies inside the stat boundary surface on $V \to X$ or $Y \to Z$ in Fig. 3.2 and so behaves elastically, we hav $H = 0$ and Eq. (3.12) becomes

$$\frac{dq'}{dp'} = \frac{2G'}{K'} = \frac{3(1 - 2v')}{(1 + v')} \tag{3.13}$$

Equations (3.12) and (3.13) describe the variation of q' and p' for one-dimensiona consolidation and unloading of an ideal soil with the mathematical model develope in Chapter 1. From these equations values for K_0 and for σ_v' and σ_h' may be calcu lated throughout a sequence of one-dimensional loading and unloading. Typica relationships between σ_v' and σ_h' and between K_0 and R_0 (where R_0 is the overcor solidation ratio in terms of σ_{vm}', the maximum past vertical effective stress) ar sketched in Fig. 3.3. Since the value of K_0 depends on the history of loading an unloading, the state of stress for soil in the ground cannot be estimated at all unles the past history of deposition, erosion, and changes of pore pressure is known.

We must not forget, however, that the calculations leading to Eq. (3.12) wer based on a number of assumptions and on a relatively simple idealization for so behaviour. It turns out that values of K_0 predicted by these calculations do no

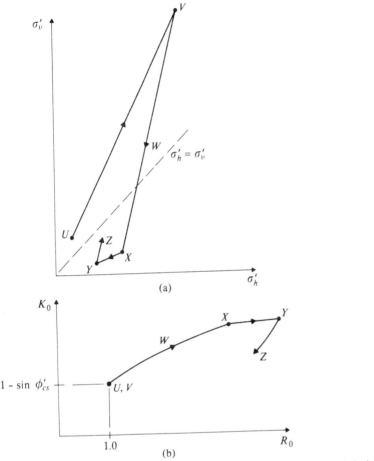

Figure 3.3 Variation of K_0 with overconsolidation for soils in the ground during deposition and erosion.

always agree well with values observed in laboratory tests but they do nevertheless show qualitatively the variation of K_0 with overconsolidation for one-dimensionally consolidated soil.

For many natural, normally consolidated soils, an empirical relationship, attributed to Jaky (1944) and given by

$$K_0 = 1 - \sin \phi' \qquad (3.14)$$

(where ϕ' may be taken equal to ϕ'_{cs}), is found to give reasonable agreement with values for K_0 found in laboratory tests. There is some evidence which suggests that, for heavily overconsolidated soils, K_0 is unlikely to exceed $\tan^2(45° + \frac{1}{2}\phi'_{cs})$, corresponding to a state on the critical state line, while for lightly overconsolidated soils K_0 may be close to 1.0. The only satisfactory method for determining a value for K_0 is by direct measurement of the horizontal stress in the ground.

CONSOLIDATION OF NATURAL SOILS

stresses in natural soils in the ground may increase or decrease owing t
c.. of total stress, changes of pore pressure, or both. Total stresses may chang
as the result of deposition or erosion of soil or as the result of growth and meltin
of glacier ice, while pore pressures may change as the result of rising and falling se
levels or other variations of ground water conditions. Although there are a numbe
of mechanisms by which a soil may become overconsolidated, the only one we wil
consider here is a reduction of effective stress due to a reduction of total stress o
to an increase in pore pressure.

We have already distinguished between lightly overconsolidated soils, whose
states lie on the wet side of critical, and heavily overconsolidated soils whose state
lie on the dry side of critical. The overconsolidation ratio at which the state of a
soil moves from the wet side to the dry side of critical may be found from the
geometry of the state boundary surface as approximately 2. We noted also that the
point at which the state of a soil moves from the wet side of critical to the dry side
of critical corresponds approximately with the point at which $K_0 = 1$ as the value
of q' changes from a positive to a negative value.

Whether a particular soil is normally consolidated or lightly or heavily overconsolidated depends on the geological history of the soil and so we may appeal to
a knowledge of physical geology for estimates of the likely overconsolidation ratio.
Of course, we cannot make any hard and fast rules and there will be exceptions to
every case, but we can make some helpful generalizations.

For natural soils in the ground we will distinguish between soils deposited
during the Quaternary period and those of Tertiary age and older. For Quaternary
soils we will distinguish also between those which have been subjected to ice loading and those deposited in lakes and near the margins of shallow seas. Almost
without exception in the world, soils of Tertiary age and older have suffered sub-
stantial reductions in total stress owing to erosion and are therefore heavily overconsolidated. For example, the youngest Tertiary soil found in any abundance in
Britain is the London Clay and this stratum, which is up to about 50 m thick in
the London basin, has been overconsolidated due to erosion of some 200–400 m
of overlying clay. Clays older than the London Clay found in Britain such as the
Weald Clay, Oxford Clay, Lias Clay and Keuper Marl are all heavily overconsolidated.
It is found that most residual soils behave as though they were heavily overconsolidated, irrespective of whether or not there has been any reduction of total or
effective stress. It is also found that the states of most naturally deposited granular
soils lie on the dry side of critical and so the behaviour of sands and gravels is
similar to that of heavily overconsolidated clay.

The Quaternary period occupied the last two to three million years of the
earth's history and was a period of ice ages. During an ice age much of the earth's
environment, except near the tropics, was glacial or periglacial and, because a large
quantity of water was bound up as glacial ice, the mean sea level was lower than it
is at present. Soil which was at any time beneath an appreciable thickness of glacial

ce became overconsolidated as the total vertical stress reduced owing to the ice melting. In addition, at the end of the glaciation the rise in sea level, which has been estimated to be of the order of 300 m because of the melting of the ice, caused overconsolidation of near coastal deposits as pore pressures rose. Thus, in general, many soils formed at any time before the end of the last ice age will be overconsolidated; of these, most will be heavily overconsolidated and their states will lie on the dry side of critical and the appropriate value of K_0 will be greater than unity.

The last major rise of sea level was complete about eight thousand years ago but since then there have been further small fluctuations both of sea level and, in many areas, of land level as well. Therefore, even recently deposited coastal soils have experienced changes of pore pressure and, in general, will be lightly overconsolidated. Indeed only in the case of lake or sea deposits, where the water level has not changed recently, will soils be truly normally consolidated.

Thus we see that truly normally consolidated soils occur only rarely in the ground and the majority of natural soils are lightly or heavily overconsolidated or, in the cases of granular soils and residual soils, behave as though they were heavily overconsolidated. We must of course accept that there will be exceptions to these broad generalizations and, in a particular location, all the relevant soils should be thoroughly investigated. Nevertheless it is true that the states of many natural soils in the ground lie within the state boundary surface and thus, so long as their states remain within the state boundary surface, their behaviour will, in theory, be elastic. We must not forget, however, that natural soils may be neither isotropic nor homogeneous.

3.5 PROFILES OF WATER CONTENT AND STRENGTH FOR NATURAL SOILS

Since the effective stresses in the ground increase with depth, as shown in Fig. 3.1(c), the water contents of natural soils will decrease with depth and their undrained shear strengths will increase. If, for simplicity, the water table is at the ground surface then the stress at a depth z is given by

$$p' = \tfrac{1}{3}(\gamma - \gamma_w)z(1 + 2K_0) \qquad (3.15)$$

Fig. 3.4(a) shows the one-dimensional consolidation behaviour of a typical soil where $ABCD$ is the normal consolidation line given by Eq. (2.116)

$$v = N_0 - \lambda \ln p' \qquad (3.16)$$

and BB', CC', and DD' are swelling lines given by

$$v = v_\kappa - \kappa \ln p' \qquad (3.17)$$

Hence the variation of specific volume with depth for a normally consolidated soil is given, from Eqs. (3.15) and (3.16), by

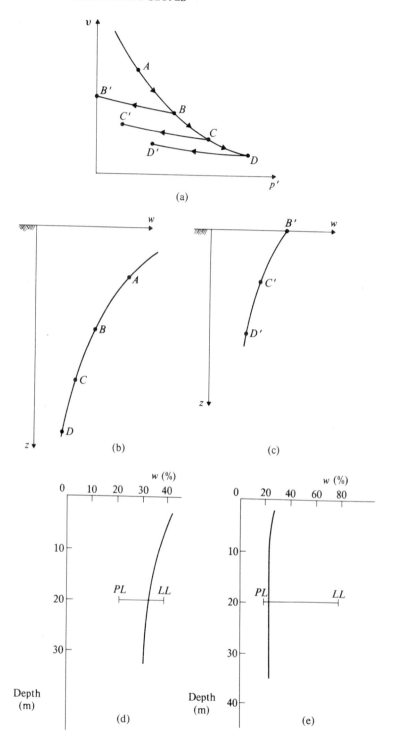

Figure 3.4 Distribution of water content with depth in the ground for normally consolidated soil and for overconsolidated soil. (*After Bjerrum 1954 and after Skempton and Henkel 1957*).

$$v = N_0 - \lambda \ln \left[\tfrac{1}{3}(\gamma - \gamma_w)z(1 + 2K_0)\right] \qquad (3.18)$$

The water content w is related to the specific volume by

$$w = \frac{v - 1}{G_s} \qquad (3.19)$$

where G_s is the specific gravity of the soil grains. Thus, from Eqs. (3.18) and (3.19) we have

$$w = \frac{1}{G_s}\{N_0 - 1 - \lambda \ln \left[\tfrac{1}{3}(\gamma - \gamma_w)z(1 + 2K_0)\right]\} \qquad (3.20)$$

and the water content for normally consolidated soil decreases with depth as illustrated in Fig. 3.4(b).

If material is removed by erosion then the soil becomes overconsolidated as stresses reduce from B to B', C to C', and D to D' in Fig. 3.4(a) and the water contents increase slightly as the states of samples in the ground move along swelling lines. If erosion occurs to a depth corresponding to the point B in Fig. 3.4(b) the resulting variation of water content with depth in the overconsolidated soil will be like that shown in Fig. 3.4(c). The water content at B' is a little greater than that at B but *at a given depth* the water content in an overconsolidated soil is substantially lower than that in the corresponding normally consolidated soil.

Figures 3.4(d) and (e) show the variations of water content with depth for normally consolidated Drammen clay (Bjerrum, 1954) and for overconsolidated London clay from Paddington (Skempton and Henkel, 1957); it has been estimated that the London clay at Paddington was overconsolidated owing to removal of the order of 200 m of soil by erosion. It is of interest to note that for normally consolidated Drammen clay the natural water content tends towards the liquid limit, especially at shallow depths, while for heavily overconsolidated London clay the natural water content tends towards the plastic limit.

From Eq. (2.45), and making use of Eq. (3.19), the undrained shear strength of soil is related to its water content by

$$c_u = \tfrac{1}{2}M \exp \left(\frac{\Gamma - 1 - wG_s}{\lambda}\right) \qquad (3.21)$$

Hence all samples of a soil with the same water content have the same undrained shear strength and the value of c_u increases with decreasing water content. The variations of undrained shear strength with depth for normally consolidated and overconsolidated soils inferred from the variations of water content with depth in Figs. 3.4(b) and (c) are shown in Figs. 3.5(a) and (b). If the water table is below ground level the undrained shear strength of normally consolidated soil will tend to increase as the water content is lowered, while the undrained shear strength of overconsolidated soil will tend to decrease as the soil becomes unsaturated,

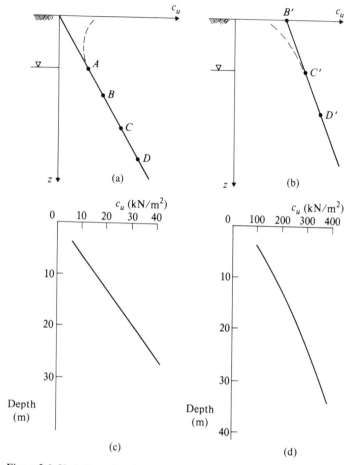

Figure 3.5 Variation of undrained shear strength with depth for normally consolidated and unconsolidated soil. (*After Bjerrum 1954 and after Skempton and Henkel 1957*).

as indicated by the broken lines. The undrained shear strength at B' is a little less than that at B, since the water content at B' is a little greater than that at B, but *at a given depth* the undrained shear strength of an overconsolidated soil is substantially greater than that of the corresponding normally consolidated soil.

For undrained loading there is no change in specific volume. Hence the specific volumes before and after loading are the same,

and, noting that
$$v_f = \Gamma - \lambda \ln p_f' = v_0 = N_0 - \lambda \ln p_0' \tag{3.22}$$

we have
$$c_u = \tfrac{1}{2} M p_f' \tag{3.23}$$

$$\frac{c_u}{p_0'} = \tfrac{1}{2} M \exp \frac{\Gamma - N_0}{\lambda} \tag{3.24}$$

where p_0' is the stress corresponding to v_0 and is the state of stress in the ground given by Eq. (3.15). In Eq. (3.24) the terms on the right hand side are soil constants and hence, for normally consolidated soil, the undrained shear strength increases linearly with depth, as shown in Fig. 3.5(a). In practice it is more convenient to relate c_u to σ_v', thus avoiding the necessity to determine K_0, and the ratio c_u/σ_v' will be constant for a given normally consolidated soil. An empirical relationship between c_u/σ_v' and the plasticity index PI was given by Skempton (1957) as

$$\frac{c_u}{\sigma_v'} = 0.11 + 0.0037\,PI \tag{3.25}$$

An analysis for the undrained shear strength of overconsolidated soil was given by Atkinson and Bransby (1978, pp. 331–334).

Figures 3.5(c) and (d) show the variations of undrained shear strength with depth for normally consolidated Drammen clay (Bjerrum, 1954) and for overconsolidated London clay from Paddington (Skempton and Henkel, 1957). The undrained shear strength of the heavily overconsolidated London clay is considerably larger than that of the normally consolidated Drammen clay.

3.6 LOADING OF SOIL IN FOUNDATIONS AND SLOPES

The loading path experienced by an element of soil in the ground during construction and loading of a soil structure depends on a number of factors; among these are the geometry of the structure and the position of the element, the kind of structure, and the rate of loading. In order to illustrate the kinds of loading paths experienced by soil elements in the ground it is convenient to examine the simple cases of quick and slow construction of a long strip foundation and a long excavated slope. Since the foundation and slope are long, soil deformations are plane strain and we define parameters for stress as

$$t' = \tfrac{1}{2}(\sigma_1' - \sigma_3') = t \tag{3.26}$$

$$s' = \tfrac{1}{2}(\sigma_1' + \sigma_3') = s - u \tag{3.27}$$

At the start of loading or construction σ_v' and σ_h' are principal stresses but as construction progresses the principal stresses may rotate and they may no longer be vertical and horizontal.

Figure 3.6(a) shows principal total stresses σ_1 and σ_3 on the faces of an element below a foundation carrying a load F and Fig. 3.6(b) shows principal stresses on the faces of an element of soil in an excavated slope. We cannot, at the moment, calculate values for σ_1 and σ_3 in either case but it is intuitively obvious that as the foundation load increases both σ_1 and σ_3 will increase (but not necessarily by the same amount) while, as the slope is excavated, σ_3 will decrease and σ_1 will remain approximately constant. Thus we may sketch the general directions of the total stress paths as $G \to F$ in Fig. 3.6(c) for the element below the foundation and as

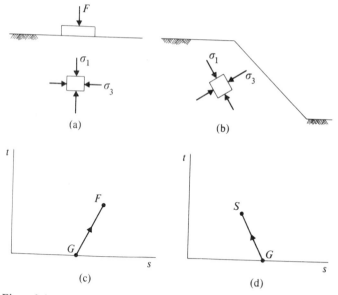

Figure 3.6 Stress paths for typical elements below a foundation and behind a slope.

$G \rightarrow S$ in Fig. 3.6(d) for the element inside the slope. However, until we can calculate the changes of σ_1 and σ_3 we cannot calculate the precise slopes of the stress paths. In Fig. 3.6 the state points G representing zero load on the foundation and before excavation of the slope have been shown for $\sigma_v = \sigma_h$ corresponding to $K_0 = 1$.

The loading paths shown in Fig. 3.6 are for total stresses, but of course we should really consider effective stresses and effective stress paths. The relationship between total and effective stresses is given by the effective stress equation (Eq. (1.1)) $\sigma' = \sigma - u$ and, from Eqs. (3.26) and (3.27), states of total and effective stress plotted with axes $t':s'$ and $t:s$ superimposed are separated horizontally by a distance equal to the magnitude of the pore pressure u, as shown in Fig. 1.13. As soil is loaded, pore pressures respond to changes of total stress and these excess pore pressures cause seepage flows to occur as the soil consolidates; the magnitude of the excess pore pressure depends on, among other things, the relative rates of loading and consolidation.

There are two limiting cases for the rate of loading of a foundation or the rate of excavation of a slope compared with the rate of consolidation of the soil. On the one hand, if the rate of loading or excavation is very slow compared with the rate of consolidation then excess pore pressures dissipate completely during construction and the loading is known as *drained*. On the other hand, if the rate of loading or excavation is so fast that there is no dissipation of pore pressure and no flow of water then the loading is known as *undrained*. For undrained loading the volumetric strain is zero, while for drained loading the pore pressure remains constant. We must be clear that it is not the absolute rate of loading which is important but the rate of loading as compared with the rate of consolidation.

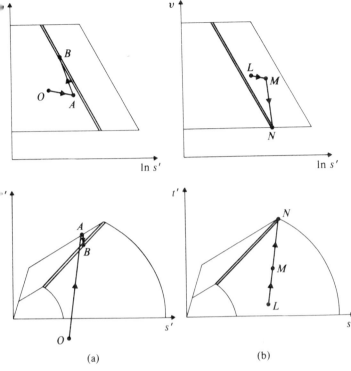

Figure 3.7 State paths for drained loading of a foundation. (a) Heavily overconsolidated soil. (b) Lightly overconsolidated soil.

Figures 3.7 to 3.10 show the approximate shapes of the state paths for drained and undrained loading and excavation of the foundation and slope shown in Figs 3.5 and 3.6. In each figure the point L represents the state of lightly overconsolidated soil before construction and the point O represents the state of heavily overconsolidated soil before construction. In Figs 3.8 and 3.10 the broken lines represent total stress paths for undrained loading and unloading for the special (and unrealistic) case when $u = 0$ before construction; thus, the horizontal distance between the total and effective stress paths is given by the magnitude Δu of the change of pore pressure. The paths in Figs 3.8 and 3.10 for undrained loading have been sketched for isotropic soil so that $\delta p' = 0$ for elastic states inside the state boundary surface; for anisotropic soil, paths such as $O \rightarrow C$ and $L \rightarrow P$ representing elastic behaviour will remain linear but they need not be vertical. In each case the effective stress paths have been shown continuing to ultimate failure on the critical state line. At this point, no further shearing stresses can be applied to the *element*, although additional loads may be applied to the foundation or the slope may be steepened if there are other elements to which additional shear stresses may be applied. Ultimately, of course, the foundation or slope will fail when there are no remaining elements to which additional shear stresses can be applied.

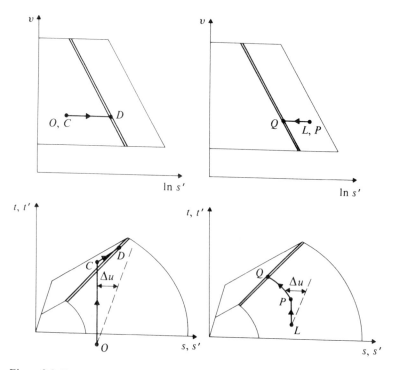

Figure 3.8 State paths for undrained loading of a foundation. (a) Heavily overconsolidated soil. (b) Lightly overconsolidated soil.

Comparison of the total and effective stress paths in Figs 3.8 and 3.10 for undrained loading and excavation shows that pore pressures rise below foundations while pore pressures drop behind slopes: thus in Fig. 3.8 the total stress path lies to the right of the effective stress path for a foundation while the opposite is true in Fig. 3.10 for a slope. This means that if the loading is terminated before undrained failure occurs then the stability of a foundation will improve as excess pore pressures diminish with time, while a slope will become less stable as excess pore pressures rise. This point is illustrated in Fig. 3.11, which shows total and effective stress paths for elements of soil below a foundation and in a slope, both loaded to states considerably below failure; the paths in Fig. 3.11 have been drawn for an initial value of $K_0 = 1$ and in both cases the states do not reach the state boundary surface. The total stress paths $G \rightarrow K$ and $G \rightarrow X$ due to the loading give rise to effective stress paths $G \rightarrow J$ and $G \rightarrow W$ and at any instant pore pressures are given by the horizontal distances between the paths. If it is assumed that the total stresses remain constant at K and X respectively, then dissipation of excess pore pressures gives rise to effective stress paths $J \rightarrow K$ and $W \rightarrow X$. It may be noted that in Fig. 3.11(a), for the foundation, the path $J \rightarrow K$ moves away from the critical state line while in Fig. 3.11(b), for the slope, the path $W \rightarrow X$ moves

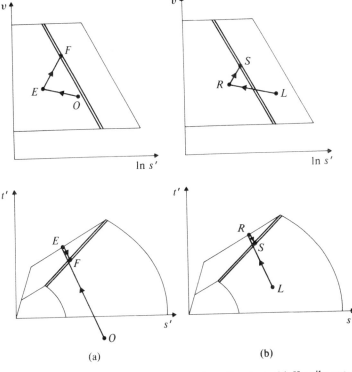

Figure 3.9 State paths for drained excavation of a slope. (a) Heavily overconsolidated soil. (b) Lightly overconsolidated soil.

towards the critical state line; thus the stability of the foundation improves while the stability of the slope deteriorates.[†]

3.7 INVESTIGATIONS, SAMPLING, AND TESTING

An essential first step in any engineering design is the determination of the mechanical properties of the materials involved. In any event, this must necessitate sampling and testing but in geotechnical engineering this also means discovering what particular soils and rocks are present. For example, a structural engineer may choose steel for a particular building and at some stage, usually at the steelworks, samples of the steel are taken and tested and suitable mechanical properties of the steel are selected for design. Similarly, if concrete is chosen the concrete mix must be designed from the results of tests on samples and further testing is usually

[†] This means that although a recently excavated slope has not yet collapsed there is no guarantee that it will not fail in the next minute. It is extremely dangerous to go into an unsupported trench.

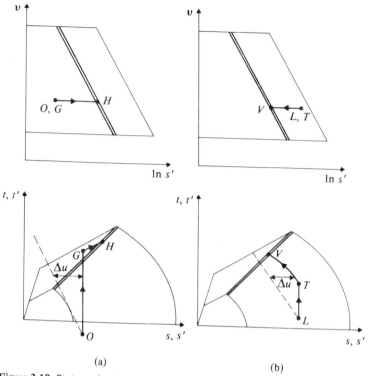

(a)

(b)

Figure 3.10 State paths for undrained excavation of a slope. (a) Heavily overconsolidated soil. (b) Lightly overconsolidated soil.

carried out for quality control purposes. In geotechnical engineering, however, the engineer usually has little choice in the selection of material and indeed will not, in the first instance, know precisely what are the materials he has to deal with. Thus the first essential step in geotechnical engineering is a site investigation which sets out to establish and classify the soils and rocks which occur at the particular

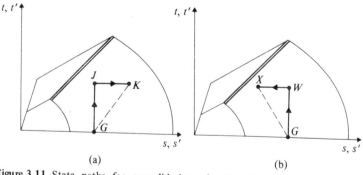

(a)

(b)

Figure 3.11 State paths for consolidation of soil below a foundation or in a slope. (a) Foundation. (b) Slope.

site in question. The second essential step is to take representative samples for each of the major strata and so determine the mechanical properties of the soils and rocks involved.

Site investigations, sampling, and testing are important parts of geotechnical engineering, but they are not topics which we will deal with here. Most standard texts on soil mechanics and foundation engineering contain chapters on site investigations and sampling methods and there are a number of special texts on these subjects; the appropriate British Standard for site investigations is CP 2001: 1957. Methods of laboratory testing for soils were discussed by Atkinson and Bransby (1978, Chapter 5) and these tests may be carried out on undisturbed samples of natural soils as well as on samples of remoulded soils. The appropriate British Standard for soil testing is BS 1377: 1975 and the standard text for triaxial testing is Bishop and Henkel (1962).

It is not always possible to obtain undisturbed samples of soils for laboratory testing and for these cases various *in situ* tests and empirical tests have been developed. Indeed, because of the unavoidable changes of total stress which occur as soil samples are removed from the ground and transferred to a laboratory testing apparatus it is doubtful whether any sample of natural soil is truly undisturbed; the question of sampling disturbance in geotechnical engineering is a subject of current research and is beyond the scope of this book.

For the present purpose we will assume that, in some way, it is possible to discover the nature of the soils occurring at a particular site and to determine suitable values for the parameters which describe their mechanical behaviour. We must appreciate that natural soils are likely to be anisotropic because of the method of their formation by deposition; although, for simplicity, and in accordance with conventional practice, we will assume that most soils may be regarded as isotropic. The validity of this assumption depends very much on the nature of the particular soil and on the kind of structure involved and it is another subject of current research. Furthermore, we must also appreciate that soils are unlikely to be homogeneous and, to take account of variations of soil properties, it is conventional to separate soil deposits into layers and to assume that each layer consists of an isotropic and homogeneous soil.

3.8 ANALYSIS OF SOIL STRUCTURES

Most problems in geotechnical engineering are essentially problems in continuum mechanics and for any such problem the complete solution requires that the conditions of equilibrium and compatibility are satisfied together with the requirements of the material properties. For soils it is necessary, in addition, to distinguish between undrained and drained loading and we may have to take account of changes of effective stress with time caused by dissipation of excess pore pressures due to consolidation. To be quite general, we should consider the complete three-dimensional state of stress and strain, allowing for seepage of pore water in any direction. For simplicity, however, we will consider the plane strain case for which all strains and pore water seepage normal to the page are zero as our discussion will concentrate on this case in later chapters of this book.

For drained loading, when pore pressures are known, calculations should be carried out in terms of effective stress. For plane strain, the conditions of equilibrium and compatibility are given by Eqs (1.69), (1.70), and (1.77) as

$$\frac{\partial \sigma_z'}{\partial z} + \frac{\partial \tau_{xz}'}{\partial x} = \gamma - \frac{\partial u}{\partial z} \tag{3.28}$$

$$\frac{\partial \sigma_x'}{\partial x} + \frac{\partial \tau_{zx}'}{\partial z} = -\frac{\partial u}{\partial x} \tag{3.29}$$

$$\frac{\partial^2 \epsilon_x}{\partial z^2} + \frac{\partial^2 \epsilon_z}{\partial x^2} - \frac{\partial \gamma_{xz}}{\partial x \, \partial z} = 0 \tag{3.30}$$

and material properties are given by Eq. (1.78) as

$$\begin{Bmatrix} \delta \epsilon_x \\ \delta \epsilon_z \\ \delta \gamma_{xz} \end{Bmatrix} = [C_{ps}'] \begin{Bmatrix} \delta \sigma_x' \\ \delta \sigma_z' \\ \delta \tau_{xz}' \end{Bmatrix} \tag{3.31}$$

where $[C_{ps}']$ is a 3×3 compliance matrix whose coefficients depend on the properties of the soil and also on its current state. Equations (3.28) to (3.31) are six independent partial differential equations in six unknowns; there are three unknown stresses and three unknown strains. In order to find a complete solution for a particular problem these must be solved everywhere throughout the region of loaded soil together with the appropriate boundary conditions. Boundary conditions may be specified as loads or stresses, as in the case of a flexible foundation, as displacements, as in the case of rigid wall moving towards or away from the soil, or as a combination of loads and displacements.

For undrained loading, when pore pressures are not known, calculations may be carried out in terms of total stresses for saturated soil for which volumetric strains are zero. The equations of equilibrium and compatibility become

$$\frac{\partial \sigma_z}{\partial z} + \frac{\partial \tau_{xz}}{\partial x} = \gamma \tag{3.32}$$

$$\frac{\partial \sigma_x}{\partial x} + \frac{\partial \tau_{zx}}{\partial z} = 0 \tag{3.33}$$

$$\frac{\partial^2 \epsilon_x}{\partial z^2} + \frac{\partial^2 \epsilon_z}{\partial x^2} - \frac{\partial^2 \gamma_{xz}}{\partial x \, \partial z} = 0 \tag{3.34}$$

and the material properties must be written by an equation of the form

$$\begin{Bmatrix} \delta\epsilon_x \\ \delta\epsilon_z \\ \delta\epsilon_{xz} \end{Bmatrix} = [C_{ps}] \begin{Bmatrix} \delta\sigma_x \\ \delta\sigma_z \\ \partial\tau_{xz} \end{Bmatrix} \qquad (3.35)$$

where the undrained compliance matrix $[C_{ps}]$ depends on the soil properties. For undrained loading of saturated soil volumetric strains are zero and hence, for plane strain, we have an additional equation

$$\delta\epsilon_x + \delta\epsilon_z = 0 \qquad (3.36)$$

but Eq. (3.35) now contains only two independent equations. Thus, Eqs (3.32) to (3.36) are six independent equations in six unknowns and for a complete solution these must be solved, together with the particular boundary conditions.

Equations (3.28) to (3.31) and (3.32) to (3.36) for drained and for undrained loading respectively are the equations governing the distribution of stress and strain throughout any soil region for plane strain: only the values of the coefficients in the matrices $[C'_{ps}]$ and $[C_{ps}]$ change for different soils and for different states for the same soil. They are indeed valid for any material whose stress–strain behaviour can be obtained in incremental form as given by Eq. (3.31) or (3.35). In Chapter 2 we examined incremental stress–strain relationships for plane strain loading of soil developed from the state boundary surface. These included stress–strain relationships for elastic deformations, for elasto–plastic deformations, and for states of ultimate failure. Thus in theory we may calculate the stresses and strains, and displacements, throughout any region of soil for any loading, up to and including failure.

The first class of solutions we will examine are concerned with *stability* and these seek to calculate the loads or conditions at which a structure will collapse so that a suitable factor of safety may be included in the design. For stability calculations we will be concerned with ultimate states of failure as soil suffers large plastic straining.

The second class of solutions is to do with *deformations* and these seek to calculate the settlements or displacements which will occur to the structure as designed with a factor of safety against collapse. For deformation calculations we will usually be concerned with states of soil which are not close to ultimate states of failure. For overconsolidated soils such states will be below the state boundary surface and will lie on elastic walls; thus elastic methods of calculation will be appropriate, but, for lightly overconsolidated soils, it may be necessary to make allowance for plastic deformations when the state of the soil reaches the state boundary surface.

The third class of solutions of practical importance is concerned with *consolidation* and these solutions seek to calculate the settlements and deformations which take place as excess pore pressures dissipate with time and the rate at which consolidation occurs.

3.9 SELECTION OF STRENGTH PARAMETERS FOR DESIGN

In Secs 2.5 and 2.9 we considered the failure of soil and we found that, for drained loading, soils have a peak strength, an ultimate or critical state strength, and a residual strength given by, respectively,

$$\tau'_n = (\tan \phi'_{cs} - \tan \phi'_h) \exp\left(\frac{\Gamma_n - v}{\lambda}\right) + \sigma'_n \tan \phi'_h \tag{3.37}$$

$$\tau'_n = \sigma'_n \tan \phi'_{cs} \tag{3.38}$$

$$\tau'_n = \sigma'_n \tan \phi'_r \tag{3.39}$$

where ϕ'_h is the Hvorslev friction angle, ϕ'_{cs} is the critical state friction angle, and ϕ'_r is the residual friction angle. For undrained loading, ultimate failure at the critical state is given by the undrained shear strength c_u and residual failure is given by the residual undrained shear strength c_{ur}.

As discussed in Sec. 2.9, the residual strength applies only for very large shear displacements, perhaps of the order of several metres. Normally, displacements of this magnitude would not be tolerated in a well designed soil structure and it would be overconservative to choose the residual strength for stability calculations. In some instances, however, there may be pre-existing or residual slip planes in which very large shear displacements have occurred, owing perhaps to ancient lanslide activity and the strength of the soil on these slip planes may have already fallen to its residual value. In this case it would be appropriate to choose the residual strength parameters ϕ'_r or c_{ur} for drained and undrained shearing respectively on the residual slip planes. Thus, an essential feature of a site investigation should determine whether there are any residual slip planes which could be reactivated by new construction.

For the usual case, when there are no residual slip planes which will influence the design, the choice of strength parameters rests between the peak or Hvorslev strength and the ultimate or critical state strength. For undrained loading, choice of the undrained shear strength c_u corresponding to ultimate failure is straightforward since, as discussed in Sec. 2.9. the 'peak' strength will be *lower* than the ultimate strength. Similarly, for drained loading of normally consolidated or lightly overconsolidiated soils whose states are on the wet side of critical, choice of the critical state friction angle ϕ'_{cs} is relatively simple, since for these soils the states do not reach the Hvorslev surface and they have no peak strength.

For drained loading of heavily overconsolidated clay and dense sand, however, the choice between the peak strength and the ultimate strength is not so easy. The important point to note is that the peak strength applies only for the small strains which correspond approximately to the end of the elastic range. In most soil structures, strains are non-uniform and there will usually be regions in which the strains are sufficient to take the state of the soil past the peak strength and towards the ultimate or critical state strength, even though the *average* strains and displacements are not large. Thus, it would be safe, and not overconservative, to base the design on the ultimate strength, taking ϕ'_{cs} or c_u for drained and for undrained loading, respectively. Then, even though some parts of the structure are strained beyond the peak the structure will not fail, as the average strength will not fall below the ultimate strength unless there are residual slip planes. Thus it is logical to adopt the critical state strength for routine design calculations and, as argued by Atkinson and Bransby (1978, pp. 351–353), it would be reasonable to use lower factors of safety than would be used if the peak strength parameters were chosen.

3.10 FACTOR OF SAFETY

Although we may calculate the conditions at collapse of a soil structure, in practice we will need to design structures with smaller loads, smaller slope angles, or lower slope heights so that there is a margin of safety against collapse. Thus foundations and slopes should be designed with reduced working loads and heights and we will need to define a *factor of safety*. We must be careful, however, because, for the case of the force supporting a wall retaining soil the working load must *exceed* the collapse load to give a suitable margin of safety. An entirely consistent factor of safety for foundations, walls, and slopes may be obtained by reducing the shear stresses in the soil by some appropriate factor. Thus we may define an *allowable shear stress* in terms of total or effective stress as

$$\tau'_a = \frac{\tau'_f}{F_s} \quad \text{or} \quad \tau_a = \frac{\tau_f}{F_s} \tag{3.40}$$

and, if collapse can occur when the soil strength is reduced to τ'_a or τ_a, the actual structure, for which the true failure stresses are τ'_f or τ_f, will have a factor of safety F_s. We must of course consider drained and undrained loading separately. For drained loading, making use of Eq. (2.22), the allowable shear stress is given by

$$\tau'_a = \sigma'_n \frac{\tan \phi'_{cs}}{F_s} = \sigma'_n \tan \phi'_a \tag{3.41}$$

and for undrained loading, making use of Eq. (2.47),

$$\tau_a = \frac{c_u}{F_s} = c_{ua} \tag{3.42}$$

where ϕ'_a is the *allowable angle of friction* and c_{ua} is the *allowable undrained shear strength*. These are given by

$$\phi'_a = \tan^{-1}\left(\frac{\tan \phi'_{cs}}{F_s}\right) \tag{3.43}$$

$$c_{ua} = \frac{c_u}{F_s} \tag{3.44}$$

where ϕ'_{cs} is the critical state friction angle, c_u is the undrained shear strength and F_s is the factor of safety.

Thus, we apply a factor of safety to the soil strength. For the next few chapters we will investigate the limiting stability of foundations, slopes, and walls for which $F_s = 1.0$ and the soil strength is given by ϕ'_{cs} for drained loading or by c_u for undrained loading. To design a structure with a given factor of safety we may conduct precisely the same calculations, but using ϕ'_a and c_{ua} from Eqs (3.43) and (3.44). On the other hand, to determine the margin of safety of an existing structure we must find the value of F_s in these equations for which the soil strength is reduced to the point where the structure just collapses. We should note that, in general, it is not possible to calculate a value of F_s directly for a given structure.

REFERENCES

Atkinson, J. H. and P. L. Bransby (1978), *The Mechanics of Soils*, McGraw-Hill, London.

Bishop. A. W. and D. J. Henkel (1962), *The Triaxial Test*, Edward Arnold, London.

Bjerrum, L. (1954), 'Geotechnical properties of Norwegian marine clays', *Geotechnique*, 4 49–69.

BS 1377: 1975, *Methods of Testing Soils for Civil Engineering Purposes*, British Standards Institution, London.

CP 2001: 1957, *Site Investigation*, British Standards Institution, London.

Holmes, A. (1965), *Principles of Physical Geology*, Nelson, London.

Jaky, J. (1944), 'The coefficient of earth pressure at rest', *J. Soc. Hungarian Architects and Engineers*, pp. 355–358.

Skempton, A. W. (1957), 'Discussion on planning and design of the new Hong Kong airport' *Proc. Instn Civil Engrs*, 7, 306.

—— and D. J. Henkel (1957), 'Tests on London clay from deep borings at Paddington Victoria and the South Bank', *Proc. 4th Int. Conf. Soil Mech. and Foundation Engng* Vol. I, London, pp. 100–105.

WORKED EXAMPLES

E3.1 Calculation of Stresses in the Ground

A soil has unit weight $\gamma = 20\,\text{kN/m}^3$ and the coefficient of earth pressure at rest is $K_0 = 0.05$. Pore pressures in the ground are hydrostatic, the water table coincides with ground level, and the unit weight of water is $\gamma_w = 9.81\,\text{kN/m}^3$. Calculate total and effective vertical and horizontal stresses in the ground at a depth of 10 m.

The vertical total stress, the pore pressure, and the vertical effective stress are given by Eqs (3.1) to (3.3) as

$$\underline{\sigma}_v = \gamma z = 20 \times 10 = \underline{200\,\text{kN/m}^2}$$

$$\underline{u} = \gamma_w z = 9.81 \times 10 = \underline{98\,\text{kN/m}^2}$$

$$\underline{\sigma}'_v = \sigma_v - u = 200 - 98 = \underline{102\,\text{kN/m}^2}$$

The horizontal total and effective stresses are given by Eqs (3.4) and (3.5), taking $\zeta = K_0$ in Eq. (3.4), as

$$\sigma_h = K_0 \sigma'_v = 0.5 \times 102 = \underline{51 \text{ kN/m}^2}$$

$$\sigma_h = \sigma'_h + u = 51 + 98 = \underline{149 \text{ kN/m}^2}$$

3.2 Calculation of K_0 for Normally Consolidated Soil

A soil has $\lambda = 0.08$, $\kappa = 0.05$, $M = 0.94$, and $v' = 0.25$. Taking the simple Cam clay equation to define the Roscoe surface, calculate the value of K_0 for normally consolidated samples.

From Eq. (3.6)

$$\frac{q'}{p'} = \frac{3(1 - K_0)}{(1 + 2K_0)}$$

and for normally consolidated soil

$$\eta'_0 = \frac{q'}{p'} = \frac{dq'}{dp'}$$

From Eq. (3.12) for one-dimensional compression

$$\frac{dq'}{dp'} = \frac{3H - 2/K' - 2H/F}{2H - 1/G' - 3HF}$$

and

$$\eta'_0 = \frac{(3 - 2/HK') - 2/F}{(2 - 1/HG') - 3F}$$

From Eqs (2.53), (2.54), 2.84), and (2.88) we have

$$H = \frac{\lambda - \kappa}{v M p'} = \frac{0.032}{v p'}$$

$$K' = \frac{v p'}{\kappa} = 20 v p'$$

$$G' = \frac{v p'}{\kappa} \frac{3(1 - 2v')}{2(1 + v')} = 12 v p'$$

$$1/F = M - \eta'_0 = 0.94 - \eta'_0$$

Hence

$$0.94 - 1/F = \frac{(3 - 2/0.64) - 2/F}{(2 - 1/0.38) - 3F} = \frac{0.125 + 2/F}{0.632 + 3F}$$

or

$$1/F^2 + 0.96 \times 1/F - 1.07 = 0$$

$$1/F = 0.66 \quad \text{or} \quad -1.62$$

Thus, taking the positive root we have

$$\eta_0' = M - 1/F = 0.94 - 0.66 = 0.28$$

$$K_0 = \frac{3 - \eta_0'}{3 + 2\eta_0'}$$

and

$$\underline{K_0 = 0.76}$$

E3.3 Calculation of K_0 for Overconsolidated Soil

A sample of the soil described in Example E3.2 is one-dimensionally normally consolidated to $p' = 600 \, \text{kN/m}^2$ and then one-dimensonally unloaded to $p' = 300$ kN/m². Calculate values of K_0 for overconsolidation ratios $R_p = 1.5$ and 2.0 assuming that the state does not reach the state boundary surface during unloading.

During unloading we have, from Eq. (3.13),

$$\frac{dq'}{dp'} = \frac{3(1 - 2\nu')}{(1 + \nu')} = 1.2$$

and, from Example E3.2, the state at $p' = 600 \, \text{kN/m}^2$ is given by

$$\frac{q'}{p'} = \eta_0' = 0.28$$

and

$$K_0 = \frac{3 - \eta_0'}{3 + 2\eta_0'} = 0.76$$

It is simplest to prepare a table with values of q' and p' calculated from each overconsolidation ratio (Table E3.1).

Table E3.1

R_p	p' kN/m²	$\Delta p'$ kN/m²	$\Delta q'$ kN/m²	q' kN/m²	η_0'	K_0
1	600			168	0.28	0.76
		-200	-240			
1.5	400			-72	-0.18	1.20
		-100	-120			
2	300			-192	-0.64	2.11

Note: Since $\eta_0' < M$, the state has not reached the state boundary surface at an overconsolidation ratio $R_p = 2.0$.

THEOREMS OF PLASTIC COLLAPSE AND THEIR APPLICATION TO SOIL STRUCTURES

1 INTRODUCTION

Clearly, engineering structures cannot be allowed to collapse and so prediction of the maximum load which can be applied to a foundation and prediction of the maximum height and slope of an excavation form an important part of geotechnical engineering. Problems such as these could, at least in theory, be solved by satisfying simultaneously conditions of equilibrium and compatibility, together with the requirements of the material properties as discussed in Sec. 3.7, seeking solutions for which some displacements become exceedingly large. Calculations such as these are not easy and they are certainly unsuitable as routine methods of stability analysis.

In order to ease stability calculations it is possible to ignore some of the conditions of equilibrium and compatibility and to make use of important theorems of plasticity theory which allow bounds to be set for collapse loads of structures. Thus, it turns out that by ignoring the equilibrium condition we may calculate an *upper bound* to the collapse load, so that if the structure is loaded to this value it must collapse; similarly, by ignoring the compatibility conditions we can set a *lower bound* to the collapse load so that if the structure is loaded to this value it cannot collapse. Clearly, the true collapse load must lie between these bounds. By ignoring the conditions of equilibrium and compatibility in turn we have naturally simplified the calculations but at the expense of certainty; thus we calculate not a specific collapse load but upper and lower bounds for the true collapse load.

2 PRINCIPLE OF VIRTUAL WORK

The principle of virtual work is required for proofs of the upper and lower bound theorems. This is a principle generally applicable for any material and it is discussed in many standard texts on structural mechanics (e.g. Palmer, 1976, Chapter 6). For the present we will give a proof of the principle of virtual work for the simple case of a bar subjected only to axial forces and we will indicate the extension of the principle to more general states of loading.

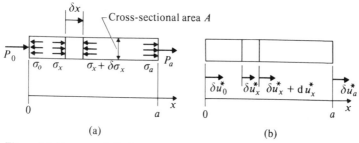

Figure 4.1 Forces and displacements for a bar subjected to axial loading only. (a) Forces a stresses. (b) Displacements.

Figure 4.1(a) shows a bar, length a and cross-sectional area A, subjected axial forces P_0 and P_a; total stresses on the faces of an element in the bar are σ_x a ($\sigma_x + \delta\sigma_x$) as shown. Defining compressive stresses as positive quantities as Chapter 1, $P_0 = A\sigma_0$ and $P_a = -A\sigma_a$ where σ_0 and σ_a are the stresses at the ends the bar. The bar and each element of it are in equilibrium and hence

$$\frac{d\sigma_x}{dx} = 0 \tag{4}$$

Figure 4.1(b) shows the same bar subjected to increments of axial displaceme δu_x^* and hence, from the definition of strain in Chapter 1,

$$\frac{d(\delta u_x^*)}{dx} = -\delta\epsilon_x^* \tag{4.}$$

It is essential to note here that the *increments of displacement δu_x^* and the incr ments of strain $\delta\epsilon_x^*$ need not have anything to do with the forces P or the stress σ_x*. Hence, since the stresses σ_x and the strains $\delta\epsilon_x^*$ are quite independent we not have to say anything about the material of the bar.

From Eq. (4.1) we may write

$$\int_0^a A\,\delta u_x^* \frac{d\sigma_x}{dx}\,dx = 0 \tag{4.}$$

and, integrating by parts,

$$[A\,\delta u_x^*\,\sigma_x]_0^a = A\int_0^a \frac{d(\delta u_x^*)}{dx}\sigma_x\,dx \tag{4.}$$

$$\therefore A\sigma_a\delta u_a^* - A\sigma_0\,\delta u_0^* = -\int_v \sigma_x\,\delta\epsilon_x^*\,d(vol.) \tag{4.}$$

where $d(vol.) = A\,dx$. Hence, noting that $P_0 = A\sigma_0$ etc., we have

$$P_a\,\delta u_a^* + P_0\,\delta u_0^* = \int_v \sigma_x\,\delta\epsilon_x^*\,d(vol.) \tag{4.}$$

and Eq. (4.6) is a simple statement of the principle of virtual work for a bar.

The loads P and the stresses σ may be real or imaginary (i.e. virtual) and the displacements δu^* and the strains $\delta\epsilon^*$ may also be real or virtual. The forces and stresses are in equilibrium with each other and the displacements and strains are compatible with each other, but otherwise forces and stresses may be either real or virtual. Now, terms like $P\,\delta u^*$ and $\int_v \sigma\,\delta\epsilon^*$ d(vol.) measure the increments of work done by the external forces and the internal stresses, and if either the forces and stresses, or the displacements and strains, or both, are virtual then the work terms are virtual also. The principle of virtual work states that the virtual work done by external loads and displacements equals the virtual work done by internal stresses and strains. In Eq. (4.6) the forces P_a and P_0 are in equilibrium with each other and with the stresses σ_x while the displacements δu_a^* and δu_0^* are compatible with the strains $\delta\epsilon_x^*$, but the set of forces and stresses (P, σ) need have nothing to do with the set of displacements and strains $(\delta u^*, \delta\epsilon^*)$, and so Eq. (4.6) is valid for any material whatsoever. Indeed, we have obtained a proof for the principle of virtual work for a bar only be integration by parts, which is simply pure mathematics, without considering material behaviour at all.

The principle of virtual work may be extended to quite general states of external loading and displacement and states of internal stress and strain. Thus, a body is loaded externally with a set of loads F which give rise to a set of internal stresses σ where the loads F may be normal loads, shearing loads, concentrated loads, or distributed loads and the internal stresses σ will contain components of normal and shear stresses; the loads F are in equilibrium with the stresses σ. The body is subjected to a set of increments of boundary displacement δw^* giving rise to a set of internal strain increments $\delta\epsilon^*$ which will contain components of normal and shear strains. Thus the general form of the principle of virtual work is

$$\sum \mathbf{F}\cdot\delta\mathbf{w}^* = \int_v \boldsymbol{\sigma}\cdot\delta\boldsymbol{\epsilon}^* \; d(\text{vol.}) \tag{4.7}$$

Note that F, σ, δw^*, and $\delta\epsilon^*$ are vector quantities and both sides of Eq.(4.7) contain the dot or scalar products of vectors and so express the work done by the external forces and displacements and by the internal stresses and strains.

4.3 THEOREMS OF PLASTIC COLLAPSE

The upper and lower bound theorems of plastic collapse set limits to the collapse load of a structure. The theorems are equally applicable to single-member structures, such as a bar, to frameworks, and to continua, but they can be proved only for materials which are *perfectly plastic*. A perfectly plastic material is one which reaches a state of non-hardening failure where the failure criterion serves as a plastic potential and so the flow rule is associated. At ultimate failure the vector of plastic strain increment is normal to the failure envelope and the forces and stresses remain constant for an increment of deformation; thus, since all forces and all stresses remain constant, elastic components of strain are zero and increments of total and plastic strain are identical.

Upper bound theorem

If there is a set of external loads and a mechanism of plastic collapse such that t increment of work done by the external loads in an increment of displaceme equals the work done by the internal stresses, collapse *must* occur and the exter loads are an upper bound to the true collapse loads.

Lower bound theorem

If there is a set of external loads which are in equilibrium with a state of str which nowhere exceeds the failure criterion for the material, collapse *cannot* occ and the external loads are a lower bound to the true collapse loads.

We may note that in the upper bound theorem nothing is said about equil rium and the mechanism of plastic collapse need not be the actual collapse mec anism. Similarly, in the lower bound theorem nothing is said about compatibili of strains and displacements and the equilibrium state of stress need not be t actual collapse state of stress. Thus, in each case we have ignored a requirement f a complete solution and, as a result, the solutions are approximate but they a bounds to the true collapse loads.

Proofs of the bound theorems may be obtained fairly easily from the princip of virtual work. For a proof of the upper bound theorem, consider a structu which collapses when subjected to a set of external loads F_c which gives rise to set of internal stresses σ_c where the subscripts c indicate that F and σ apply to t actual collapse of the structure. We seek an upper bound set of external loads I which give rise to a set of internal stresses σ_u; these are associated with a set boundary displacements δw_u and a set of internal strain increments $\delta \varepsilon_u$ whi together make up a compatible mechanism of collapse. From the statement of tl upper bound theorem, loads F_u must cause collapse if

$$\sum F_u \cdot \delta w_u = \int_v \sigma_u \cdot \delta \varepsilon_u \, d(\text{vol.}) \tag{4.}$$

where the term on the left is the increment of work done by the external loads a the term on the right is the increment of work done by the internal stresses. addition, from the principle of virtual work

$$\sum F_c \cdot \delta w_u = \int_v \sigma_c \cdot \delta \varepsilon_u \, d(\text{vol.}) \tag{4.}$$

where F_c and σ_c are the true loads and stresses and δw_u and $\delta \varepsilon_u$ are virtual d placements and strains.

In Fig. 4.2 the line *FF* is a failure envelope which, for a perfectly plast material, serves also as a plastic potential and which cannot be concave. Bot vectors of stress σ_c and σ_u touch the failure envelope, since the structure collaps with either state of stress and the vector of strain increment $\delta \varepsilon_u$ is normal to tl plastic potential since elastic components of strain are zero at collapse. For un

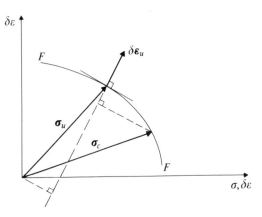

igure 4.2 Proof for upper bound theorem.

rain increment, the scalar product $\sigma \cdot \delta\varepsilon$ is given by the projection of σ on to $\delta\varepsilon$
d, from Fig. 4.2,

$$\sigma_u \cdot \delta\varepsilon_u \geqslant \sigma_c \cdot \delta\varepsilon_u \qquad (4.10)$$

ence, from Eqs (4.8) to (4.10),

$$F_u \geqslant F_c \qquad (4.11)$$

nd loads F_u found from Eq. (4.8) are always greater than or equal to loads F_c
hich actually cause collapse.

For a proof of the lower bound theorem, consider a lower bound set of
xternal loads F_l which are in equilibrium with internal stresses σ_l which do not
xceed the failure criterion. For the true collapse conditions the virtual work
quation becomes a real work equation

$$\sum F_c \cdot \delta w_c = \int_v \sigma_c \cdot \delta\varepsilon_c \, d(\text{vol.}) \qquad (4.12)$$

nd for the lower bound loads and stresses Eq. (4.7) becomes

$$\sum F_l \cdot \delta w_c = \int_v \sigma_l \cdot \delta\varepsilon_c \, d(\text{vol.}) \qquad (4.13)$$

roceeding to calculate scalar products as before, from Fig. 4.3

$$\sigma_l \cdot \delta\varepsilon_c \leqslant \sigma_c \cdot \delta\varepsilon_c \qquad (4.14)$$

ence, from Eqs (4.12) to (4.14)

$$F_l \leqslant F_c \qquad (4.15)$$

nd loads F_l are always less than or equal to the loads F_c which actually cause
ollapse.

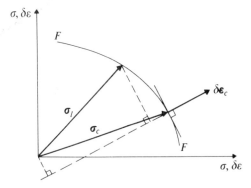

Figure 4.3 Proof for lower bound theorem.

4.4 USE OF BOUND THEOREMS FOR THE COLLAPSE OF A BEAM

In order to illustrate the use of the bound theorems we will use them to estimate the collapse load for the simple case of a prismatic beam, built in at both ends and carrying a central concentrated load, as shown in Fig. 4.4. The beam is fabricated from steel, which has the stress–strain curve for uniaxial tension and compression shown in Fig. 4.5(a); the steel is assumed to be perfectly elastic and perfectly plastic with the same yield stress and failure stress σ_f. The relationship between moment and rotation for the beam is shown in Fig. 4.5(b); as the bending moment is increased, the outer fibres of steel first yield and fail when $M = M_y$, but the complete member does not fail until $M = M_p$, where M_p is known as the fully plastic moment. It is assumed that readers will know, or will be able to show, that for a beam of depth d and breadth b

and
$$M_y = \tfrac{1}{6}\sigma_f bd^2 \tag{4.16}$$
$$M_p = \tfrac{1}{4}\sigma_f bd^2 \tag{4.17}$$

The derivations of these relationships are given in most standard texts on the strength of materials (e.g. Case and Chilver, 1971, pp. 264–265). If the maximum moment in the beam is less than M_y then the maximum stress is less than σ_f and the state of stress does not exceed the failure criterion while, if plastic hinges form so that the structure becomes a mechanism, M_p is the moment at each plastic hinge.

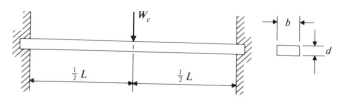

Figure 4.4 Collapse of simple steel beam.

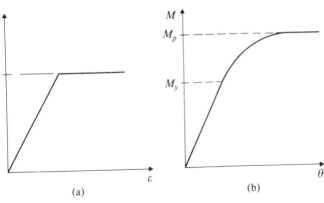

Figure 4.5 Behaviour of steel and beam. (a) Stress–strain behaviour of steel. (b) Moment–rotation behaviour of beam.

First we calculate a lower bound W_l for the collapse load. Since for a lower bound the state of stress is everywhere below yield, the structure is elastic and linear and, using the principle of superposition, the bending moments may be found by the conventional methods of structural analysis described by, for example, Heyman (1974, Chapter 1). The maximum bending moments are $M = \pm \frac{1}{8}WL$ and occur at the ends and the centre of the beam as shown in Fig. 4.6, and the beam cannot collapse so long as $M \leqslant M_y$. Hence a lower bound for the collapse load is given by

$$W_l = \frac{4\sigma_f bd^2}{3L} \tag{4.18}$$

Second we calculate an upper bound W_u for the collapse load by introducing a number of plastic hinges, so converting the beam to a mechanism. The encastré beam shown in Fig. 4.4 has two degrees of statical indeterminacy and so it may be changed into a mechanism by adding three plastic hinges; the positions of the plastic hinges are arbitrary, provided of course that they produce a mechanism, but the better the choice of position for the hinges the closer the upper bound load will be to the true collapse load. Figure 4.7 shows a suitable choice of three hinge positions and a small increment of displacement δv of the load corresponding to the marked rotations of the hinges. The increment of work done by the external load is $W_u \, \delta v$ and that done by the internal stresses is $\Sigma M_p \, \delta\theta$ for all the hinges. Hence the upper bound load is given by

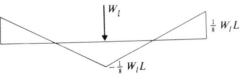

Figure 4.6 Equilibrium bending moments.

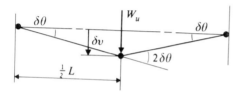

Figure 4.7 Mechanism of plastic collapse.

$$W_u \, \delta v = 4M_p \, \delta\theta \qquad (4.19$$

or, noting that $\delta v = \frac{1}{2}L \, \delta\theta$ from the geometry of Fig. 4.7, and using Eq. (4.17

$$W_u = \frac{2\sigma_f b d^2}{L} \qquad (4.20$$

The bound theorems state specifically that the true collapse load W_c must li
between these bounds and hence is given by

$$\frac{4\sigma_f b d^2}{3L} \leqslant W_c \leqslant \frac{2\sigma_f b d^2}{L} \qquad (4.21$$

It is very difficult to calculate a true value for the collapse load W_c and the calcu
lations involved are very much more complicated than the simple upper and lowe
bound calculations described above.

4.5 FAILURE CRITERIA FOR SOILS

In order to make use of these bound theorems, we must extend the ideas developed
for the steel beam to a soil continuum and first we must specify suitable failure
criteria for soils. The bound theorems are strictly valid only for perfectly plastic
materials which reach a state of ultimate failure where elastic strains are zero and
where the failure criterion serves as a plastic potential. Since many problems of
practical importance are concerned with the stability of long walls, long foundations, and long slopes, we will concentrate our attention on conditions of plane
strain, as discussed in Sec. 1.2, and, unless otherwise stated, we will consider the
stability of a strip of unit thickness normal to the page.

In Sec. 3.9 we argued that for routine design calculations it is appropriate to
take the ultimate or critical state strength. Use of the peak or Hvorslev strength
may lead to unsafe designs, unless it can be shown that the strains everywhere in
the soil are less than those which will move the state of the soil beyond the peak
and towards the ultimate state, while use of the residual strength will be unduly
conservative. At ultimate failure, the state remains on the critical state line and the
soil deforms plastically with zero elastic strain.

For undrained loading of saturated soil the failure criterion appropriate for ultimate failure is

$$\tau = t = c_u \tag{4.22}$$

where c_u, the undrained shear strength, given by Eqs (2.44) and (2.45), depends only on the (constant) specific volume v and on some soil parameters. For undrained loading, the angle of dilation is zero (i.e. $\psi = 0$) and, as discussed in Sec. 2.8, the failure envelope given by Eq. (4.22) serves as a plastic potential. For drained loading, the failure criterion appropriate for ultimate failure is

$$\tau'_n = \sigma'_n \tan \phi'_{cs} \text{ or } t' = s' \sin \phi'_{cs} \tag{4.23}$$

where ϕ'_{cs} is the critical state angle of friction, but, as we found in Sec. 2.8, Eq. (4.23) does not serve as a plastic potential, since at ultimate failure at the critical state volumetric strains are zero (i.e. $\psi = 0$). Thus the angle of dilation ψ does not equal the critical state angle of friction ϕ'_{cs} and soils are not perfectly plastic for drained loading.

In order to calculate bounds for soil for drained loading when the normality condition does not hold, we make use of a subsidiary theorem for upper bound calculations and we make a gross assumption for lower bound calculations. A theorem in plasticity theory states:

Any set of loads which causes collapse for a perfectly plastic material for which the normality condition holds will also cause collapse for a material with the same failure criterion, but for which vectors of strain increment at failure are not normal to the failure envelope.

Thus, if we calculate an upper bound for soil for drained loading by assuming that $\psi = \phi'_{cs}$ then the calculated loads are upper bounds even though, in fact, $\psi = 0$ at the critical state.

The proof of this theorem follows very simply from the proof of the upper bound theorem given in Sec. 4.3. Figure 4.8 is similar to Fig. 4.2 but shows also the actual vector of strain increment $\delta\varepsilon_c$ at collapse which is not normal to the failure envelope FF. This vector of strain increment $\delta\varepsilon_c$ does not appear in the proof of the upper bound theorem in Sec. 4.3. Hence the upper bound loads F_u associated with stresses σ_u and a vector of strain increment $\delta\varepsilon_u$ which is normal to the failure envelope are related to the actual collapse loads F_c, as in Sec. 4.3, by

$$F_u \geqslant F_c \tag{4.24}$$

In order to calculate a lower bound for drained loading of soil we simply deem that the normality condition holds and that $\psi = \phi'_{cs}$. The consequences of making this assumption are that it is no longer absolutely certain that the lower bound calculated for drained loading of soil is a true lower bound for the actual collapse load. It has been suggested (Palmer, 1966) that for soil whose failure criterion is of the form given by Eq. (4.23) a lower bound calculated by assuming that $\psi = \phi'_{cs}$ will be close to the true lower bound for soil with the same value of ϕ'_{cs} but with

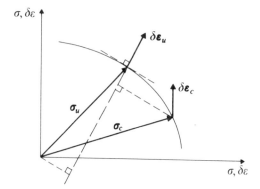

Figure 4.8 Proof of upper bound theorem for a material which is not perfectly plastic.

$\psi = 0$. Detailed discussions of the lower bound for frictional materials are beyond the scope of this book and, in any case, the difficulties have not been fully resolved and the topic forms the subject of current research.[†]

4.6 MECHANISMS FOR PLANE PLASTIC COLLAPSE

Framed structures, such as the simple beam discussed in Sec. 4.4, may be converted to mechanisms by adding a number of plastic hinges; in a similar fashion a continuum may be converted to a mechanism by adding a number of slip planes. Thus the plane rectangular block loaded as shown in Fig. 4.9(a) may be converted to mechanism by adding a single slip plane $A-B$ as shown in Fig. 4.9(b) and plastic collapse can occur as the blocks slide past one another. In Fig. 4.9 a mechanism

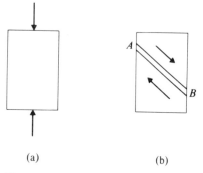

(a)   (b)

Figure 4.9 Simple mechanism of plastic collapse.

[†] It is worth noting in additon that it is, in any case, often rather difficult to calculate lower bound loads which are very close to the true collapse loads. Thus, the approximate lower bounds calculated for a material with $\psi \neq \phi'_{cs}$ by assuming that $\psi = \phi'_{cs}$ are unlikely to exceed the true collapse loads.

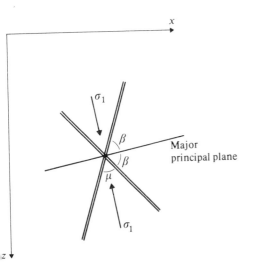

Figure 4.10 Directions of slip planes.

has been obtained by adding a single straight slip plane, but it will not usually be so simple to construct a suitable mechanism.

If slip planes occur in a material which is also suffering continuous strain, the directions of the slip planes must coincide with the directions of zero normal strain as discussed in Sec. 1.3 and as shown in Fig. 1.8 and these are angled at $\pm \beta$ to the major principal plane, where

$$\beta = (45° + \tfrac{1}{2}\psi) \tag{4.25}$$

Thus, in a material suffering continuous strain, any slip planes that occur must intersect at an angle μ, as shown in Fig. 4.10, where

$$\mu = (90° - \psi) \tag{4.26}$$

In an upper bound mechanism of plastic collapse, however, it is assumed that the material remains rigid while all deformations in an increment of collapse occur due to relative sliding across the slip planes; thus, since there are no continuous strains there are no restrictions on the directions of the slip planes which make up the mechanism. Nevertheless, suitable upper bounds can often be obtained by having slip planes intersecting at $(90° - \psi)$ to each other; thus for undrained loading for which $\psi = 0$ we will seek slip planes intersecting at 90°, while for drained loading for which it is assumed that $\psi = \phi'_{cs}$ we will seek slip planes intersecting at $(90° - \phi'_{cs})$, but it is not strictly necessary for the directions of slip planes to satisfy Eq. (4.26) so long as material outside the slip planes remains rigid.

Slip planes may be straight or they may be curved. Fig. 4.11(a) shows a short section of a slip plane; the material on one side is stationary, while the material on the other side undergoes an increment of displacement δw at an angle ψ to the slip plane, as discussed in Sec. 1.3. Figure 4.11(b) shows a section of a curved slip plane

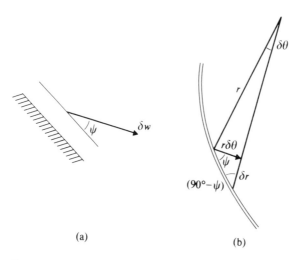

(a)   (b)

Figure 4.11 Permissible shapes of slip planes.

between two radii r and $(r + \delta r)$ at an angle $\delta\theta$; from the geometry of Fig. 4.11(b) and in the limit,

$$\frac{dr}{r \, d\theta} = \tan \psi \tag{4.27}$$

hence

$$\frac{r_B}{r_A} = \exp (\Delta\theta \tan \psi) \tag{4.28}$$

where $\Delta\theta$ is the angle between the radii r_A and r_B. Thus, from Eq. (4.28) the slip plane is a logarithmic spiral for $\psi > 0$, but for $\psi = 0$

$$\frac{r_B}{r_A} = \exp (0) = 1 \tag{4.29}$$

and the slip plane is a circular arc. Furthermore, as $r_A \to \infty$ the slip plane tends to a straight line. Thus, slip planes may be straight lines or logarithmic spirals for drained loading of soil for which ψ is assumed to equal ϕ'_{cs}, while slip planes may be straight lines or circular arcs for undrained loading of soil for which $\psi = 0$, although other shapes are permissible if continuous strains occur in the material outside the slip planes. In Fig. 4.11(b) the radii intersect the curved slip surface at a constant angle $(90° - \psi)$ and hence radii may also be slip planes.

A number of slip planes may be assembled to form a mechanism of plastic collapse in a number of ways and a few simple examples for undrained loading for a vertical cut slope and for a foundation placed at the ground surface are illustrated in Fig. 4.12. These mechanisms containing straight lines or circular arcs are valid only for undrained loading and, for drained loading, when the assumption $\psi = \phi'_{cs}$ is made, slip planes must be logarithmic spirals or straight lines. A particular mechanism may contain both straight lines and circular arcs or both straight lines

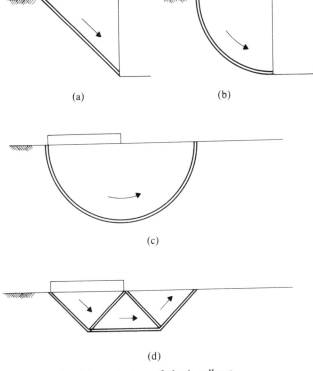

Figure 4.12 Possible mechanisms of plastic collapse.

and logarithmic spirals, but obviously circular arcs and logarithmic spirals cannot occur together in a single mechanism.

Figure 4.12(d) shows a mechanism in which slip planes meet at a point and it is not immediately apparent that collapse can occur because of the possibility of interference between adjacent sliding blocks at these junctions. Such mechanisms are regarded as permissible if, when small holes are drilled at the junctions as shown in Fig. 4.13(a), an increment of plastic collapse can occur as shown in Fig. 4.13(b).

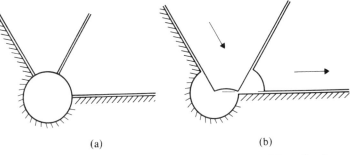

Figure 4.13 Compatibility of displacement at the junction of three slip planes.

4.7 INCREMENTS OF WORK DONE DURING·PLASTIC COLLAPS

For upper bounds we are required to calculate the increments of work done by th external loads and by the internal stresses for an increment of plastic collapse. Th increment of work done by a force is simply the scalar or dot product of the forc and its increment of displacement but, as usual, we must consider drained an undrained loading separately.

Figure 4.14(a) shows an element with unit weight γ and volume δV acted o by forces $\mathbf{F}$, each applied at a point, and total stresses $\mathbf{p}$, applied over areas δA During an increment of collapse the corresponding displacements are δw_γ, δw and δw_p. For undrained loading, the increment of work δE done by the extern: forces and stresses is given by

$$\delta E = \sum \delta w_f \cdot \mathbf{F} + \int_A \delta w_p \cdot \mathbf{p} \ dA + \int_V \delta w_\gamma \cdot \gamma \ dV \qquad (4.30$$

where the summation is for all concentrated loads and the integrals are taken ove the loaded areas and the volume of the body. Equation (4.30) is written in terms o total stresses and the total unit weight γ, and it is valid only for undrained loading

For drained loading Eq. (4.30) should be written in terms of effective stresse and to determine the correct form it is simplest to examine the work done by : force equivalent to the applied stresses and body weight forces. Figure 4.14(b shows an element of saturated soil with unit weight γ surrounded by water with unit weight γ_w; in order to maintain the integrity of the element, it is enclosed ir a permeable membrane so that pore pressures are everywhere hydrostatic and, a the element moves, the water remains stationary. The volume of the element is δV, its length is δL, and the area of a side is δA; the water pressures are u at the top and $(u + \delta u)$ at the bottom and $\delta u = \gamma_w \delta L$. The element is in equilibrium with a force $\mathbf{F}_\gamma$ as shown and, resolving vertically,

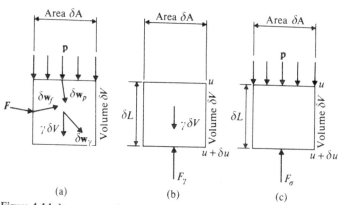

Figure 4.14 Increment of work done by external forces for an increment of displacement. (a) For undrained loading. (b) and (c) For drained loading.

$$\mathbf{F}_\gamma + (u + \delta u)\,\delta A = \gamma\,\delta V + u\,\delta A \qquad (4.31)$$

nd, noting that $\delta u\,\delta A = \gamma_w\,\delta L\,\delta A = \gamma_w\,\delta V$, and hence

$$\mathbf{F}_\gamma = (\gamma - \gamma_w)\,\delta V \qquad (4.32)$$

Figure 4.14(c) shows the same element, but for the case for which the soil rains are taken to be weightless and a stress p is applied to the top surface. We must e very careful here. The stress **p** is the sum of the stress applied by a foundation r by a wall and the stress applied by the external water pressure; hence, if there is o wall or foundation, but only external water, $\mathbf{p} = u$. The element is in equilibrium vith a force $\mathbf{F}_\sigma$ as shown, and, resolving vertically,

$$\mathbf{F}_\sigma + (u + \delta u)\,\delta A = \mathbf{p}\,\delta A + \gamma_w\,\delta V \qquad (4.33)$$

nd

$$\mathbf{F}_\sigma = (\mathbf{p} - u)\,\delta A \qquad (4.34)$$

Thus, noting that the water remains stationary and so the water pressures do no vork, the increment of work δE for drained loading is given by

$$\delta E = \sum \delta\mathbf{w}_f \cdot \mathbf{F} + \int_A \delta\mathbf{w}_p \cdot (\mathbf{p} - u)\,\delta A + \int_V \delta\mathbf{w}_\gamma \cdot (\gamma - \gamma_w)\,\mathrm{d}V \qquad (4.35)$$

For dry soil we simply put $u = \gamma_w = 0$ in Eq. (4.35). The scalar or dot product of wo vectors **a** and **b** is $ab\cos\theta$ where θ is the angle between the positive directions of the vectors. Thus, in Eqs (4.30) and (4.35) the scalar products may be found as he products of the forces and the components of the increments of displacement resolved in the directions of the appropriate forces.

For a material which is perfectly plastic, elastic strains at failure are zero and the increment of work done by the internal stresses is completely dissipated in plastic distortion. Strictly, we should consider both continuous and discontinuous plastic distortions, but since we will be concerned with mechanisms of collapse which consist only of discontinuous slipping on slip planes, we need not consider the work dissipated during continuous straining. We must, however, consider drained and undrained loading separately.

Figure 4.15 shows a slip zone δy thick containing an element δl long, which suffers an increment of discontinuous slipping similar to that shown in Fig. 1.9. Figure 4.15(a) shows positive total stresses τ_n and σ_n and there is a pore pressure u. Figure 4.15(b) shows an increment of displacement δw with components $-\delta m$ and $-\delta n$ such that the shear and volumetric strains are positive. For compressive volumetric strain, the angle of dilation is $-\psi$ and the change of volume of the element is $-\delta V = \delta V_w$, where δV_w is the volume of water expelled from the element. Thus the increment of work done δW per unit volume is

$$\delta W = 1/V[-\delta n(\sigma_n\,\delta l) - \delta m(\tau_n\,\delta l) - u\,\delta V_w] \qquad (4.36)$$

where $V = \delta y\,\delta l$ is the volume of the element for unit thickness normal to the page. Hence, making use of Eqs (1.20) and (1.21), we have

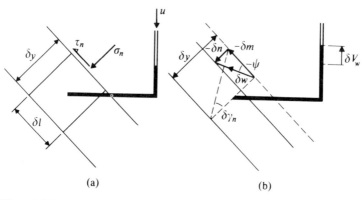

Figure 4.15 Stresses and displacements across a slip plane.

$$\delta W = [\sigma_n\,\delta\epsilon_v + \tau_n\,\delta\gamma_n - u\,\delta\epsilon_v] = [\sigma'_n\,\delta\epsilon_v + \tau'_n\,\delta\gamma_n] \tag{4.37}$$

At ultimate failure at the critcal state $\tau'_n = \sigma'_n \tan\phi'_{cs}$ and, making use of Eq. (1.16), Eq. (4.37) may be written

$$\delta W = \tau'_n\,\delta\gamma_n\left[1 - \frac{\tan\psi}{\tan\phi'_{cs}}\right] \tag{4.38}$$

But for an upper bound calculation we must take $\phi'_{cs} = \psi$, and hence for drained loading

$$\delta W = 0 \tag{4.39}$$

and the increment of work done by the internal stresses during an increment of drained plastic collapse is zero. This is a surprising result, and it presents difficulties which we will not explore here. The implication is that, while a perfectly plastic material is dissipative, a perfectly plastic frictional material is neither dissipative nor conservative. The conclusion must be that the flow rule for a frictional material cannot be associated. Nevertheless, the result given by Eq. (4.39) is extremely convenient and may be used to calculate upper bounds for frictional materials like soil.

For undrained loading, the volumetric strain is zero and $\delta n = \psi = 0$, while from Fig. 4.15(b) $\delta w = -\delta m$. Thus the increment of work done per unit length of slip plane and for unit thickness normal to the page is given by

$$\delta W = 1/\delta l[-\delta m(\tau_n\,\delta l)] = \tau_n\,\delta w \tag{4.40}$$

and δW is independent of the thickness δy of the slip plane. Now, at ultimate failure at the critical state for undrained loading, $\tau_n = c_u$, where the undrained shear strength c_u depends only on the (constant) specific volume. Hence, for a complete collapse mechanism consisting of a number of separate slip planes, the increment of work done by the internal stresses and dissipated in an increment of plastic collapse is

$$\delta W = \sum c_u L \, \delta w \qquad (4.41)$$

where L is the length of each slip plane.

4.8 DISPLACEMENT DIAGRAMS

In order to carry out an upper bound calculation for a particular mechanism we must calculate the increments of displacement for all external loads, including those due to the weights of the sliding blocks, and the increments of relative displacement across all the slip planes. The simplest way of calculating the displacements of the various components of a mechanism for an increment of collapse is to proceed graphically, making use of a displacement diagram. We assume that readers are familiar with the theory and use of displacement diagrams in mechanics and for the present we will simply illustrate their use to calculate increments of displacement for mechanisms of plastic collapse like those shown in Fig. 4.12.

To construct a displacement diagram all the regions are labelled with a capital letter, including stationary material which is given the label O; thus, in Fig. 4.16(a) two sliding blocks are labelled A and B and all stationary material is labelled O. In a displacement diagram the displacement of each region is represented by a single point (provided there is no rotation) labelled with the corresponding lower-case letter; thus, in Fig. 4.16(b) the points o, a, and b represent the displacements of the regions O, A, and B in Fig. 4.16(a). A displacement diagram has the general property that the vector joining two points represents the relative displacement of the corresponding regions; thus a line such as ab represents both the direction and the magnitude of the relative displacement δw_{ba} between the regions A and B across the slip plane separating them. Thus Fig. 4.16(b) allows the relative displacements across all the slip planes in Fig. 4.16(a) to be determined very simply.

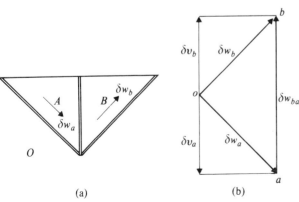

(a) (b)

Figure 4.16 Displacement diagram for a simple mechanism of plastic collapse for undrained loading.

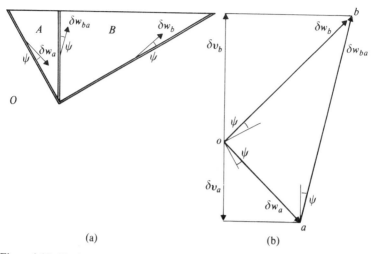

(a)   (b)

Figure 4.17 Displacement diagram for a simple mechanism of plastic collapse for drained loading.

In Fig. 4.16(a) the directions of displacement of the blocks A and B are parallel with the slip planes between them and the stationary region O; hence $\psi = 0$ and Fig. 4.16 is relevant for undrained loading. For drained loading, the displacements of the blocks must be angled at ψ to the slip planes as shown in Fig. 4.17(a) where the relative displacement between the blocks A and B is of course directed at an angle ψ to the slip plane separating them. The displacement diagram for the increment of displacement in Fig. 4.17(a) is shown in Fig. 4.17(b). Vectors representing displacements may be resolved graphically. Thus δv_a and δv_b in Figs. 4.16(b) and 4.17(b) represent the vertical components of the increments of displacement of the blocks A and B in Figs. 4.16(a) and 4.17(a). Displacement diagrams may therefore be employed to evaluate scalar products of force and increment of displacement as required for Eqs (4.30) and (4.33), since such scalar products are simply the products of the force and the component of the increment of displacement resolved in the direction of the appropriate force.

4.9 SLIP FANS

A special arrangement of slip planes of particular interest is known as a *slip fan*. A compatible mechanism of plastic collapse cannot be constructed for the rigid blocks A and B in Fig. 4.18(a) by having the fan between them rotate as a rigid body without gaps opening as shown in Fig. 4.18(a). If, however, extra radial slip planes, each separated by a small angle $\delta\theta$, are added to the fan, as shown in Fig. 4.19(a), the mechanism becomes compatible and a displacement diagram can be constructed as shown in Fig. 4.19(b). In the limit, as the angles $\delta\theta$ tend to zero,

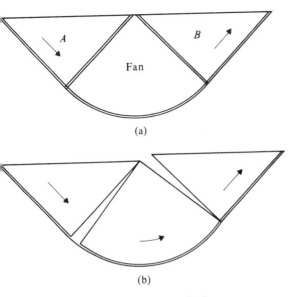

Figure 4.18 Incompatible deformations of a fan.

the outer limit of the slip fan, and the vectors ac, cd, de, etc. in the displacement diagram tend to smooth curves. For undrained loading for which $\psi = 0$, slip planes become circular arcs, as shown in Sec. 4.6, and the appropriate sections of the displacement diagram are also circular arcs, as shown in Fig. 4.19(b). From the geometry of Fig. 4.19 we have

$$r_b = r_a \qquad \delta w_b = \delta w_a \qquad (4.42)$$

and so the radius of the fan and the increment of displacement remain constant through a slip fan for undrained loading.

For drained loading for which $\psi > 0$, the directions of the increments of displacement are at an angle ψ to the slip planes. Hence slip planes become logarithmic spirals, as shown in Sec. 4.6, and the appropriate sections of displacement diagrams are also logarithmic spirals, as shown in Fig. 4.20(b). From the geometry of Fig. 4.20 we have

$$r_b = r_a \exp (\theta_f \tan \psi) \qquad (4.43)$$

$$\delta w_b = \delta w_a \exp (\theta_f \tan \psi) \qquad (4.44)$$

where θ_f is the fan angle between the radius r_a, where the increment of displacement is δw_a, and the radius r_b, where the increment of displacement is δw_b. It should be noted, however, that both for drained loading and for undrained loading the increment of displacement remains constant along any radius, since each small triangular block in a slip fan is assumed to remain rigid.

From Eq. (4.38), the increment of work done by the internal stresses in a slip fan during an increment of plastic collapse for drained loading for which $\psi = \phi'_{cs}$ is

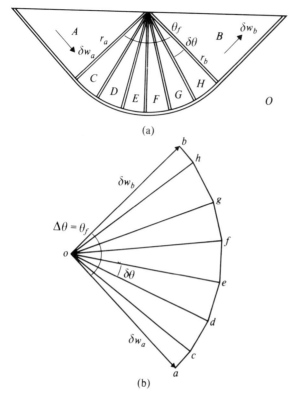

Figure 4.19 Compatible mechanism for a fan zone and the corresponding displacement diagram for undrained loading.

zero. For undrained loading, however, the increment of work done by the internal stresses in a fan is given by Eq. (4.41), summing over the circular arc and the radial slip planes. Figure 4.21(a) shows a fan of radius R and angle θ_f with radial slip planes each separated by a small angle $\delta\theta$ of which only two are shown. The rigid blocks either side of the fan suffer increments of displacement δw and the corresponding displacement diagram for the increment is shown in Fig. 4.21(b). From Eq. (4.41), summing for the elements of the circular arc and for the radial slip planes, the increment of work done by the internal stresses in the fan is given by

$$\delta W = \sum c_u R(\delta w\,\delta\theta) + \sum c_u (R\,\delta\theta)\,\delta w \tag{4.45}$$

Hence, in the limit

$$\delta W = \int_0^{\theta_f} 2c_u R\,\delta w\,d\theta \tag{4.46}$$

and

$$\delta W = 2c_u R\,\Delta\theta\,\delta w \tag{4.47}$$

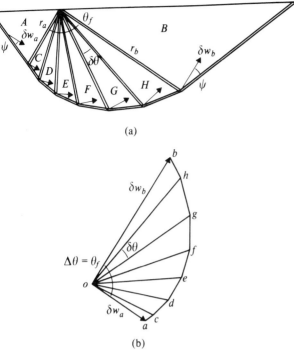

(a)

(b)

Figure 4.20 Compatible mechanism for a fan zone and the corresponding displacement diagram for drained loading.

Slip fans are often of considerable use in mechanisms of plastic collapse for linking together rigid blocks sliding in different directions. It may be noted that for drained and for undrained loading the fan angle θ_f is equal to the change of direction $\Delta\theta$ of the vector of displacement δw, as shown in Figs 4.19 and 4.20.

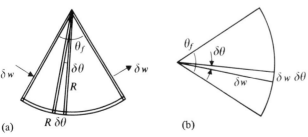

Figure 4.21 Work done by the internal stresses in a fan zone for undrained loading. (a) Fan zone. (b) Displacement diagram.

4.10 DISCONTINUOUS STRESS STATES

In order to calculate a lower bound we are required to calculate a state of stress which is in equilibrium with the external loads and which nowhere exceeds the appropriate failure criterion. A suitable state of stress may vary smoothly from place to place or there may be sudden jumps or discontinuities, but in all cases the conditions of equilibrium must be satisfied.

For undrained loading of saturated soil for which calculations may be carried out in terms of total stresses, the conditions of equilibrium for a smoothly varying state of stress as given by Eqs (1.67) and (1.68) are

$$\frac{\partial \sigma_z}{\partial z} + \frac{\partial \tau_{xz}}{\partial x} = \gamma \qquad (4.48)$$

$$\frac{\partial \sigma_x}{\partial x} + \frac{\partial \tau_{zx}}{\partial z} = 0 \qquad (4.49)$$

For drained loading, when pore pressures are known, calculations should be carried out in terms of effective stresses and the conditions of equilibrium are given by Eqs (1.69) and (1.70) as

$$\frac{\partial \sigma_z'}{\partial z} + \frac{\partial \tau_{xz}'}{\partial x} = \gamma - \frac{\partial u}{\partial z} \qquad (4.50)$$

$$\frac{\partial \sigma_x'}{\partial x} + \frac{\partial \tau_{zx}'}{\partial z} = -\frac{\partial u}{\partial x} \qquad (4.51)$$

Figure 4.22(a) shows an element of soil divided by a stress discontinuity. The state of stress in region A to one side of the discontinuity need not be the same as the state of stress on the other side, but conditions of equilibrium for the element must be satisfied. Resolving in a direction normal to the discontinuity and taking moments about a corner gives

$$\sigma_{na} = \sigma_{nb} \qquad \tau_{na} = \tau_{nb} \qquad (4.52)$$

and these are sufficient conditions for the element to be in equilibrium. In particular, it should be noted that the normal stresses σ_{ta} and σ_{tb} on planes which are themselves normal to the discontinuity need not be equal for the element to be in equilibrium. For drained loading, for which pore pressures u_a and u_b in the parts of the element either side of the discontinuity are equal, Eqs (4.52) become

$$\sigma_{na}' = \sigma_{nb}' \qquad \tau_{na}' = \tau_{nb}' \qquad (4.53)$$

Figure 4.22(b) shows the Mohr's circles of total stress for the states of stress in the parts of the element in the regions A and B either side of the discontinuity. Both circles pass through a common point C where the states of stress $(\sigma_{na}, -\tau_{na})$ and $(\sigma_{nb}, -\tau_{nb})$ are those on planes parallel with the discontinuity; the states of

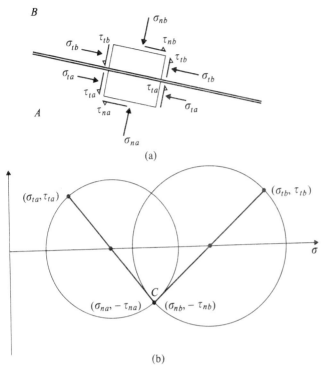

Figure 4.22 States of stress across a discontinuity.

stress (σ_{ta}, τ_{ta}) and (σ_{tb}, τ_{tb}) at opposite ends of the diameters from C represent the stresses on the planes normal to the discontinuity.

Figure 4.23 shows the same element and the same Mohr's circles as those in Fig. 4.22. The poles of the circles are found by drawing $P_a - C - P_b$ parallel with the discontinuity, and hence the major principal planes are given by the broken lines in Fig. 4.23(b) and the directions of the major principal total stresses in Fig. 4.23(a) are normal to the major principal planes. It is a property of the Mohr's circle construction that the angle subtended at the centre by two states of stress on the circumference is *double* the angle between the directions of the appropriate stresses and hence we may mark the angles $2\theta_a$ and $2\theta_b$ as shown. The rotation $\delta\theta$ of the direction of the major principal stress from region A to region B is given by

$$\delta\theta = \theta_b - \theta_a \qquad (4.54)$$

and we will define counterclockwise angles as positive. The states of stress in the regions A and B represented by the Mohr's circles of stress in Figs 4.22 and 4.23 may be defined by the parameters (s_a, t_a) and (s_b, t_b) as shown in Fig. 4.23(b), where t and s are given by Eqs (1.24) and (1.25) and are appropriate for plane strain. For lower bound calculations the permissible states of stress must not exceed the appropriate failure criterion for soil and this restriction limits the

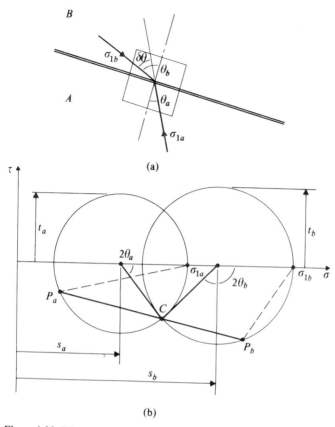

Figure 4.23 Directions of major principal stress across a discontinuity.

allowable sizes of the Mohr's circles to those which just touch the appropriate failure envelope. For undrained loading the failure envelope for soil is given by

$$\tau = t = c_u \qquad [4.21]$$

and for drained loading the failure envelope is given in terms of effective stresses by

$$\tau' = \sigma'_n \tan \phi'_{cs} \text{ or } t' = s' \sin \phi'_{cs} \qquad [4.23]$$

Figure 4.24 shows the directions of the major principal total stresses across a discontinuity of stress and the corresponding Mohr's circles of total stress for the case when the soil in both regions A and B is in a state of undrained failure so that both Mohr's circles just touch the undrained failure envelope given by Eq. (4.21). From the geometry of Fig. 4.24(b), noting that the radius $AC = c_u$, we have

$$\delta s = 2c_u \sin \delta\theta \qquad (4.55)$$

or

$$(s_b - s_a) = 2c_u \sin (\theta_b - \theta_a) \qquad (4.56)$$

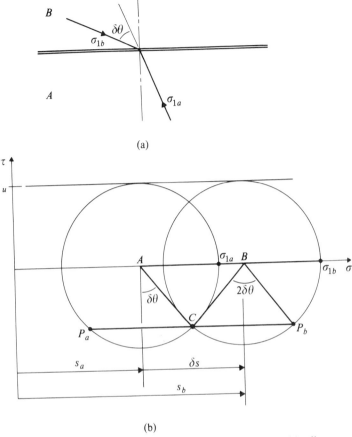

(a)

(b)

Figure 4.24 Change of stress across a discontinuity for undrained loading.

Hence the change δs of the state of total stress across a discontinuity is simply related to the rotation $\delta \theta$ of the direction of the major principal total stress.

For drained loading, the principles of the analysis are the same but the geometry of the problem is more complex. Figure 4.25 shows directions of the major principal effective stresses across a discontinuity and the corresponding Mohr's circles of effective stress for the case when the soil in both regions A and B is in a state of drained failure so that both Mohr's circles just touch the drained failure envelope given by Eq. (4.23). The point C' in Fig. 4.25(b) has coordinates $(\sigma'_{na}, -\tau'_{na})$ and $(\sigma'_{nb}, -\tau'_{nb})$ and hence the angle ρ' is the angle of shearing resistance mobilized on the plane of the discontinuity.

Figure 4.26 shows again the Mohr's circles corresponding to the states of stress in Fig. 4.25. It is convenient to define an angle P[†] as shown, where

---

[†] Some texts define this angle by the symbol Δ but the symbol P (capital rho) is used here to avoid confusion with the use of Δ to mean an increment of.

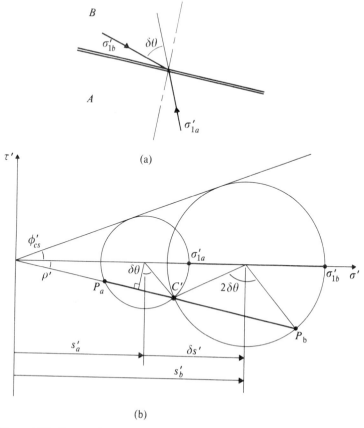

Figure 4.25 Change of stress across a discontinuity for drained loading.

$$P = (90° - \delta\theta) \tag{4.57}$$

From the geometry of Fig. 4.26, noting that the radius $A'C' = t'_a$, we have

$$\sin P = \frac{A'D'}{t'_a} \qquad \sin \rho' = \frac{A'D'}{s'_a} \tag{4.58}$$

Hence,

$$\sin \rho' = \sin P \sin \phi'_{cs} \tag{4.59}$$

and, from Eq. (4.57),

$$\sin \rho' = \cos \delta\theta \sin \phi'_{cs} \tag{4.60}$$

With the aid of the constructions shown in Fig. 4.26, or otherwise, we have

$$\frac{O'E'}{s'_a} = \sin (P + \rho') \qquad \frac{O'F'}{s'_b} = \sin (P - \rho') \tag{4.61}$$

and

$$O'E' = O'F' \tag{4.62}$$

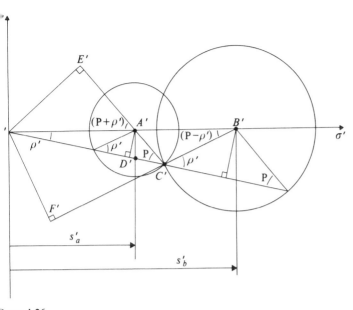

nd hence

$$\frac{s_b'}{s_a'} = \frac{\sin (P + \rho')}{\sin (P - \rho')} \tag{4.63}$$

nd, from Eq. (4.57)

$$\frac{s_b'}{s_a'} = \frac{\cos (\delta\theta - \rho')}{\cos (\delta\theta + \rho')} \tag{4.64}$$

where the mobilized angle of shearing resistance ρ' in given by Eq. (4.60).

Hence the change of the state of effective stress across a discontinuity is simply elated to the rotation $\delta\theta$ of the direction of the major principal stress. In theory, $'$ can be eliminated from Eqs (4.60) and 4.64) but the resulting expression is omplicated and it is usually better to leave the result in its present form.

.11 STRESS FANS†

n the previous section we investigated the change of stress across a single discon-inuity but we could instead consider a change of stress from one region to another ccurring as a number of small changes across a number of discontinuities arranged s a fan. Figure 4.27 shows a fan of discontinuities separating region A from region B.

---

† A stress fan, which consists of a radial fan of stress discontinuities, must be distinguished rom a slip fan, which consists of a radial fan of slip planes, discussed in Sec. 4.9.

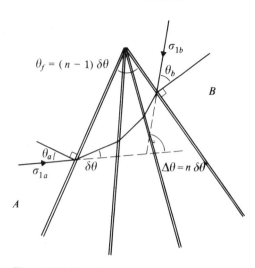

Figure 4.27 Rotation of the direction of the major principal stress through a fan discontinuities.

The rotation of the direction of the major principal stress across each discontinuity $\delta\theta$ and hence the total rotation across the fan is $\Delta\theta = n\,\delta\theta$ where n is the number of discontinuities. The change of stress across the fan is $\Delta s = n\delta s$. For n discontinuities the fan angle θ_f in Fig. 4.27 is given by

$$\theta_f = (n-1)\,\delta\theta = \left(\frac{n-1}{n}\right)\Delta\theta \qquad (4.6$$

and, from the geometry of the figure, $\theta_b - \theta_a = \delta\theta$, where θ_b and θ_a are the angle between the major principal planes in the regions B and A and the outer discontinuities. As before, we must consider separately the cases for drained loading and for undrained loading.

Figure 4.28(a) is for undrained loading and shows a stress fan of four discontinuities separating the regions A and B. The corresponding five Mohr's circles of total stress shown in Fig. 4.28(b) all just touch the undrained failure envelope given by Eq. (4.21). The points C_a and C_b in Fig. 4.28(b) correspond to the point C in Fig. 4.24; they are the points of intersection of adjacent Mohr's circles and give the stresses on the outer discontinuities. From the geometry of Figs 4.24 and 4.28, the directions of the major principal stresses are given by

$$\theta_a = (45° - \tfrac{1}{2}\delta\theta) \qquad \theta_b = (45° + \tfrac{1}{2}\delta\theta) \qquad (4.66$$

as shown in Fig. 4.28(a) and hence $\theta_b - \theta_a = \delta\theta$ as required. The change of stress across a single discontinuity is given by Eq. (4.55), and hence for n discontinuities the total change of stress Δs is given by

$$\Delta s = n\{2c_u \sin \delta\theta\} = n\{2c_u \sin [\theta_f/(n-1)]\} \qquad (4.6$$

where θ_f is the fan angle.

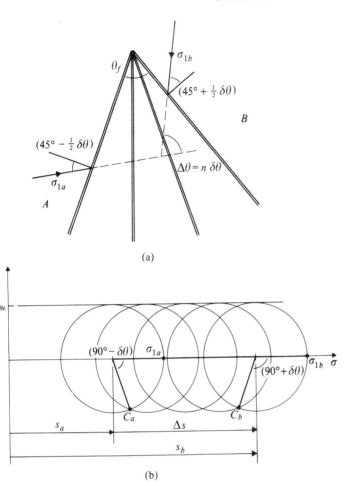

(a)

(b)

Figure 4.28 States of stress across a fan of discontinuities for undrained loading.

Alternatively, we may consider a stress fan as an infinity of very closely spaced discontinuities so that the state of stress varies smoothly through the fan zone from that in region A to that in region B. As the number of discontinuities becomes large and $\delta\theta \to 0$ we have θ_b and $\theta_a \to 45°$ and $\theta_f \to \Delta\theta$, and the fan is as shown in Fig. 4.29(a). The corresponding Mohr's circles of total stress for the regions A and B are shown in Fig. 4.29(b) and there will be a very great number of Mohr's circles, each corresponding to the state of total stress in a sector of the fan, between these limiting circles. It may be noted that as $\delta\theta \to 0$, adjacent circles come closer together and points such as C_a and C_b become closer to the apex of each Mohr's circle and hence θ_b and θ_a become closer to 45°. In the limit, as $\delta\theta \to 0$, we have $\sin \delta\theta \to \delta\theta$ and Eq. (4.55) becomes

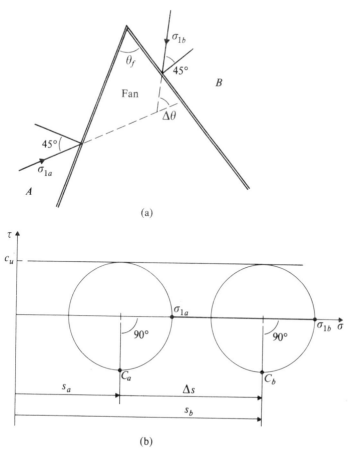

Figure 4.29 States of stress across a fan for undrained loading.

$$\frac{ds}{d\theta} = 2c_u \qquad (4.68)$$

Hence, integrating through the fan from region A to region B

$$\Delta s = s_b - s_a = 2c_u \theta_f = 2c_u \Delta\theta \qquad (4.69)$$

where θ_f is the fan angle and $\Delta\theta$ is the change of the direction of the major principal stress.

Figure 4.30(a) is for drained loading and shows a fan of four discontinuities. The corresponding five Mohr's circles of effective stress, all just touching the drained failure envelope given by Eq. (4.23), are shown in Fig. 4.30(b). The points C'_a and C'_b correspond to the point C' in Fig. 4.25 and represent the states of stress on the outer discontinuities. From the geometry of Figs 4.26 and 4.30,

$$\theta_a = (45° + \tfrac{1}{2}\rho' - \tfrac{1}{2}\delta\theta) \qquad \theta_b = (45° + \tfrac{1}{2}\rho' + \tfrac{1}{2}\delta\theta) \qquad (4.70)$$

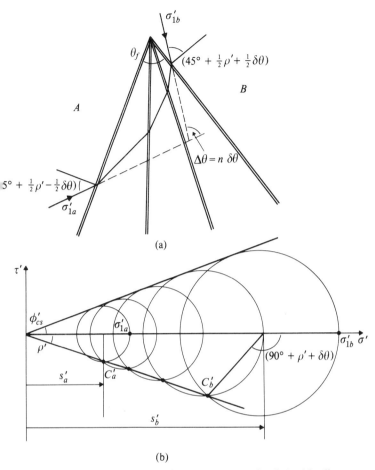

Figure 4.30 States of stress across a fan of discontinuities for drained loading.

where ρ' is the mobilized angle of shearing resistance given by Eq. (4.60). The change of stress across a single discontinuity is given by Eq. (4.64) as

$$\frac{s_b'}{s_a'} = \frac{\cos(\delta\theta - \rho')}{\cos(\delta\theta + \rho')} \qquad [4.64]$$

and

$$\frac{\delta s'}{s'} = 2\frac{\sin\delta\theta\,\sin\rho'}{\cos(\delta\theta + \rho')} \qquad (4.71)$$

where ρ' is given by Eq. (4.60) as

$$\sin\rho' = \cos\delta\theta\,\sin\phi_{cs}' \qquad [4.60]$$

Hence the change of stress $\Delta s'$ across the whole fan must be found by summing the changes of stress $\delta s'$ across each discontinuity in the fan.

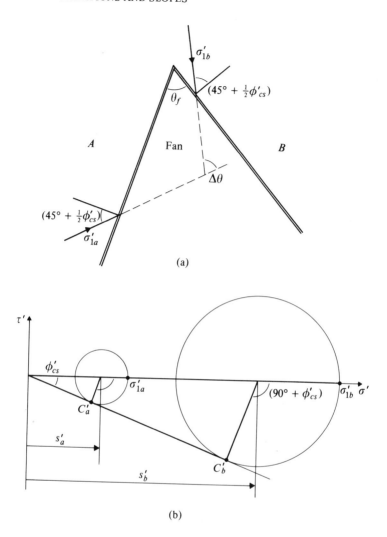

Figure 4.31 States of stress across a fan for drained loading.

Alternatively, we may proceed as before and consider a stress fan to consist of an infinity of discontinuities so that the state of stress varies smoothly through the fan. As the number of discontinuities becomes large, $\delta\theta \rightarrow 0$ and, from Eq. (4.60), $\rho' \rightarrow \phi'_{cs}$. Thus we have $\theta_f = \Delta\theta$ and $\theta_a = \theta_b = (45° + \frac{1}{2}\phi'_{cs})$, as shown in Fig. 4.31. The corresponding Mohr's circles of effective stress for the regions A and B are shown in Fig. 4.31(b) and there will be an infinity of circles, each corresponding to the state of stress in a sector of the fan, between these outer circles. In the limit, as $\delta\theta \rightarrow 0$, we have $\sin \delta\theta \rightarrow \delta\theta$ while $\cos \delta\theta \rightarrow 1$. Hence, with $\rho' \rightarrow \phi'_{cs}$ and from Eq. (4.71)

$$\frac{ds'}{d\theta} = 2s' \tan \phi'_{cs} \tag{4.72}$$

d, integrating through the fan from region A to region B,

$$\frac{s'_b}{s'_a} = \exp[2\theta_f \tan \phi'_{cs}] = \exp[2\Delta\theta \tan \phi'_{cs}] \tag{4.73}$$

here θ_f is the fan angle and $\Delta\theta$ is the change in the direction of the major principal ress.

.12 α AND β DISCONTINUITIES

Fig. 4.22(a) the shear stresses on the discontinuity τ_{nb} and τ_{na} are clockwise and plot as negative quantities at C in the Mohr's circles in Fig. 4.22(b). It is quite ossible, however, for the case to arise when the shear stresses on the discontinuity e counterclockwise and so plot as positive quantities in the Mohr's circle diagram, deed, it is quite common to have discontinuities of stress associated with clockise shearing stresses close to, and intersecting, discontinuities associated with ounterclockwise shearing stresses and it is necessary to distinguish two families of iscontinuities. Discontinuities of stress associated with counterclockwise and ositive shearing stresses will be known as α discontinuities while those associated ith clockwise and negative shearing stresses will be known as β discontinuities.

Figure 4.32 shows stresses across an α discontinuity and the corresponding [ohr's circles of total stress intersecting at a point C_α; Fig. 4.33 shows stresses ross a β discontinuity and the corresponding Mohr's circles of total stress inter-cting at a point C_β. Figure 4.33(a) is simply a mirror image of Fig. 4.32(a) and e corresponding Mohr's circles are mirror images of each other about the σ axis. ll the stress discontinuities in Figs 4.23 to 4.31 are members of the β family ssociated with clockwise shear stresses; the corresponding α family associated with ounterclockwise shear stresses are simply mirror images of the β family and the orresponding Mohr's circle constructions are mirror images of the Mohr's circles Figs 4.23 to 4.31.

The angle $\delta\theta$ through which the direction of the major principal stress rotates cross a discontinuity is always measured positively counterclockwise and the hanges of stress across β discontinuities, for undrained loading and for drained ading respectively, are

$$\delta s = 2c_u \sin \delta\theta \tag{4.55}$$

$$\delta s' = 2s' \frac{\sin \delta\theta \sin \rho'}{\cos(\delta\theta + \rho')} \tag{4.71}$$

here ρ' is given by Eq. (4.60). For an α discontinuity, however, we must intro-uce negative signs into Eqs (4.55) and (4.71), since $\delta\theta$ is still measured positively ounterclockwise. Thus, for an α discontinuity we have

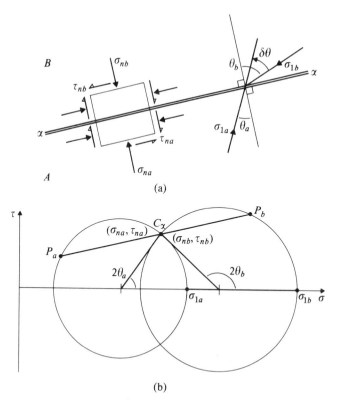

Figure 4.32 States of stress across an α discontinuity.

$$\delta s = -2c_u \sin \delta\theta \tag{4.74}$$

$$\delta s' = -2s' \frac{\sin \delta\theta \sin \rho'}{\cos (\delta\theta + \rho')} \tag{4.75}$$

where ρ' is given by Eq. (4.60). We may generalize these and write, for undrained loading and for drained loading respectively,

$$\delta s = \pm 2c_u \sin \delta\theta \tag{4.76}$$

$$\delta s' = \pm 2s' \frac{\sin \delta\theta \sin \rho'}{\cos (\delta\theta + \rho')} \tag{4.77}$$

where the positive signs are for β discontinuities and the negative signs are for α discontinuities. Since the value of $\delta\theta$ must lie in the range $-\frac{1}{2}\pi \leqslant \delta\theta \leqslant \frac{1}{2}\pi$, the value of ρ', given by Eq. (4.60), has the same sign as ϕ'_{cs} and is therefore always positive.

Similarly, for the variation of stress through a fan we may generalize Eqs. (4.68) and (4.72) to

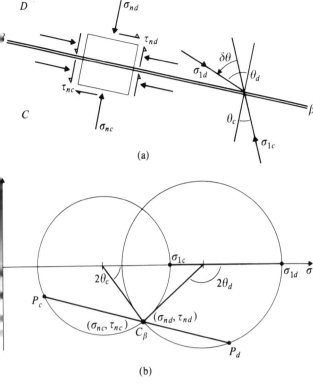

Figure 4.33 States of stress across a β discontinuity.

$$\frac{ds}{d\theta} = \pm 2c_u \tag{4.78}$$

$$\frac{ds'}{d\theta} = \pm 2s' \tan \phi'_{cs} \tag{4.79}$$

where the positive signs must be taken where the fan consists of β discontinuities and the negative sign must be taken where it consists of α dicontinuities.

4.13 SUMMARY

Instead of trying to calculate the collapse load of a structure exactly we may use relatively simple analyses to find upper and lower bounds.

To find an upper bound, a mechanism of collapse must be postulated and, for an increment of displacement, the work δE done by the external loads equated to the work δW done by the internal stresses. Mechanisms for undrained loading may consist of straight lines or circular arcs and mechanisms for drained loading may consist of straight lines or logarithmic spiral arcs. For undrained loading increments of work are given by

$$\delta E = \sum \delta \mathbf{w}_f \cdot \mathbf{F} + \int_A \delta \mathbf{w}_p \cdot \mathbf{p} \, dA + \int_V \delta \mathbf{w}_\gamma \cdot \gamma \, dV \qquad [4.30]$$

$$\delta W = \sum c_u L \, \delta w \qquad \text{(for single slip planes)} \qquad [4.41]$$

or $\qquad \delta W = 2c_u R \, \Delta\theta \, \delta w \qquad \text{(for a slip fan)} \qquad [4.47]$

and, for drained loading, they are given by

$$\delta E = \sum \delta \mathbf{w}_f \cdot \mathbf{F} + \int_A \delta \mathbf{w}_p \cdot (\mathbf{p} - u) \, dA + \int_V \delta \mathbf{w}_\gamma \cdot (\gamma - \gamma_w) \, dV \qquad [4.35]$$

$$\delta W = 0 \qquad [4.39]$$

To find a lower bound, a state of stress must be postulated which is in equilibrium with the external loads and which nowhere exceeds the appropriate failure criterion. Conditions of equilibrium for smoothly varying states of stress for undrained loading are given by

$$\frac{\partial \sigma_z}{\partial z} + \frac{\partial \tau_{xz}}{\partial x} = \gamma \qquad [4.48]$$

$$\frac{\partial \sigma_x}{\partial x} + \frac{\partial \tau_{zx}}{\partial z} = 0 \qquad [4.49]$$

and for drained loading they are given by

$$\frac{\partial \sigma_z'}{\partial z} + \frac{\partial \tau_{xz}'}{\partial x} = \gamma - \frac{\partial u}{\partial z} \qquad [4.50]$$

$$\frac{\partial \sigma_x'}{\partial x} + \frac{\partial \tau_{zx}'}{\partial z} = -\frac{\partial u}{\partial x} \qquad [4.51]$$

The changes of stress across discontinuities for undrained loading are given by

$$\delta s = \pm 2c_u \sin \delta\theta \qquad \text{(for a single discontinuity)} \qquad [4.76]$$

or $\qquad \dfrac{ds}{d\theta} = \pm 2c_u \qquad \text{(for a stress fan)} \qquad [4.78]$

and for drained loading they are given by

$$\delta s' = \pm 2s' \frac{\sin \delta\theta \sin \rho'}{\cos (\delta\theta + \rho')} \qquad \text{(for a single discontinuity)} \qquad [4.77]$$

$$\frac{ds'}{d\theta} = \pm\, 2s' \tan \phi'_{cs} \qquad \text{(for a stress fan)} \qquad [4.79]$$

here

$$\sin \rho' = \cos \delta\theta \sin \phi'_{cs} \qquad [4.60]$$

these expressions the positive signs are taken for β discontinuities and the egative signs are taken for α discontinuities: shear stresses on a β discontinuity e clockwise and shear stresses on an α discontinuity are counterclockwise. The gle $\delta\theta$ is measured positively counterclockwise.

EFERENCES

se, J. and A. H. Chilver (1971), *Strength of Materials and Structures*, Edward Arnold, London.

eyman J. (1974), *Beams and Framed Structures*, 2nd edn, Pergamon, Oxford.

lmer, A. C. (1966), 'A limit theorem for materials with non-associated flow rules', *J. de Mécanique*, **5**(2), 217–22.

——— (1976), *Structural Mechanics*, Oxford University Press.

UNDRAINED STABILITY OI
SOIL STRUCTURE

5.1 INTRODUCTION

We are now in a position to calculate upper and lower bounds for the stability c soil structures, using the methods described in the previous chapter. Calculatio₁ may be carried out either for drained loading in terms of effective stress or fc undrained loading in terms of total stress, but it is essential to distinguish clearl between the two methods of calculation. In this chapter we will discuss upper an lower bound calculations for the stability of slopes and foundations and retainin walls for *undrained* loading; we will consider the same problems for drained loadin in the next chapter.

In distinguishing between drained and undrained loading, note that, as discusse in Sec. 2.2, it is important to consider the rate of loading, or the rate of constru tion, compared with the rate of consolidation of the soil. For undrained loadin the rate of loading is very fast compared with the rate of consolidation, and it assumed that volumetric strains are zero; for drained loading, on the other han the rate of loading is very slow compared with the rate of consolidation, and it assumed that excess pore pressures are zero. For any calculation for the stabilit of soil structures it is essential to choose the most appropriate loading and drainag condition.

Figure 5.1 illustrates the kinds of problem commonly encountered in geotec nical engineering. Figure 5.1(a) shows a section of a slope cut vertically into so for which it is required to calculate the maximum height H for which the slop just remains stable. Figure 5.1(b) shows part of an infinitely long slope of so over strong rock at a depth H and it is required to calculate the maximum angl i for which the slope just remains stable. Figure 5.1(c) shows a section of a lon foundation placed on the surface of soil where the width of the foundation i B and it is required to calculate the maximum load F for which the foundatio is just stable. Figure 5.1(d) shows a section of a vertical wall retaining soil to height H and it is required to calculate the maximum (or minimum) force P o₁ the wall as it just moves towards (or away from) the soil. These are four ver idealized examples but they are representative of the more common stabilit problems in soil engineering.

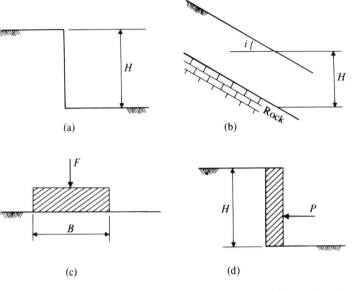

Figure 5.1 Stability problems in soil engineering. (a) Vertical cut slope. (b) Infinite slope. (c) Foundation. (d) Retaining wall.

Each structure is regarded as being long normal to the page and so deformations and collapse occur in plane strain. It is assumed that the soil is saturated and that it is isotropic and homogeneous with unit weight γ. For undrained loading, the failure criterion for soil in terms of total stress is

$$\tau_n = c_u \tag{5.1}$$

where the undrained shear strength c_u is given by

$$c_u = \sin \phi'_{cs} \exp\left(\frac{\Gamma_p - v}{\lambda}\right) = \tan \phi'_{cs} \exp\left(\frac{\Gamma_n - v}{\lambda}\right) \tag{5.2}$$

Thus the undrained shear strength c_u depends only on the specific volume for a particular soil. In practice values for c_u are determined from undrained laboratory shear box, triaxial, or unconfined compression tests or from *in situ* tests. If a site investigation reveals the presence of residual slip planes which may be reactivated then it may be necessary to replace c_u with the residual undrained shear strength c_{ur}. We will not discuss the methods for determining c_u or c_{ur} here and we will assume that, in some way, the appropriate undrained shear strength of the soil has been found as a result of site investigations and laboratory testing. For undrained loading where the failure criterion is written in terms of total stress, as in Eq. (5.1), the failure envelope serves as a plastic potential and flow rule satisfies the normality condition. Thus, at ultimate failure, when the state of the soil lies on the critical state line, undrained soil is regarded as being perfectly plastic and the upper and lower bound theorems are valid.

5.2 BOUND CALCULATIONS FOR UNDRAINED LOADING

In order to calculate upper and lower bounds we have two quite separate calcu‐
lations to perform; one gives an upper bound F_u or H_u or P_u for which collapse
must occur, while the other gives a lower bound F_l or H_l or P_l for which collapse
cannot occur. These calculations are quite separate and the one does not depend
on the other.

For an upper bound calculation we are required to construct a compatible
mechanism of plastic collapse and, for an increment of collapse, to equate the
increment δE of work done by the external loads to the increment δW of work
done by the internal stresses. For undrained loading, a mechanism of plastic
collapse may consist only of straight lines or circular arcs as discussed in Sec. 4.6.
Any compatible mechanism of plastic collapse will do, but one close to the true
collapse mechanism will give an upper bound close to the true value. We assume
that, at collapse, displacements due to continuous strains are negligible compared
with displacements due to discontinuous slipping and we consider only the case
of plane strain.

From the results obtained in Sec. 4.7, the increment of work δW done by the
internal stresses, for increments of displacement δw and for unit thickness normal
to the page, is given by

$$\delta W = \sum c_u L \, \delta w + \sum 2c_u R\theta_f \, \delta w \qquad (5.3)$$

where the terms $c_u L \, \delta w$ are summed for all slip planes of length L and the terms
$2c_u R\theta_f \, \delta w$ are summed for all slip fans of radius R and angle θ_f. From Sec. 4.7
the increment of work δE done by the external forces and stresses and by the
body weight forces is given by

$$\delta E = \sum \delta \mathbf{w} \cdot \mathbf{F} + \int_A \delta \mathbf{w} \cdot \mathbf{p} \, dA + \int_V \delta \mathbf{w} \cdot \gamma \, dV \qquad (5.4)$$

where $\mathbf{F}$ are boundary forces, $\mathbf{p}$ are total boundary stresses applied to areas A, γ is
the unit weight of a volume V of soil and $\delta \mathbf{w}$ are appropriate increments of dis‐
placement.

All the terms in Eq. (5.4) contain the scalar or dot product of vectors of force
and vectors of displacement. Thus we must obtain the product of the forces and
their displacements resolved into the directions of the appropriate forces and so
terms in Eq. (5.4) may be positive, negative, or zero, depending on the directions
of the forces and their displacements. A simple method of calculation and one we
will adopt is to make use of a displacement diagram to obtain the components of
the increments of the displacements in the directions of the appropriate forces.
On the other hand, all the terms in Eq. (5.3) are positive, irrespective of the direc‐
tions of slip, and a displacement diagram is used only to obtain the magnitudes of
the increments of relative displacement across each slip plane in the mechanism.

For a lower bound calculation we are required to find an equilibrium state of stress which nowhere exceeds the undrained failure criterion and which is also in equilibrium with the external lower bound loads. The equilibrium state of stress may vary smoothly from place to place or there may be discontinuities of stress which are, nevertheless, in equilibrium. For a smoothly varying state of stress, from Eqs (4.48) and (4.49)

$$\frac{\partial \sigma_z}{\partial z} + \frac{\partial \tau_{xz}}{\partial x} = \gamma \tag{5.5}$$

$$\frac{\partial \sigma_x}{\partial x} + \frac{\partial \tau_{zx}}{\partial z} = 0 \tag{5.6}$$

where the z axis is positive downwards so that the vertical stress σ_z increases with depth. The change δs of the state of stress across a single discontinuity, and the change Δs across a fan of discontinuities, for undrained loading, are given respectively by

$$\delta s = \pm 2c_u \sin \delta\theta \tag{5.7}$$

$$\Delta s = \pm 2c_u \Delta\theta \tag{5.8}$$

where $\delta\theta$ and $\Delta\theta$ are the rotations of the directions of the major principal total stress across the discontinuity and across the fan, respectively. In Eqs (5.7) and (5.8) the positive signs apply for β discontinuities and the negative signs apply for α discontinuities and the angles $\delta\theta$ and $\Delta\theta$ are positive for counterclockwise rotations.

5.3 UNDRAINED STABILITY OF CUTS AND SLOPES

We begin by considering the undrained stability of a vertical cut slope, and, in order to simplify the problem slightly, we assume that strong rock occurs immediately below the base of the cut slope, as shown in Fig. 5.2. The presence of this strong rock means that collapse mechanisms cannot pass below the base of the cut and we need not examine the states of stress in the rock below the cut. The relevant soil properties are c_u and γ and it is required to calculate the critical height H_c at which collapse just occurs.

1. Upper bound for a vertical cut

A simple mechanism of plastic collapse consists of a single straight slip plane at an angle 45° to the vertical, as shown in Fig. 5.3(a); the sliding wedge is denoted by the letter A. The displacement diagram for an increment of displacement δw down the slip plane is the single line oa in Fig. 5.3(b) and the vertical component of δw is given by the line ov. From the geometry of Fig. 5.3(a), the length L of the slip plane and the volume V of the wedge (for unit thickness normal to the page) are given by

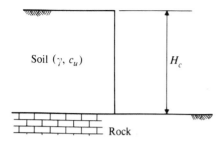

Figure 5.2 Simple vertical cut in soil for undrained loading.

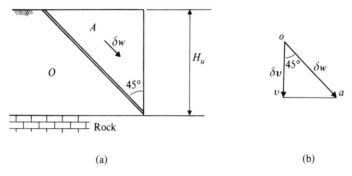

(a)   (b)

Figure 5.3 Mechanism of plastic collapse for a vertical cut slope for undrained loading.

$$L = \sqrt{2}H_u \qquad V = \tfrac{1}{2}H_u^2 \qquad (5.9$$

where H_u is an upper bound for the height of the slope at collapse. From the geometry of Fig. 5.3(b) we have

$$\delta v = \frac{1}{\sqrt{2}}\,\delta w \qquad (5.10$$

The only external forces are those due to the self weight of the sliding soil and from Eqs (5.3) and (5.4); using Eqs (5.9) and (5.10) we have

$$\delta W = \sum c_u L\,\delta w = c_u\sqrt{2}H_u\,\delta w \qquad (5.11$$

$$\delta E = \int_V \delta \mathbf{w} \cdot \gamma\,\mathrm{d}V = \frac{1}{\sqrt{2}}\,\delta w\,\gamma\,\tfrac{1}{2}H_u^2 \qquad (5.12$$

Hence, equating $\delta W = \delta E$, an upper bound for the height of the cut slope at collapse is given by

$$H_u = \frac{4c_u}{\gamma} \qquad (5.13$$

Lower bound for a vertical cut

e must now calculate a distribution of stress which is in equilibrium with the
xternal loads and which nowhere exceeds the undrained failure criterion; the
econd condition is satisfied if we can show that the Mohr's circles for each and
very element of soil have radii not greater than c_u. Figure 5.4(a) shows a state
f stress in which shear stresses on vertical and horizontal planes are zero (i.e.
$_{xz} = \tau_{zx} = 0$), which is clearly correct at the ground surface and at the cut face.
fence, from Eqs (5.5) and (5.6) the states of stress throughout the soil are given by

$$\frac{\partial \sigma_z}{\partial z} = \gamma \qquad \frac{\partial \sigma_x}{\partial x} = 0 \qquad (5.14)$$

ntegrating with the limits $\sigma_z = 0$ at the soil surface and $\sigma_x = 0$ at the cut face, we
ave

$$\sigma_z = \gamma z \qquad \sigma_x = 0 \qquad (5.15)$$

nd, since $\tau_{xz} = \tau_{zx} = 0$, these are principal stresses.

Mohr's circles of stress for the elements A and B in Fig. 5.4(a) are shown in
ig. 5.4(b). The Mohr's circle A does not cross the undrained failure envelope when

$$\gamma H_l = 2c_u \qquad (5.16)$$

nd hence a lower bound for the height of the cut is given by

$$H_l = \frac{2c_u}{\gamma} \qquad (5.17)$$

The Mohr's circle B is smaller than circle A and is within the undrained failure
envelope. From Eqs (5.15), the stresses in the soil at a given depth are the same
nd hence the Mohr's circles in Fig. 5.4(b) represent the states of stress everywhere
throughout the soil in Fig. 5.4(a). Thus for a cut height H_l given by Eq. (5.17) we
have found a distribution of stress which is in equilibrium with the (zero) boundary
stresses and which nowhere exceeds the failure criterion: hence H_l given by
Eq. (5.17) is a lower bound for the height of the cut at collapse.

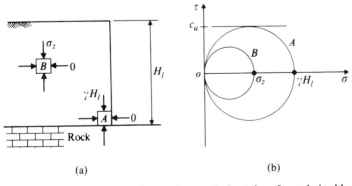

(a)   (b)

Figure 5.4 Equilibrium state of stress for a vertical cut slope for undrained loading.

If the true height of the cut slope at collapse is H_c, then, from the boun
theorems,

$$\frac{4c_u}{\gamma} \geqslant H_c \geqslant \frac{2c_u}{\gamma} \qquad (5.18$$

Thus, by means of two relatively simple calculations, we have obtained an estimat
for the collapse of a quickly excavated cut slope. It should be noted that th
collapse mechanism was a simple straight slip plane and the angle it made with th
horizontal was arbitrarily chosen; furthermore, the state of stress examined had zer
shear stresses on vertical and horizontal planes, a condition which again was quit
arbitrarily chosen. Thus neither the collapse mechanism nor the state of stress nee
have anything to do with the true collapse of the slope and, moreover, they nee
have nothing to do with each other.

The case shown in Fig. 5.2, where strong rock occurs at the base of the slope
is rather artificial, but it is very simple and well illustrates the principles and method
of the upper and lower bound calculations. To continue, we will examine the mor
general case of the undrained stability of a vertical cut slope in homogeneous soi
shown in Fig. 5.5.

3. Upper bounds for a vertical cut

The mechanism of plastic collapse shown in Fig. 5.3 serves also as a mechanism
of plastic collapse for the cut slope in Fig. 5.5 and hence an upper bound for the
height of the slope at collapse is given by Eq. (5.13) as

$$H_u = \frac{4c_u}{\gamma} \qquad [5.13]$$

Another mechanism of plastic collapse consisting of a circular arc is shown in
Fig 5.6. The sliding block is rigid and displaces by rotation about O at the top of
the cut face, and we consider an increment of rotation $\delta\theta$. The length of the slip
plane L and the increment of relative displacement across the slip plane δw are
given by

$$L = \tfrac{1}{2}\pi H_u \qquad \delta w = H_u\,\delta\theta \qquad (5.19)$$

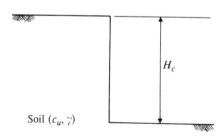

Soil (c_u, γ)

Figure 5.5 Vertical cut slope in homogeneous soil for undrained loading.

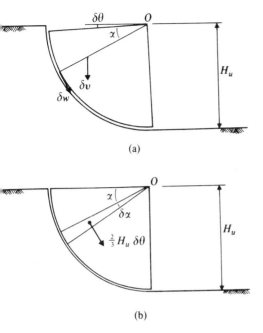

(a)

(b)

Figure 5.6 Mechanism of plastic collapse for a vertical cut slope for undrained loading.

where H_u is an upper bound for the height at which the cut face collapses. Hence, from Eq. (5.3), the increment of work done by the internal stresses is given by

$$\delta W = \sum c_u L\, \delta w = \tfrac{1}{2}\pi H_u^2 c_u\, \delta\theta \qquad (5.20)$$

The only external forces are those due to the self weight of the sliding block. For a small sector as shown in Fig. 5.6(b) the volume is

$$V = \tfrac{1}{2} H_u^2\, \delta\alpha \qquad (5.21)$$

and its weight acts at a radial distance $\tfrac{2}{3} H_u$ from the centre of rotation. The vertical component of displacement of the centre of mass of the sector is

$$\delta v = \tfrac{2}{3} H_u\, \delta\theta \cos\alpha \qquad (5.22)$$

Hence, from Eq. (5.4), the increment of work done by the external loads is

$$\delta E = \int_V \delta\mathbf{w}\cdot\gamma\, dV = \int_0^{\pi/2} \tfrac{2}{3} H_u \delta\theta \cos\alpha \gamma \tfrac{1}{2} H_u^2\, d\alpha \qquad (5.23)$$

and

$$\delta E = \tfrac{1}{3}\gamma H_u^3\, \delta\theta \qquad (5.24)$$

Thus, equating $\delta W = \delta E$, an upper bound for the height of the cut slope at collapse is given by

$$H_u = \frac{3\pi c_u}{2\gamma} = \frac{4.71 c_u}{\gamma} \tag{5.25}$$

The value of H_u given by Eq. (5.25) is greater than that given by Eq. (5.13) and so we have not improved our estimate of collapse and the mechanism shown in Fig. 5.3 is better than that shown in Fig. 5.6.

4. Lower bound for a vertical cut

The state of stress shown in Fig. 5.4 is insufficient as a lower bound for the vertical cut in homogeneous soil, because we have not examined the state of stress in the soil below the cut. Figure 5.7(a) shows a state of stress with two discontinuities separating three regions of soil. Shear stresses on horizontal and vertical planes are everywhere zero and hence the stresses are given by Eqs (5.14) and (5.15). A

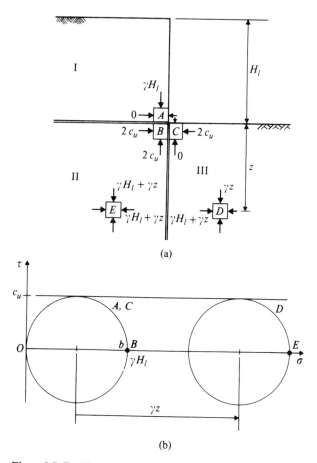

(a)

(b)

Figure 5.7 Equilibrium state of stress for a vertical cut slope for undrained loading.

:fore (p. 151), the state of stress in region I is in equilibrium and does not exceed
ιe undrained failure criterion when the height of the cut is

$$H_l = \frac{2c_u}{\gamma} \tag{5.26}$$

he states of stress in the elements A, B, and C are marked on Fig. 5.7(a) and the
ɔrresponding Mohr's circles are shown in Fig. 5.7(b). The Mohr's circle for the
.otropic state of stress $\sigma_x = \sigma_z$ in the element B is the single point B in Fig. 5.7(b)
ιnd the same point b represents the stresses on both discontinuities. The states of
:ress in the elements D and E at a depth z are given by the Mohr's circle D and
ιe point E in Fig. 5.7(b). The states of stress in Fig. 5.7(a) are everywhere in
quilibrium and nowhere exceed the undrained failure criterion, since none of the
Λohr's circles in Fig. 5.7(b) cross the failure envelope. Thus, the height H_l given by
'q. (5.26) is a lower bound for the height of the cut at collapse.

From the upper and lower bound theorems the true height of the cut at
ɔllapse H_c is given from Eqs (5.13) and (5.26) as

$$\frac{4c_u}{\gamma} \geqslant H_c \geqslant \frac{2c_u}{\gamma} \tag{5.27}$$

Γhus the bounds we have calculated so far for a vertical cut in homogeneous soil
ιre the same as those given by Eq. (5.18) for the case where rock occurs in the
ɔase of the cut, although it should be noted that the actual heights of the cuts at
ɔollapse may not be the same for each case.

The average of the upper and lower bound solutions given by Eq. (5.27) is
$H = 3c_u/\gamma$ and hence the bounds differ from the average by $\pm$ 33 per cent. Unfor-
:unately it is not easy to improve these estimates. The problem is discussed in detail
ɔy Heyman (1973), who gives an upper bound $H_u = 3.83c_u/\gamma$ and a lower bound
$H_l = 2.83c_u/\gamma$.

The case for an infinitely long slope is shown in Fig. 5.1(b). In order to limit
the depth of slipping soil, strong rock occurs at a depth H below ground level and
this is a common occurrence where a relatively thin mantle of soil overlies rock in
a hillside. In an infinitely long slope, the length down the slope is large compared
with the depth H and it is required to calculate the limiting slope angle i_c for
which collapse occurs.

1. Upper bound for an infinite slope

Figure 5.8(a) shows a mechanism of plastic collapse consisting of a slip plane
through the soil at the rock level and, for convenience, we consider a block of
soil length l measured down the slope. The corresponding displacement diagram
for an increment of displacement δw is shown in Fig. 5.8(b). For an infinitely
long slope, the forces on any such block are the same as those on any other similar
block and so the forces F_1 and F_2 are equal and opposite. From the geometry of
Fig. 5.8(a), the weight of the block (for unit thickness normal to the page) is

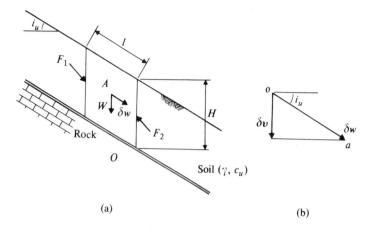

Figure 5.8 Mechanism of plastic collapse for an infinitely long slope for undrained failure.

$$W = \gamma Hl \cos i_u \qquad (5.28)$$

and from Fig. 5.8(b) the vertical component of displacement is

$$\delta v = \delta w \sin i_u \qquad (5.29)$$

where i_u is an upper bound for the limiting slope angle. Hence, from Eqs (5.3) and (5.4), noting that the increments of work done by the equal and opposite forces F_1 and F_2 sum to zero, we have

$$\delta W = c_u l\, \delta w \qquad (5.30)$$

$$\delta E = \gamma Hl \cos i_u\, \delta w \sin i_u \qquad (5.31)$$

and, equating $\delta W = \delta E$, an upper bound for the critical slope angle is given by

$$\sin i_u \cos i_u = \frac{c_u}{\gamma H} \qquad (5.32)$$

or

$$i_u = \tfrac{1}{2} \sin^{-1} \frac{2c_u}{\gamma H} \qquad (5.33)$$

2. Lower bound for an infinite slope

Figure 5.9(a) shows an infinite slope whose angle i_l is a lower bound for the limiting angle. The state of stress in the soil increases linearly with depth from zero at the surface and the maximum shear stresses $\tau = c_u$ occur on planes parallel with the slope. For an infinite slope, as before, the forces F_1 and F_2 are equal and opposite and the weight of a block of soil of length l is $W = \gamma Hl \cos i_l$. Hence, resolving normal to and along the slope, we have

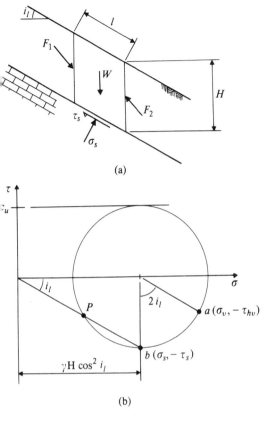

(a)

(b)

Figure 5.9 Equilibrium state of stress for an infinite slope for undrained loading.

$$\sigma_s = \gamma H \cos^2 i_l \qquad \tau_s = \gamma H \sin i_l \cos i_l \qquad (5.34)$$

where σ_s and τ_s are the normal and shear stresses in the soil on the plane parallel to the slope at a depth H. The Mohr's circle of total stress for an element of soil just above the rock is shown in Fig. 5.9(b). The pole is at P and points a and b represent the states of stress on a horizontal plane and on a plane parallel with the slope, respectively, and the angle subtended at the centre of the circle is $2i_l$. The Mohr's circle just touches the undrained failure envelope and so the state of stress in the slope does not exceed the undrained failure criterion given by Eq. (5.1). From the geometry of Fig. 5.9(b), making use of Eq. (5.34), a lower bound for the critical slope angle is given by

$$\tan i_l = \frac{\tau_s}{\sigma_s} = \frac{c_u}{\gamma H \cos^2 i_l} \qquad (5.35)$$

and hence

$$i_l = \tfrac{1}{2} \sin^{-1} \frac{2c_u}{\gamma H} \qquad (5.36)$$

Comparing Eqs (5.33) and (5.36) we find that the upper bound solution exactly equals the lower bound solution and so both must equal the exact solution. Hence the limiting slope angle i_c for undrained loading of an infinite slope is given by

$$i_c = \tfrac{1}{2} \sin^{-1} \frac{2c_u}{\gamma H} \qquad (5.37)$$

There is of course no point in seeking to find better bounds.

We have been fortunate to obtain such good bound solutions and normally, as was the case for the vertical cut, we will only be able to find upper and lower bounds which differ from one another. Even though the upper and lower bounds may differ, one or other may correspond to the exact solution but we will have no means of knowing which, if either, bound is exact. Because the upper and lower bounds given by Eq. (5.37) are equal, the mechanism of plastic collapse shown in Fig. 5.8(a) must correspond to the state of stress shown in Fig. 5.9(a). This correspondence of the displacements and stresses leads to the *slip line* method of analysis which we will discuss in Chapter 7.

5.4 UNDRAINED STABILITY OF A SMOOTH RETAINING WALL

Figure 5.10(a) shows a rigid, vertical wall retaining soil whose unit weight is γ and whose undrained shear strength is c_u. The height of the supported soil is H and of course H is greater than H_c, the height of an unsupported cut face at collapse. To illustrate simple upper and lower bound calculations it is convenient to assume that strong rock occurs at the base of the wall, so that we do not have to investigate states of stress and mechanisms of plastic collapse below the base of the wall. The wall is assumed to be smooth and so shear stresses between the wall and the soil are zero; we will consider the case for a rough wall in a later section. The horizontal force on the wall is P per unit length normal to the page, applied so that the wall moves horizontally without rotation and without any vertical component of displacement.

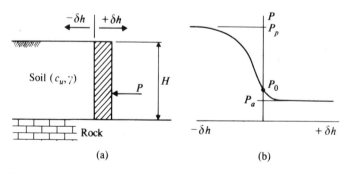

Figure 5.10 Displacement and failure of a retaining wall.

The variation of P with horizontal displacement $\pm \delta h$ of the wall away from or *wards the soil is indicated in Fig. 5.10(b). As the wall moves towards the soil, the aximum force P_p is known as the *passive force* and the associated normal stresses n the wall are known as *passive pressures*; as the wall moves away from the soil, ie minimum force P_a is known as the *active force* and the associated stresses on ie wall are known as *active pressures*. The problem of a retaining wall illustrated Fig. 5.10(a) is applicable not only to walls retaining soil in excavations and cut opes but also to the forces in ground anchors, to the forces on a bulldozer blade, id to a number of other similar cases.

. Upper bound for the passive case

'e begin by considering the passive force P_p for which collapse occurs as the wall loves towards the soil. Figure 5.11(a) shows a mechanism of plastic collapse onsisting of a single slip plane at an angle $45°$ to the vertical and Fig. 5.11(b) iows the corresponding displacement diagram for an increment of displacement w across the slip plane. From the geometry of Fig. 5.11(a) the length L of the ip plane and the volume V of the sliding wedge (for unit thickness normal to the age) are given by

$$L = \sqrt{2}H \qquad V = \tfrac{1}{2}H^2 \qquad (5.38)$$

nd, from the geometry of the displacement diagram in Fig. 5.11(b), the horizontal nd vertical components of the increment of displacement are

$$\delta v = \delta h = \frac{1}{\sqrt{2}} \delta w \qquad (5.39)$$

'he external forces are those due to the self weight of the slipping soil and P_{pu} the pper bound for the passive force. Hence, from making use of Eqs (5.38) and 5.39), and noting that the wall is smooth, we have

$$\delta W = c_u \sqrt{2}H \,\delta w \qquad (5.40)$$

$$\delta E = P_{pu} \frac{1}{\sqrt{2}} \delta w - \frac{1}{\sqrt{2}} \delta w \tfrac{1}{2}\gamma H^2 \qquad (5.41)$$

vhere the negative sign appears in Eq. (5.41) because δv is *upward* while the weight f the wedge acts *downwards*. Equating $\delta W = \delta E$ an upper bound for the passive orce is given by

$$P_{pu} = \tfrac{1}{2}\gamma H^2 + 2c_u H \qquad (5.42)$$

This is an upper bound and hence the wall must fail by moving towards the soil if he passive force exceeds the value of P_{pu} given by Eq. (5.42).

2. Lower bound for the passive case

'igure 5.12(a) shows a state of stress where shear stresses on horizontal and vertical lanes are zero, which clearly satisfies the conditions at the soil surface and at the mooth wall. Hence, putting $\tau_{xz} = \tau_{zx} = 0$ into Eqs (5.5) and (5.6) and integrating

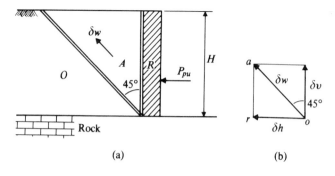

Figure 5.11 Mechanism of plastic collapse for a retaining wall for undrained loading: passive case

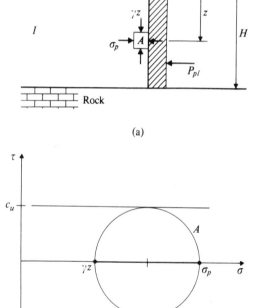

Figure 5.12 Equilibrium state of stress for a retaining wall for undrained loading: passive case

with the limits $\sigma_z = 0$ at the soil surface and $\sigma_x = \sigma_p$ at the wall, the stresses throughout the soil are given by

$$\sigma_z = \gamma z \qquad \sigma_x = \sigma_p \qquad (5.43)$$

The Mohr's circle of total stress for the element A at a depth z is shown in Fig. 5.12(b) and the circle does not cross the undrained failure envelope when the passive stress σ_p at a depth z is given by

$$\sigma_p = \gamma z + 2c_u \tag{5.44}$$

 e state of stress shown in Fig. 5.12 is in equilibrium and does not exceed the
 drained failure criterion and hence a lower bound for the passive force is given by

$$P_{pc} = \int_0^H \sigma_p \, dz = \tfrac{1}{2}\gamma H^2 + 2c_u H \tag{5.45}$$

 his is a lower bound and the wall cannot fail by moving towards the soil unless
 e passive force exceeds the value of P_{pl} given by Eq. (5.45).

Comparing Eqs (5.42) and (5.45), we find that the upper bound solution
 actly equals the lower bound solution, and so both must equal the exact solu-
 on. Hence the passive force at collapse P_{pc} for a smooth wall moving towards the
 il is given by

$$P_{pc} = \tfrac{1}{2}\gamma H^2 + 2c_u H \tag{5.46}$$

 d of course there is no point in investigating other bounds. Thus, as was the case
 r an infinite slope, we have been fortunate to obtain exceedingly good bound
 lutions and the mechanism of plastic collapse shown in Fig. 5.11(a) must corre-
 ond to the state of stress shown in Fig. 5.12(a).

We now consider the active force P_a for which collapse occurs as the wall
 oves away from the soil. This case is rather different from the passive case, since
 the wall is not very high then it may be removed completely to leave an un-
 pported face. Thus, as shown in Fig. 5.13(a), the wall need not extend to the
 ll height of the soil and the height H_c of the unsupported soil is given by the
 pper and lower bounds given in the previous section as

$$\frac{4c_u}{\gamma} \geqslant H_c \geqslant \frac{2c_u}{\gamma} \tag{5.27}$$

 ndeed, unsupported faces may occur anywhere in the soil behind the wall and
 hese are known as *tension cracks*. Such tension cracks are common occurrences
 n soil behind walls and at the top of slopes; they may fill with water but for the
 resent we assume that cracks remain dry.

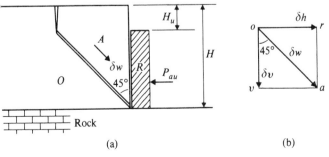

(a)   (b)

 igure 5.13 Mechanism of plastic collapse for a retaining wall for undrained loading: active case.

3. Upper bound for the active case

Figure 5.13(a) shows a mechanism of plastic collapse, consisting of a single straight line slip plane at an angle $45°$ to the vertical and meeting the bottom of a tension crack whose depth H_u, corresponding to the upper bound for H_c, is given by

$$H_u = \frac{4c_u}{\gamma} \qquad [5.13]$$

Figure 5.13(b) shows the displacement diagram for an increment of displacement δw across the slip plane as the block A moves downwards and to the right. Proceeding as before, we have

$$\delta W = c_u \sqrt{2}(H - H_u)\, \delta w \qquad (5.47)$$

$$\delta E = -P_{au} \frac{1}{\sqrt{2}} \delta w + \frac{1}{\sqrt{2}} \delta w \tfrac{1}{2}\gamma(H^2 - H_u^2) \qquad (5.48)$$

where the negative sign appears in Eq. (5.48) because δh is to the *right*, while P_a acts to the *left* in Fig. 5.13. Hence, equating $\delta W = \delta E$, an upper bound for the active force is given by

$$P_{au} = \tfrac{1}{2}\gamma(H^2 - H_u^2) - 2c_u(H - H_u) \qquad (5.49)$$

where H_u is given by Eq. (5.13). This is an upper bound and the wall must fail by moving away from the soil if the active force falls below the value of P_{au} in Eq. (5.49). We must be very careful here to note that although P_{au} given by Eq. (5.49) is an *upper* bound, collapse must occur if the active force falls *below* this value.

4. Lower bound for the active case

Figure 5.14(a) shows a state of stress consisting of regions I and II separated by horizontal broken line at a depth H_l; this is not a stress discontinuity in the sense described in Sec. (4.10), and it merely separates region I, where horizontal stresses are everywhere zero, from region II, where the horizontal stresses are equal to the active stress σ_a. Tension cracks occur throughout region I and their depth H_l corresponding to the lower bound for H_c, is given by

$$H_l = \frac{2c_u}{\gamma} \qquad [5.17]$$

Shear stresses on horizontal and vertical planes are everywhere zero, which clearly satisfies the conditions at the surface and at the smooth wall and hence, from Eqs (5.5) and (5.6), the states of stress throughout the soil in region I are given by

$$\sigma_z = \gamma z \qquad \sigma_x = \sigma_a \qquad (5.50)$$

The Mohr's circles of total stress for the elements A, B, and C are shown in Fig. 5.14(b) and none cross the undrained failure envelope when this active stress σ_a at a depth z is given by

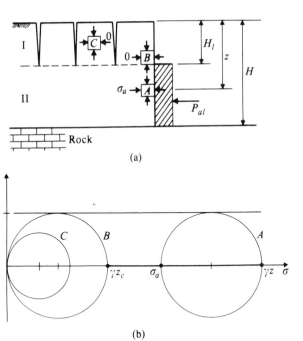

Figure 5.14 Equilibrium state of stress for a retaining wall for undrained loading: active case.

$$\sigma_a = \gamma z - 2c_u \tag{5.51}$$

Thus the state of stress in Fig. 5.14(a) is in equilibrium and does not exceed undrained failure criterion, and a lower bound for the active force is given by

$$P_{al} = \int_{H_l}^{H} (\gamma z - 2c_u)\, dz = \tfrac{1}{2}\gamma(H^2 - H_l^2) - 2c_u(H - H_l) \tag{5.52}$$

where H_l is given by Eq. (5.17). This is a lower bound and the wall cannot fail by moving away from the soil unless the active forces falls below the value of P_{al} in Eq. (5.52). We must be careful to note that although P_{al} given by Eq. (5.52) is a *lower* bound, collapse cannot occur if the active force *exceeds* this value.

From the bound theorems the active force P_{ac} as the wall collapses by moving away from the soil is given by

$$[\tfrac{1}{2}\gamma(H^2 - H_u^2) - 2c_u(H - H_u)] \leqslant P_{ac} \leqslant [\tfrac{1}{2}\gamma(H^2 - H_l^2) - 2c_u(H - H_l)] \tag{5.53}$$

where H_u and H_l are upper and lower bounds respectively for the height of an unsupported cut given by Eqs (5.13) and (5.17). For most cases the bounds given by Eqs (5.53) are relatively close to each other.

5.5 UNDRAINED STABILITY OF A FOUNDATION

Figure 5.15(a) shows a section of a long foundation, width B, at the surface of soil whose unit weight is γ and whose undrained shear strength is c_u. Loads per unit length normal to the page cause a *bearing pressure* $q = F/B$, which assumed to be uniform, and a uniform stress $p^\dagger$ is applied to the soil surface outsi the area of the foundation. As the foundation loading is raised, settlements increase approximately as indicated in Fig. 5.15(b). When the load reaches t collapse load F_c, settlements are able to continue with no further increase loading (at least for settlements which are relatively small when compared wi the width of the foundation) and the collapse pressure $q_c = F_c/B$ is known as t *bearing capacity* of the foundation.

For the present we suppose that the load F is increased very rapidly. Hen the loading is assumed to be undrained and we are required to estimate the u drained capacity q_c of the foundation. For the case of undrained loading, it convenient to separate the contribution made to the bearing capacity by t undrained shear strength of the soil from the contribution made by any surfa pressures. First we will consider the stability of a foundation where the surfa pressures outside the area of the foundation are zero and the stability is due sole to the undrained shear strength of the soil.

1. Upper bound for a foundation

Figure 5.16 shows a mechanism of plastic collapse consisting of a rigid block soil slipping on a semicircular slip plane centred on a corner of the foundatio this mechanism does not consist of a slip fan, since collapse can occur by rig body rotation about the centre of the arc. For a small increment $\delta\theta$ of angul

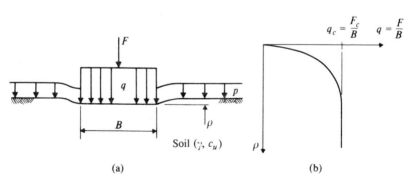

Figure 5.15 Settlement and collapse of a foundation for undrained loading.

† It should be noted that the stresses q and p here are not the same as the parameters q ar p defined by Eqs (1.27) and (1.28) and used to represent the state of stress in an element f axial symmetry.

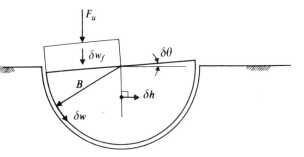

gure 5.16 Mechanism of plastic collapse for a foundation for undrained loading.

tation the vertical settlement of the centre of the foundation is δw_f but the
ntre of mass of the sliding block of soil moves horizontally and so body weight
rces do no work. From the geometry of Fig. 5.16

$$\delta w_f = \tfrac{1}{2}B\,\delta\theta \qquad \delta w = B\,\delta\theta \qquad (5.54)$$

ence, from Eqs (5.3) and (5.4), using Eq. (5.54),

$$\delta W = c_u \pi B \cdot B\,\delta\theta \qquad (5.55)$$

$$\delta E = F_u \cdot \tfrac{1}{2}B\,\delta\theta \qquad (5.56)$$

id, equating $\delta W = \delta E$, an upper bound for the collapse load of the foundation
given by

$$F_u = 2\pi B c_u \qquad (5.57)$$

. Lower bound for a foundation

igure 5.17(a) shows a state of stress with two vertical stress discontinuities. That
n the right is an α discontinuity and that on the left is a β discontinuity and
ne state of stress is symmetrical about the centreline of the foundation. Shear
resses on horizontal and vertical planes are zero and hence, from Eqs (5.5) and
5.6), the vertical stresses in regions I and III are

$$\sigma_z = \gamma z \qquad (5.58)$$

ne vertical stresses in regions II and IV are

$$\sigma_z = q_1 + \gamma z \qquad (5.59)$$

nd these are principal stresses. Mohr's circles of total stress for elements A and B
re shown in Fig. 5.17(b) and for elements C and D in Fig. 5.17(c). The Mohr's
ircles all just touch the undrained failure envelope and each pair — A and B, C
nd D — satisfy conditions of equilibrium across the appropriate discontinuity. The
oint a in Fig. 5.17(b) represents the state of stress on the α discontinuity and the
oint b in Fig. 5.17(c) represents the state of stress on the β discontinuity. From
he geometry of Figs 5.17(b) and (c) we have

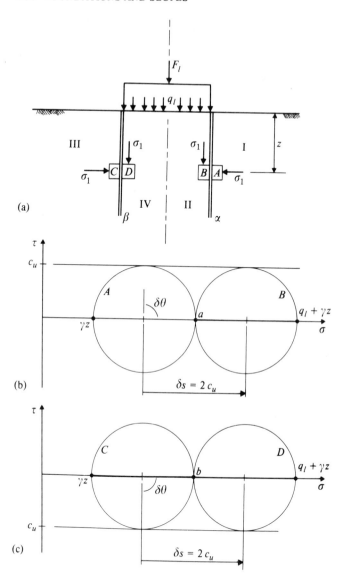

Figure 5.17 Equilibrium state of stress for a foundation for undrained loading.

and hence

$$q_l + \gamma z = 4c_u + \gamma z \tag{5.60}$$

$$F_l = 4c_u B \tag{5.61}$$

The state of stress in Fig. 5.17(a) is everywhere in equilibrium and nowhere exceeds the undrained failure criterion; hence F_l given by Eq. (5.61) is a lower bound for the collapse load.

Alternatively, we may proceed by considering the rotations of the directions the major principal stresses, making use of Eq. (5.7):

$$\delta s = \pm 2c_u \sin \delta\theta \qquad [5.7]$$

or the α discontinuity, $\delta\theta = -90°$ from region I to region II and we take the negative sign in Eq. (5.7): for the β discontinuity, $\delta\theta = 90°$ from region III to gion IV and we take the positive sign in Eq. (5.7). Hence, in both cases, we have

$$\delta s = 2c_u \qquad (5.62)$$

shown in Figs 5.17(b) and (c). For the Mohr's circles A and B we have

$$s_A = \gamma z + c_u \qquad s_B = q_l + \gamma z - c_u \qquad (5.63)$$

d for the Mohr's circles C and D

$$s_C = \gamma z + c_u \qquad s_D = q_l + \gamma z - c_u \qquad (5.64)$$

d
$$\delta s = (s_B - s_A) = (s_D - s_C) \qquad (5.65)$$

ence, from Eqs (5.62) and (5.65), noting that $F_l = q_l B$, we have, as before

$$F_l = 4c_u B \qquad [5.61]$$

From Eqs (5.57) and (5.61) the collapse load F_c of the foundation is given by

$$2\pi B c_u \geqslant F_c \geqslant 4B c_u \qquad (5.66)$$

he mean of the upper bound and lower bound solutions gives a value of $F_c \approx$ .14c_u and hence the bounds differ from the mean by about $\pm$ 20 per cent. If we ear in mind the difficulties of obtaining true values for the undrained shear strength for natural soils which may not be either isotropic or homogeneous, these latively simple bounds may be all that are required for design purposes. However, order to illustrate other aspects of the bound calculations, we will examine some ternative mechanisms of plastic collapse and some alternative distributions of stress.

. Upper bound for a foundation

igure 5.18(a) shows a mechanism of plastic collapse consisting of three triangular edges and Fig. 5.18(b) is the corresponding displacement diagram for an increment w_f of settlement of the foundation. In Fig. 5.18(a) the foundation remains horiontal rather than rotating about one edge as in Fig. 5.16(a), but both mechanisms re equally allowable. From the geometry of Fig. 5.18, the components of dislacement of the blocks are given by

$$\delta w_a = \delta w_c = \sqrt{2}\delta w_f \qquad \delta w_b = 2\delta w_f \qquad (5.67)$$

he increments of work done by the body weight forces sum to zero, since block B oves horizontally while the vertical components of blocks A and C are equal and pposite. Thus, from Eq. (5.4),

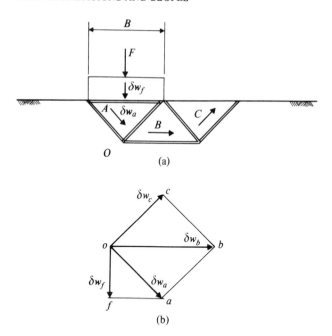

Figure 5.18 Mechanism of plastic collapse for a foundation for undrained loading.

$$\delta E = F_u \, \delta w_f \qquad (5.6$$

In order to calculate a value for δW from Eq. (5.3) it is convenient to tabula $c_u, L,$ and δw for each slip plane. Thus, from Table 5.1, noting that for a smoo foundation shear stresses between the soil and the foundation are zero

$$\delta W = 6 c_u B \, \delta w_f \qquad (5.6$$

Table 5.1

Slip plane	Shear stress	Length	Displacement	$\delta W = c_u L \, \delta$
oa	c_u	$\dfrac{1}{\sqrt{2}}B$	$\sqrt{2}\,\delta w_f$	$c_u B \, \delta w_f$
ob	c_u	B	$2\,\delta w_f$	$2c_u B \, \delta w_f$
oc	c_u	$\dfrac{1}{\sqrt{2}}B$	$\sqrt{2}\,\delta w_f$	$c_u B \, \delta w_f$
ab	c_u	$\dfrac{1}{\sqrt{2}}B$	$\sqrt{2}\,\delta w_f$	$c_u B \, \delta w_f$
bc	c_u	$\dfrac{1}{\sqrt{2}}B$	$\sqrt{2}\,\delta w_f$	$c_u B \, \delta w_f$
fa	0	B	δw_f	0
			Total	$6c_u B \, \delta w_f$

d, equating $\delta W = \delta E$, an upper bound for the collapse load of the foundation is
ven by

$$F_u = 6Bc_u \qquad (5.70)$$

is upper bound is lower than, and hence better than, that given by Eq. (5.61)
d the mechanism shown in Fig. 5.18(a) is an improvement on that shown in
g. 5.16.

Lower bound for a foundation

gure 5.19(a) shows a state of stress with a number of inclined discontinuities.
ose to the right are α discontinuities and those on the left are β discontinuities
d the state of stress is symmetrical about the centreline of the foundation. In
gions I and III shear stresses on horizontal and vertical planes are zero, and
nce, from Eqs (5.5) and (5.6), the vertical stress in region I is

$$\sigma_z = \gamma z \qquad (5.71)$$

e vertical stress in region III is

$$\sigma_z = q_l + \gamma z \qquad (5.72)$$

d these are principal stresses.

The major principal stress in region I is horizontal and the major principal
ress in region III is vertical and from region I to region III we have $\Delta\theta = 90°$;
nce, from Eq. (4.72), with $n = 2$, the angle between the discontinuities is
$= 45°$, as shown in Fig. 5.19(a) and $\delta\theta = 45°$ for each discontinuity. Mohr's
rcles of total stress for elements at the points A to F in Fig. 5.19(a) are shown
Figs 5.19(b) and (c). The Mohr's circles all just touch the undrained failure
velope and each adjacent pair satisfies conditions of equilibrium across the
propriate discontinuity. The points a to d in Figs 5.19(b) and (c) represent
e stresses on the appropriate α discontinuities in Fig. 5.19(a). From the geometry
Fig. 5.19(b) with $\delta\theta = 45°$, we have

$$q_l + \gamma z = 2c_u + 2\sqrt{2}c_u + \gamma z \qquad (5.73)$$

d hence

$$F_l = 2(1 + \sqrt{2})Bc_u \qquad (5.74)$$

he state of stress in Fig. 5.19(a) is everywhere in equilibrium and nowhere exceeds
e undrained failure criterion and hence F_l given by Eq. (5.74) is a lower bound
r the collapse load.

Alternatively, we may proceed using Eq. (5.7) with $\delta\theta = -45°$ and taking
e negative sign for each α discontinuity. Hence we have

$$\Delta s = 2\delta s = 4c_u \sin 45° = 2\sqrt{2}c_u \qquad (5.75)$$

or the Mohr's circles A and C we have

$$s_A = \gamma z_1 + c_u \qquad s_C = q_l + \gamma z_1 - c_u \qquad (5.76)$$

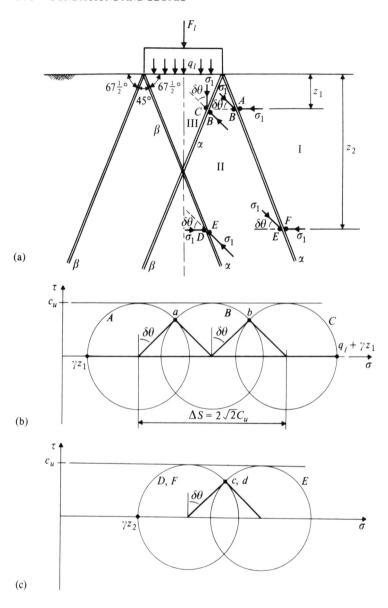

Figure 5.19 Equilibrium states of stress for a foundation for undrained loading.

$$\Delta s = s_C - s_A \tag{5.7?}$$

and hence, noting that $F_l = q_l B$, we have, as before,

$$F_l = 2(1 + \sqrt{2})Bc_u \tag{5.74}$$

is lower bound is larger than, and hence better than, that given by Eq. (5.61)
d the state of stress shown in Fig. 5.19(a) is an improvement on that shown in
g. 5.17(a).

From Eqs (5.70) and (5.74), the collapse load F_c of the foundation is given by

$$6Bc_u \geqslant F_c \geqslant (2 + 2\sqrt{2})Bc_u \tag{5.78}$$

e bounds given by Eq. (5.78) are within, and so are better than, those given by
. (5.66). The mean of the bounds given by Eq. (5.78) has a value of $F_c \approx 5.41\,c_u$
d hence the bounds differ from the mean by about ± 11%; thus by examining
ghtly more complicated mechanisms of plastic collapse and equilibrium states of
ess we have significantly improved the accuracy of our bounds. For practical
rposes it is probably hardly worth trying to find new mechanisms and new states
stress to improve these bounds, but for the present we will continue our calcu-
ion for a foundation in order to illustrate the use of fans of slip planes and fans
discontinuities.

Upper bound for a foundation

gure 5.20(a) shows a mechanism of plastic collapse consisting of two wedges
d a fan of slip planes and Fig. 5.20(b) shows the displacement diagram for an
crement δw_f of settlement of the foundation. From the geometry of Fig. 5.20(b),
e have

$$\delta w_a = \delta w_b = \sqrt{2}\delta w_f \tag{5.79}$$

e increments of work done by the body weight forces sum to zero and thus,
om Eq. (5.4),

$$\delta E = F_u \,\delta w_f \tag{5.80}$$

e radius of the fan is $R = B/\sqrt{2}$ and the fan angle is $\theta_f = \tfrac{1}{2}\pi$. Hence, from
. (4.69), making use of Eq. (5.79), the increment of work done by the internal
resses through the fan is

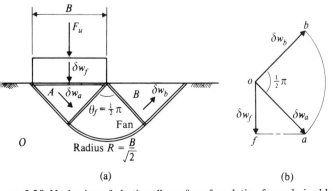

(a)   (b)

gure 5.20 Mechanism of plastic collapse for a foundation for undrained loading.

Table 5.2

Slip plane	Shear stress	Length	Displacement	$\delta W = c_u L \, \delta w$
oa	c_u	$\dfrac{1}{\sqrt{2}}B$	$\sqrt{2}\,\delta w_f$	$c_u B \,\delta w_f$
ob	c_u	$\dfrac{1}{\sqrt{2}}B$	$\sqrt{2}\,\delta w_f$	$c_u B \,\delta w_f$
Fan	c_u	–	–	$\pi c_u B \,\delta w_f$
fa		B	δw_f	0
Total				$(2 + \pi)\, c_u B \, \delta w$

$$\delta W = 2c_u R \theta_f \, \delta w_a = \pi c_u B \, \delta w_f \tag{5.8}$$

Tabulating values for δW for each slip plane, as before, and noting that for smooth foundation shear stresses between the soil and the foundation are zero, we have, from Table 5.2,

$$\delta W = (2 + \pi)c_u B \, \delta w_f \tag{5.8}$$

Hence, equating $\delta W = \delta E$, an upper bound for the collapse of the foundation given by

$$F_u = (2 + \pi)Bc_u \tag{5.8}$$

This upper bound is lower than, and hence better than, that given by Eq. (5.70), and the mechanism shown in Fig. 5.20(a) is an improvement on that shown in Fig. 5.18(.

6. Lower bound for a foundation

Figure 5.21(a) shows a state of stress with two stress fans marked II and IV which overlap in region VI. Fan II consists of α discontinuities and fan IV consists of β discontinuities and the state of stress is symmetrical about the centreline of the foundation. In regions I and III shear stresses on horizontal and vertical planes are zero and hence, from Eqs (5.5) and (5.6), the vertical stress in region I is

$$\sigma_z = \gamma z \tag{5.8}$$

the vertical stress in region III is

$$\sigma_z = q_1 + \gamma z \tag{5.8}$$

and these are principal stresses.

The major principal stress in region I is horizontal and the major principal stress in region III is vertical and from region I to region III we have $\Delta\theta = 90$ and hence the fan angle is $\theta_f = 90°$ as shown in Fig. 5.21(a). The Mohr's circle for elements at the points A and C are shown in Fig. 5.21(b). There is an infinity of circles between these limiting circles, each corresponding to the states of stress small elements along radii in the stress fan II. The points a and c in Fig. 5.21(b) represent the states of stress on the limiting discontinuities of the fan.

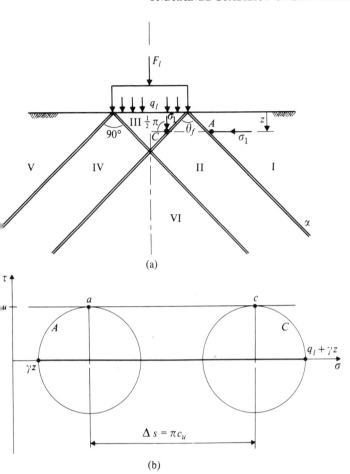

Figure 5.21 Equilibrium state of stress for a foundation for undrained loading.

From Eq. (5.8), taking the negative sign for the fan of α discontinuities and for $\Delta\theta = -\frac{1}{2}\pi$, the change in the state of stress from region I to region III is

$$\Delta s = \pi c_u \tag{5.86}$$

For the Mohr's circles A and C we have

$$s_A = \gamma z + c_u \qquad s_C = q_l + \gamma z - c_u \tag{5.87}$$

$$\Delta s = s_C - s_A \tag{5.88}$$

and hence, noting that $F_l = q_l B$, we have

$$F_l = (2 + \pi)Bc_u \tag{5.89}$$

It must be noted that in this analysis we have not examined the state of str
in region VI in Fig. 5.21(a), where the stress fans II and IV overlap, and theref
we cannot yet be certain that F_l given by Eq. (5.89) is a true lower bound. It is
fact possible to calculate states of stress in region VI which are in equilibrium a
which do not exceed the undrained failure criterion, but a simple analysis is lengtl
An analysis which examines the state of stress everywhere below a foundation
undrained loading but which uses a different approach from that used here is giv
by Chen (1975, Chapter 6) and this analysis gives a lower bound which is the sa
as that given by Eq. (5.85).

Comparing Eqs (5.83) and (5.89), we find that the upper and lower bou
solutions are the same and so both must equal the exact solution. Hence the lc
on the foundation at collapse is given by

$$F_c = (2 + \pi)Bc_u \qquad (5.9$$

Thus, as was the case for the passive forces on the retaining wall, we have ag.
reached the satisfactory position where the upper and lower bounds are equal.

Again, the mechanism of plastic collapse shown in Fig. 5.20 must correspo
to the state of stress shown in Fig. 5.21 and the two taken together can be used
develop the slip line method of analysis described in Chapter 7. Although we ha
proceeded to an exact solution, in most cases of practical importance we wor
probably have been justified in stopping at Eq. (5.78) for which the upper a
lower bounds differed from the mean by about 11%.

We now consider the case where a uniform pressure p is applied to the s
surface outside the foundation, as shown in Fig. 5.15. For these calculations
would guess that the most suitable mechanism is that shown in Fig. 5.20 and t
most suitable stress distribution is like that shown in Fig. 5.21.

7. Upper bound for a foundation with surcharge pressure

Figure 5.22(a) shows a mechanism of plastic collapse and Fig. 5.22(b) shows t
displacement diagram for an increment δw_f of settlement of the foundation. T
calculations proceed exactly as for the mechanism shown in Fig. 5.20, except tl
a term must be included to account for the increment of work done by the surfa
stresses p given by

$$\int_A \delta w \cdot p \, dA = -\delta w_s \, pC \qquad (5.9$$

where, from the geometry of Fig. 5.22,

$$C = B \qquad \delta w_s = \delta w_f \qquad (5.9$$

and the negative sign arises because the directions of p and δw_s are opposite. T
increment of work done by the external forces is therefore

$$\delta E = F_u \, \delta w_f - \delta w_f \, pB \qquad (5.9$$

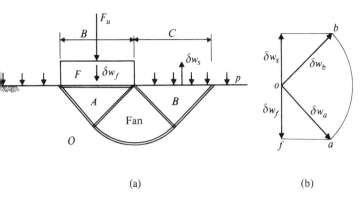

(a)   (b)

Figure 5.22 Mechanism of plastic collapse for a foundation for undrained loading.

and, as before, the increment of work done by the internal stresses is given by Eq. (5.81) as

$$\delta W = \pi c_u B\, \delta w_f \qquad [5.81]$$

Hence, equating $\delta E = \delta W$, we find that an upper bound F_u for the collapse load of the foundation is given by

$$F_u = (2 + \pi)c_u B + pB \qquad (5.94)$$

Lower bound for a foundation with surcharge pressure

Figure 5.23(a) shows a state of stress similar to that shown in Fig. 5.21(a) and Fig. 5.23(b) shows the Mohr's circles of total stress for elements at a depth z. The Mohr's circles in Fig. 5.23(b) are the same as those in Fig. 5.21(b) but shifted to the right by a distance equal to the magnitude of the surface pressure p. Calculations for the separation Δs of the Mohr's circles proceed as before and hence a lower bound for the collapse load is given by

$$F_l = (2 + \pi)c_u B + pB \qquad (5.95)$$

From Eqs (5.94) and (5.95), the upper and lower bounds are the same and so both must equal the exact solution given by

$$F_c = (2 + \pi)c_u B + pB \qquad (5.96)$$

Again we have obtained an exact solution and the mechanism of plastic collapse shown in Fig. 5.22(a) must correspond to the state of shear stress shown in Fig. 5.23(b).

Bearing capacity factors

It is conventional to write Eq. (5.96) is the form

$$F_c = c_u BN + pBM \qquad (5.97)$$

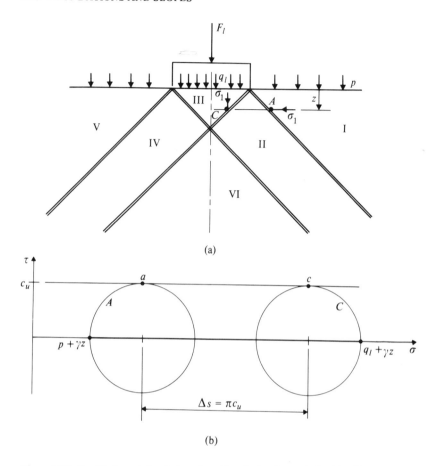

(a)

(b)

Figure 5.23 Equilibrium state of stress for a foundation for undrained loading.

where N and M are *bearing capacity factors* where, for undrained loading and f
plane strain,

$$N = (2 + \pi) \qquad M = 1 \tag{5.9}$$

Equation (5.97) has the same form as the bearing capacity equation given by Terzag
(1943, p. 126) and by most texts on soil mechanics and foundation engineerin
We must be careful to appreciate that Eq. (5.97) was obtained for undrain
loading of saturated soil and it is not applicable for any other condition. T
values of the bearing capacity factors N and M given by Eq. (5.98) were obtain
for plane strain loading of a foundation placed at the soil surface and differe
values will be appropriate for circular, square, or rectangular foundations a
for those buried below the soil surface. These cases will be considered furth
in Chapter 9.

6 UNDRAINED STABILITY OF A ROUGH RETAINING WALL

Sec. 5.4 we examined the case of a retaining wall which was assumed to be 100th so that shear stresses between the wall and the soil were zero. We now amine the more general and more realistic case where the wall is rough and shear :esses at failure between the soil and the wall, for undrained loading, are c_w, here, of course, $c_w \leqslant c_u$. In practice, a value for c_w may be measured in the oratory by conducting an undrained shear box test in which the lower half of e shear box contains the material of the wall; we will not discuss the methods ' measuring c_w here and we will assume that, in some way, the undrained shear rength of the soil and of the soil–wall interface are known.

We consider the passive case shown in Fig. 5.24. As the wall moves to the left e soil tends to rise upwards and the shear stresses applied by the wall to the soil e clockwise. The force P_p required to support the wall has a component N_p ormal to the wall and a component V_p as shown in Fig.5.24, where

$$\int_A V_p = c_w \, dA = c_w H \tag{5.99}$$

is simplest to calculate the normal component of the passive force N_p and then calculate the passive force P_p as the vector sum of its components N_p and V_p.

. Upper bound for a rough wall

igure 5.25(a) shows a mechanism of plastic collapse similar to that shown in ig. 5.11(a), and Fig. 5.25(b) shows the corresponding displacement diagram or an increment of displacement δw across the slip plane. The calculation for 1 upper bound N_{pu} for the normal component of the passive force follows osely that given in Sec. 5.4 for a smooth wall. The wall is assumed to move orizontally without rotation and so the external force V_p does no work, but a rm must be included in the expression for δW to account for the work dissipated 1 shearing between the soil and the wall. Hence, from Eqs (5.40) and (5.41) e have

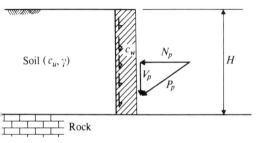

igure 5.24 Loads on a rough retaining wall for undrained loading: passive case.

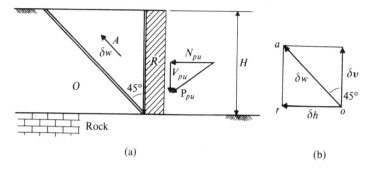

Figure 5.25 Mechanism of plastic collapse for a rough retaining wall for undrained loadir passive case.

$$\delta W = c_u \sqrt{2} H \, \delta w + c_w H \frac{1}{\sqrt{2}} \delta w \qquad (5.10$$

and

$$\delta E = N_{pu} \frac{1}{\sqrt{2}} \delta w - \frac{1}{\sqrt{2}} \delta w \, \gamma \tfrac{1}{2} H^2 \qquad (5.10$$

Equating $\delta W = \delta E$, an upper bound for the normal component of the passiv force is given by

$$N_{pu} = \tfrac{1}{2}\gamma H^2 + 2 c_u H \left(1 + \frac{c_w}{2 c_u}\right) \qquad (5.10$$

2. Lower bound for a rough wall

Figure 5.26(a) shows a state of stress consisting of regions I and II separated by β discontinuity. For the passive case there is, of course, no question of the existen of tension cracks in the soil. The shear stresses on horizontal and vertical planes i region I are zero and hence, from Eq. (5.5) we have

$$\sigma_z = \gamma z \qquad (5.10$$

The shear stresses on horizontal and vertical planes in region II however are c_w an the direction of the major principal stress is inclined at an angle $\delta\theta$ to the horizont as shown in Fig. 5.26(a). Figures 5.26(b) and (c) show Mohr's circles of total stre for elements A and B at a depth z in Fig. 5.26(a): the circle B in Fig. 5.26(b) repeated in Fig. 5.26(c) for clarity. The points w and b represent the stresses on th face of the wall and on the discontinuity respectively and P_a and P_b are the poles c the circles. The broken line bP_aP_b is parallel with the discontinuity and the broke line aP_b is parallel with the major principal plane in region II in Fig. 5.26(a). Th Mohr's circles do not cross the undrained failure envelope and they satisfy con ditions of equilibrium across the discontuity and at the wall. Thus the state of stre in Fig. 5.26(a) is in equilibrium and does not exceed the undrained failure criterior From the geometry of Fig. 5.26(b), the angle $\delta\theta$ is given by

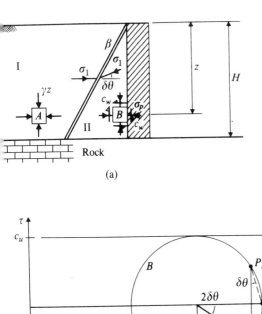

(a)

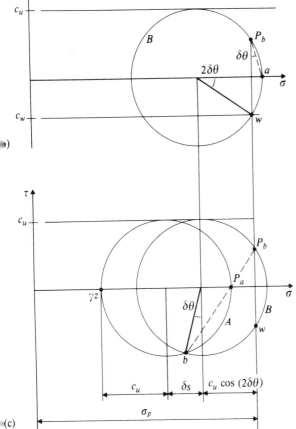

(c)

Figure 5.26 Equilibrium state of stress for a rough retaining wall for undrained loading: passive case.

$$\sin(2\delta\theta) = \frac{c_w}{c_u} \tag{5.10}$$

and, moving from region I to region II, $\delta\theta$ is counterclockwise and has a positive value. From Eq. (5.7), taking the positive sign for a β discontinuity, the change in the state of stress from region I to region II is

$$\delta s = 2c_u \sin \delta\theta \tag{5.10}$$

where $\delta\theta$ is given by Eq. (5.104). For the Mohr's circles A and B we have

$$s_A = \gamma z + c_u \qquad s_B = \sigma_p - c_u \cos(2\delta\theta) \tag{5.10}$$

$$\delta s = s_B - s_A \tag{5.10}$$

Hence, from Eqs (5.105) to (5.107), or from the geometry of Fig. 5.26(c), we have

$$\sigma_p = \gamma z + c_u[1 + 2\sin\delta\theta + \cos(2\delta\theta)] \tag{5.10}$$

where $\delta\theta$ is given by Eq. (5.104) in terms of c_w and c_u. Thus a lower bound for the normal component of the passive force on the wall is given by

$$N_{pl} = \int_0^H \sigma_p \, dz = \tfrac{1}{2}\gamma H^2 + c_u H[1 + 2\sin\delta\theta + \cos(2\delta\theta)] \tag{5.10}$$

where $\delta\theta$ is given by Eq. (5.104). From the bound theorems the normal component of the passive force on the wall at collapse is given by

$$N_{pu} \geqslant N_{pc} \geqslant N_{pl} \tag{5.110}$$

where N_{pu} and N_{pl} are given by Eqs (5.102) and (5.109). In both cases the vertical component of the force on the wall V_p is given by Eq. (5.99) and the bounds for the passive force P_p may be found from the vector sum of its components.

Similar calculations are applicable for the case of active collapse of a rough wall moving away from the soil but, as in Sec. 5.4, allowance must be made for the presence of tension cracks near the soil surface. We will not pursue these calculations here, since the main purpose of this section was to demonstrate simple upper and lower bound calculations for cases where loads are applied across rough boundaries.

5.7 EFFECT OF EXTERNAL WATER PRESSURES

For undrained loading we have been able to work with total, not effective, stresses, and so pore water pressures have not appeared in our calculations. Indeed, for undrained loading of saturated soil, knowledge of pore pressures is never necessary for stability calculations. We must, however, consider the cases where a cut slope forms a river or canal bank, where rainwater may collect in tension cracks, or where foundations are placed on the sea floor as indicated in Fig. 5.27.

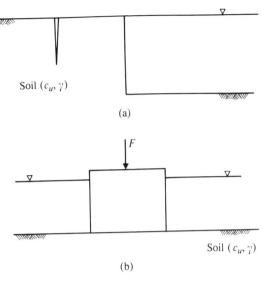

(a)

(b)

Figure 5.27 Soil structures with free water present for undrained loading. (a) River bank with water filled tension crack. (b) Foundation placed on the sea floor.

In these cases the free water should be considered separately from the pore water. The free water pressure is everywhere hydrostatic and it exerts *total* stresses on the soil, while the pore water pressures are determined by their initial values before loading and on the changes of stress which occurred during loading. Consequently, the magnitudes of the pressures in the free water, which act as total stresses on the soil, will not in general be the same as the magnitudes of the pore pressures in the adjacent soil. It is this lack of equilibrium between the pore water pressures and the free water pressures (which will be zero if there is no free water present) which gives rise to consolidation as positive or negative excess pore pressures dissipate with the passage of time.

For calculations of the stability of soil structures for undrained loading, any free water pressures must be considered as total boundary stresses.

As an example of stability calculations involving free water, we will obtain upper and lower bounds for the undrained stability of a vertical river bank where strong rock occurs in the river bed, as illustrated in Fig. 5.28(a). Thus the problem is similar to that shown in Fig. 5.2 and discussed in the first part of Sec. 5.3, except that we now consider the case where there is free water to the right of the vertical cut slope.

1. Upper bound for a river bank

Figure 5.28(a) shows a simple mechanism of plastic collapse consisting of a single slip plane at an angle $45°$ to the vertical and Fig. 5.28(b) shows the corresponding displacement diagram for an increment of displacement δw across the slip plane.

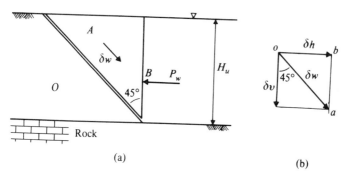

Figure 5.28 Mechanism of plastic collapse for a sumberged vertical cut slope for undrained loading.

The total stresses applied to the vertical soil face by the river water are $\sigma_w = \gamma_w z$ where γ_w is the unit weight of water and hence, integrating over the depth of the river, the total force P_w applied by the water to the soil is given by

$$P_w = \int_A \sigma_w \, dA = \tfrac{1}{2}\gamma_w H_u^2 \tag{5.111}$$

where H_u is an upper bound for the height of the river bank. Following Sec. 5.3 we have, for the increment of displacement δw across the slip plane,

$$\delta W = c_u \sqrt{2} H_u \, \delta w \tag{5.112}$$

$$\delta E = \frac{1}{\sqrt{2}} \delta w \, \gamma \tfrac{1}{2} H_u^2 - P_w \frac{1}{\sqrt{2}} \delta w \tag{5.113}$$

Hence, equating $\delta E = \delta W$, an upper bound for the height of the river bank at collapse H_u is given by

$$H_u = \frac{4c_u}{\gamma - \gamma_w} \tag{5.114}$$

2. Lower bound for a river bank

Figure 5.29(a) shows a state of stress in which shear stresses on vertical and horizontal planes are zero. Hence, from Eqs (5.5) and (5.6), with $\sigma_x = \gamma_w z$ at the vertical face, the stresses in element B at a depth z are

$$\sigma_z = \gamma z \qquad \sigma_x = \gamma_w z \tag{5.115}$$

Mohr's circles of total stress for elements A and B are shown in Fig. 5.29(b). The Mohr's circle A does not cross the undrained failure envelope when

$$\gamma H_l - \gamma_w H_l = 2c_u \tag{5.116}$$

and hence a lower bound for the height of the cut at collapse is given by

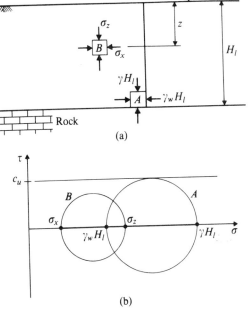

Figure 5.29 Equilibrium state of stress for a submerged vertical cut slope for undrained loading.

$$H_l = \frac{2c_u}{\gamma - \gamma_w} \tag{5.117}$$

The Mohr's circle B is smaller than the circle A and is within the undrained failure envelope. Moreover, the circle B represents the state of stress anywhere within the soil, which is everywhere in equilibrium and which nowhere exceeds the undrained failure criterion.

Thus the critical height of a vertical river bank is given by

$$\frac{4c_u}{\gamma - \gamma_w} \geqslant H_c \geqslant \frac{2c_u}{\gamma - \gamma_w} \tag{5.118}$$

Comparing Eqs (5.27) and (5.118), and noting that $\gamma \approx 2\gamma_w$ for most soils, the critical height of a submerged vertical cut slope for undrained loading is approximately twice that of a similar cut slope in air.

3. Upper and lower bounds for a submerged foundation

As a second example of a structure where free water is present, Fig. 5.30 shows a foundation on the sea bottom or on the bed of a river or lake. The weight of the foundation is W_f, its width is B, its depth is H, and the depth of water is H_w, so that free water pressures p_w at sea bottom level are

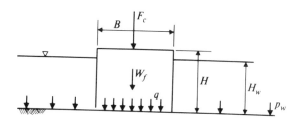

Figure 5.30 Stability of a submerged foundation for undrained loading.

$$p_w = \gamma_w H_w \tag{5.119}$$

We assume first that the contact between the foundation and the soil is no perfect, so that free water pressures exist between the foundation and the soil The submerged foundation is partially buoyant, and the upthrust U on the base due to the water pressures between the soil and the foundation is

$$U = \gamma_w B H_w \tag{5.120}$$

Thus, the *total* stress q applied by the loaded foundation and the free water pressures beneath it is given by

$$qB = F_c + W_f - U + \gamma_w H_w B = F_c + W_f \tag{5.121}$$

If, on the other hand, we assume that the contact between the soil and the foundation is perfect so that no free water pressures exist there then the foundation is no longer partially buoyant and

$$qB = F_c + W_f \tag{5.122}$$

Thus, it makes no difference, so far as total stresses are concerned, whether we assume the contact between the soil and the foundation to be perfect or imperfect.

The free water applies a total stress $p_w = \gamma_w H_w$ to the soil surface outside the foundation and hence, from Eq. (5.97), with values for the bearing capacity factors M and N given by Eq. (5.98), the collapse load F_c is given by

$$F_c + W_f = (2 + \pi)c_u B + \gamma_w H_w B \tag{5.123}$$

If the foundation is hollow so that its weight is negligible we have, for a submerged foundation,

$$F_c = (2 + \pi)c_u B + \gamma_w H_w B \tag{5.124}$$

and if the soil is very weak so that its strength c_u is negligible then we have

$$F_c = \gamma_w H_w B \tag{5.125}$$

Equation (5.125) is of course simply a statement of the principle of Archimedes that the upthrust on a submerged body is equal to the weight of fluid displaced.

8 DISCUSSION

this chapter we have examined upper and lower bound calculations for un-
ained loading of foundations, slopes, and retaining walls. In some cases we
•tained upper and lower bounds which were equal and which, therefore, equalled
.e exact solution, but in other cases the best upper and lower bounds obtained
ere different. Although the examples considered were relatively simple, the
.ethods are equally applicable to more general cases. We have examined calcu-
·tions for rough walls and for the presence of free water but all the methods in
lis chapter are applicable only for undrained loading.

REFERENCES

hen, W. F. (1975), *Limit Analysis and Soil Plasticity*, Elsevier, New York.
leyman, J. (1973), 'The stability of a vertical cut', *Int. J. Mech. Sci.*, **15**, 845–854.
·erzaghi, K. (1943), *Theoretical Soil Mechanics*, Wiley, New York.

WORKED EXAMPLES

E5.1 Stability of a Loaded Slope

A slope with angle i and height H is cut in saturated soil above strong rock. The
undrained shear strength of the soil is c_u and its unit weight is taken as zero. A
uniform normal stress q is applied to the soil surface and a uniform normal stress
p ($<q$) is applied to the slope. Obtain upper and lower bounds for the stress q
for a given value of p for undrained loading.

Figure E5.1(a) shows a mechanism of plastic collapse consisting of two wedges
separated by a slip fan of radius R and fan angle $\Delta\theta$ and Fig. E5.1(b) is a displacement diagram for an increment of displacement δw_q of the surface. Since the soil
is assumed to be weightless, the only external loads are P due to the stresses on the
slope and an upper bound Q_u due to the upper bound stresses q_u; their displacements are δw_p and δw_q, respectively. For a slice 1 m thick we have

$$P = pH/\sin i \qquad Q_u = q_u H/\sin i$$

$$\delta w_p = \delta w_q = \frac{1}{\sqrt{2}}\delta w$$

and, from Eq. (4.30)

$$\delta E = Q_u \delta w_q - P\,\delta w_p$$

$$\delta E = \frac{H}{\sqrt{2}\,\sin i}[q_u - p]\,\delta w$$

In the mechanism there are straight slip planes and a slip fan and, from Eqs (4.41)
and (4.47),

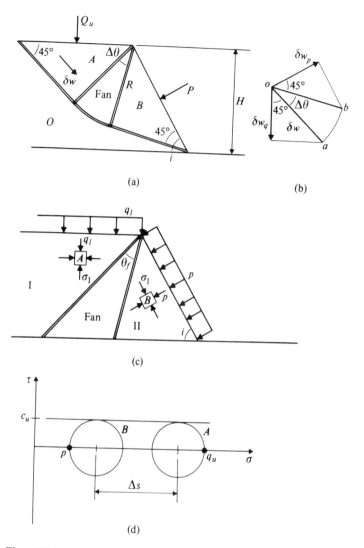

Figure E5.1

$$\delta W = \sum c_u L \, \delta w + \sum 2c_u R \, \Delta\theta \, \delta w$$

From Fig. E5.1(a) the radius of the fan is $R = H/\sqrt{2} \sin i$, the fan angle is $\Delta\theta = (90° - i)$, and the increment of displacement through the fan is δw. Hence for the fan we have

$$2c_u R \, \Delta\theta \, \delta w = \frac{\sqrt{2}c_u H}{\sin i} \left(\tfrac{1}{2}\pi - i\right) \delta w$$

Table E5.1

Plane	c_u	Length	Displacement	$c_u L\, \delta w$
t	c_u	$\dfrac{H}{\sqrt{2}\sin i}$	δw	$\dfrac{c_u H\, \delta w}{\sqrt{2}\sin i}$
b	c_u	$\dfrac{H}{\sqrt{2}\sin i}$	δw	$\dfrac{c_u H\, \delta w}{\sqrt{2}\sin i}$
fan	c_u	—	—	$\dfrac{\sqrt{2}c_u H\, \delta w(90° - i)}{\sin i}$
Total				$\dfrac{\sqrt{2}c_u H\, \delta w}{\sin i}(1 + \tfrac{1}{2}\pi - i)$

Values for the lengths of the straight slip planes are found from Fig. E5.1(a) and values for the increments of displacement across them are found from Fig. E5.1(b) and, making use of Table E5.1, we have

$$\delta W = \frac{\sqrt{2}c_u H}{\sin i}(1 + \tfrac{1}{2}\pi - i)\,\delta w$$

Hence, equating $\delta E = \delta W$, we have

$$q_u = c_u(2 + \pi - 2i) + p$$

Figure E5.1(c) shows a state of stress with regions I and II separated by a stress fan with a fan angle $\theta_f = (90° - i)$. In region I shear stresses on horizontal and vertical planes are zero and in region I shear stresses on planes normal to and parallel with the slope are zero. Figure E5.1(d) shows the Mohr's circles of total stress for elements A and B in regions I and II respectively, and the directions of the major principal stresses are shown in Fig. E5.1(c). The change of stress Δs through the fan is obtained from Eq. (4.77) as

$$\Delta s = 2c_u\, \Delta\theta = c_u(\pi - 2i)$$

and, from Fig. E5.3(b)

$$q_1 = c_u(2 + \pi - 2i) + p$$

Thus the upper bound for the collapse mechanism shown in Fig. E5.1(a) and the lower bound for the state of stress shown in Fig. E5.1(c) are equal and both equal the exact solution. The solutions for a foundation and for a retaining wall for weightless soil may be found with $i = 0$ and $i = \tfrac{1}{2}\pi$, respectively.

E5.2 Loads on Trench Struts

A trench is excavated to a depth of 5 m through saturated soil with undrained shear strength $c_u = 15$ kN/m² and unit weight $\gamma = 20$ kN/m³. Strong rock occurs at the base of the trench and there is a uniform surcharge of 80 kN/m² at the surface. The

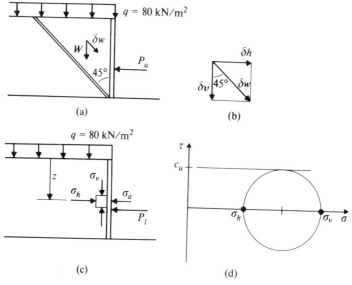

Figure E5.2

sides of the trench are stabilized by smooth, rigid sheet piles held apart by struts at intervals of 1 m normal to the page, placed so that the sheet piles do not rotate. Calculate upper and lower bounds for the strut loads required to maintain the stability of the trench for undrained loading (1) when the trench is empty and (2) when it is full of sea water with unit weight $\gamma_w = 10 \, \text{kN/m}^3$. (It may be assumed that the surcharge load is sufficiently large to prevent the formation of tension cracks.)

1. Figure E5.2(a) shows a mechanism of plastic collapse with a single straight slip plane and Fig. E5.2(b) is the displacement diagram for an increment of displacement δw down the plane. The external forces are the weight W of the sliding block of soil, the surcharge stress q, and an upper bound P_u for the strut load. For a slice 1 m thick normal to the page we have, from Eq. (4.30),

$$\delta E = \int_V \delta v \, \gamma \, dV + \int_A \delta v \, q \, dA - P_u \, \delta h$$

where

$$\delta w = \sqrt{2} \delta h = \sqrt{2} \delta v$$

$$\int_V \gamma \, dV = \tfrac{1}{2} \times 20 \times 5^2 = 250 \, \text{kN/m}$$

$$\int_A q \, dA = 80 \times 5 = 400 \, \text{kN/m}$$

and

$$\delta E = \frac{1}{\sqrt{2}} (650 - P_u) \delta w$$

here is only one slip plane and, from Eq. (4.41),

$$\delta W = c_u L \, \delta w$$

here

d

$$L = \sqrt{2}H = 5\sqrt{2}$$

$$\delta W = 15 \times 5\sqrt{2} \times \delta w = 75\sqrt{2} \times \delta w$$

ence, equating $\delta E = \delta W$, we have

$$\frac{1}{\sqrt{2}}(650 - P_u)\delta w = 75\sqrt{2} \, \delta w$$

$$\underline{P_u = 500 \, \text{kN}}$$

igure E5.2(c) shows a state of stress in which shear stresses on horizontal and ertical planes are zero and Fig. E5.2(d) shows the Mohr's circle of total stress or an element at a depth z below the surface. The total active stress between the oil and the sheet piles is $\sigma_a = \sigma_h$ where, from Fig. E5.2(d),

$$\sigma_h = \sigma_v - 2c_u = (\sigma_v - 30)$$

$$\sigma_v = q + \gamma z = (80 + 20z)$$

nd

$$\sigma_a = \sigma_h = (50 + 20z) \, \text{kN/m}^2$$

A lower bound for the strut load P_l is given by

$$P_l = \int_0^H \sigma_a \, dz = \int_0^5 (50 + 2z) \, dz$$

$$= [50z + 10z^2]_0^5$$

$$\underline{P_l = 500 \, \text{kN}}$$

Thus the upper bound for the collapse mechanism in Fig. E5.2(a) and the lower ound for the state of stress in Fig. E5.2(c) are equal and so both must equal the exact solution. Hence to maintain the stability of the trench the capacity of the struts must exceed 500 kN.

2. For the case when the trench is filled with sea water with unit weight $\gamma_w = 10 \, \text{kN/m}^3$, we assume that the sheet piles contain holes so that hydrostatic water pressures exist between the piles and the soil. The water pressures $p_w = \gamma_w z$ apply a total horizontal force to the soil given by

$$\int_A p_w \, dA = \tfrac{1}{2} \times 10 \times 5^2 = 125 \, \text{kN/m}$$

Hence, proceeding as before for the mechanism shown in Fig. E5.2(a), and con-sidering a slice 1 m thick normal to the page, we have

$$\delta E = \int_V \delta v \gamma \, dV + \int_A \delta v q \, dA - P_u \, \delta h - \int_A \delta h \, p_w \, dA$$

and

$$\delta E = \frac{1}{\sqrt{2}}(525 - P_u)\,\delta w$$

As before, for the single slip plane we have

$$\delta W = c_u L\,\delta w = 75\sqrt{2}\,\delta w$$

and, equating $\delta E = \delta W$,

$$\frac{1}{\sqrt{2}}(525 - P_u)\,\delta w = 75\sqrt{2}\,\delta w$$

$$\underline{P_u = 375\,kN}$$

For a lower bound, the calculation proceeds as in the previous example, except that the total horizontal stresses in the soil are given by

$$\sigma_h = \sigma_a + \sigma_w$$

where σ_a is the stress applied by the sheet piles and

$$\sigma_h = q + \gamma z - 2c_u = (50 + 20z)$$

and

$$\sigma_w = \gamma_w z = 10z$$

$$\sigma_a = (50 + 10z)\,kN/m^2$$

A lower bound for the strut load P_l is given by

$$P_l = \int_0^H \sigma_a\,dz = \int_0^5 (50 + 10z)\,dz$$

$$= [50z + 5z^2]_0^5$$

$$\underline{P_l = 375\,kN}$$

For these calculations we have assumed that the sheet piles were not impermeable and hence the sea water applied equal and opposite stresses to both sides of the sheet piles and to the soil. Alternatively, it may be assumed that the sheet piles are impermeable, in which case the water pressures act only on the strut side of the sheet piles. Hence, by statics, the strut loads are simply reduced by a force equal to $\int_A p_w\,dA = 125\,kN/m^2$ applied by the water pressures. In each case we have $P_u = P_l = 375\,kN$, and, to maintain the stability of the trench when it is full of sea water, the capacity of the struts must exceed $375\,kN$.

E5.3 Force on a Bulldozer Blade

A bulldozer blade 1 m high and 3 m wide pushes saturated soil across the top of strong rock and the blade does not rotate. The soil has undrained shear strength $c_u = 40\,kN/m^2$ and unit weight $\gamma = 20\,kN/m^3$ and the shear stress between the

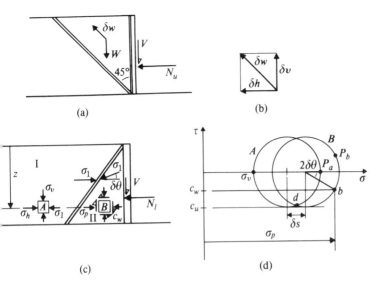

Figure E5.3

oil and the blade is $c_w = 20\,\text{kN/m}^2$. Calculate upper and lower bounds for the orce P which the bulldozer must apply to its blade. (It is assumed that the problem s plane strain and any three-dimensional effects at the ends of the blade may be neglected.)

Figure E5.3(a) shows a mechanism of plastic collapse with a single straight slip plane and Fig. E5.3(b) is the displacement diagram for an increment of displacement δw up the plane. The external forces are the weight W of the block of soil, the vertical component V of the force applied by the bulldozer, and an upper bound N_u for the horizontal component of the force applied by the bulldozer, but, as the blade moves horizontally, the vertical force V does no work. For a slice 1 m thick normal to the page we have, from Eq. (4.30),

$$\delta E = -\int_V \delta v\,\gamma\,\mathrm{d}V + N_u\,\delta h$$

where

$$\delta v = \delta h = \frac{1}{\sqrt{2}}\,\delta w$$

$$W = \int_V \gamma\,\mathrm{d}V = \tfrac{1}{2} \times 20 \times 1^2 = 10\,\text{kN/m}$$

and

$$\delta E = (N_u - 10)\frac{1}{\sqrt{2}}\,\delta w$$

For shearing through the soil along the slip plane and against the wall we have, from Eq. (4.41),

$$\delta W = c_u L\,\delta w + c_w H\,\delta v$$

where

and
$$L = \sqrt{2}H = \sqrt{2}\,\text{m}$$

$$\delta W = \left(40\sqrt{2} + \frac{20}{\sqrt{2}}\right)\delta w$$

Hence, equating $\delta E = \delta W$, we have

$$(N_u - 10)\frac{1}{\sqrt{2}}\,\delta w = \left(40\sqrt{2} + \frac{20}{\sqrt{2}}\right)\delta w$$

$$N_u = 110\,\text{kN/m}$$

An upper bound P_u for the force applied by the bulldozer to the blade is given by the vector sum of the components V and N_u where

$$V = \int_A c_w \, dA = 20\,\text{kN/m}$$

Hence, noting that the blade is 3 m wide normal to the page, we have

$$P_u = 3(V^2 + N_u^2)^{1/2} = 3(20^2 + 110^2)^{1/2}$$

$$\underline{P_u = 335\,\text{kN}}$$

Figure E5.3(c) shows a state of stress containing a single β discontinuity separating regions I and II. In region I shear stresses on horizontal and vertical planes are zero and the Mohr's circle for an element A at a depth z is shown in Fig. E5.3(d). The pole of the circle is at P_a and we have

and
$$\sigma_v = \gamma z$$

$$\sigma_h = \gamma z + 2c_u = \sigma_1$$

In region II shear stresses on horizontal and vertical planes are equal to the shear stresses $c_w = 20\,\text{kN/m}^2$ between the soil and the blade, and the Mohr's circle for an element B at a depth z is shown in Fig. E5.3(d); the pole is at P_b, the point b gives the stresses on the face of the blade, and the point d gives the stresses on the discontinuity. The angle between the direction of the major principal stress and the horizontal in region II is $\delta\theta$ and, from the geometry of Fig. E5.3(d),

and
$$\sin(2\delta\theta) = \frac{c_w}{c_u} = 0.5$$

$$\delta\theta = 15°$$

The distance δs between the centres of the two circles, corresponding to the change of stress across the discontinuity, is given by Eq. (4.76) as

$$\delta s = 2c_u \sin\delta\theta = 2 \times 40 \sin 15°$$

$$\delta s = 21\,\text{kN/m}^2$$

he total normal stress on the blade is σ_p, and, from Fig. E5.3(d),

$$\sigma_p = \gamma z + c_u + \delta s + c_u \cos 2\delta\theta$$

$$= 20z + 40 + 21 + 40 \cos 30°$$

$$= 96 + 20z$$

lower bound for the total normal force N_l is given by

$$N_l = \int_0^H \sigma_p \, dz = \int_0^1 (96 + 20z) \, dz$$

$$= [96z + 10z^2]_0^1$$

nd

$$N_l = 106 \text{ kN/m}$$

lower bound P_l for the force applied by the bulldozer is found from the vector um of the components V and N_l. Hence, noting that $V = 20$ kN/m as before, and hat the blade is 3 m wide normal to the page, we have

$$P_l = 3(20^2 + 106^2)^{1/2}$$

$$\underline{P_l = 324 \text{ kN}}$$

Thus we have simple bounds $P_u = 335$ kN and $P_l = 324$ kN, which are not equal but are relatively close to one another. These bounds may be improved by making use of stress fans and slip fans.

DRAINED STABILITY OF SOIL STRUCTURE

6.1 INTRODUCTION

In Chapter 5 we carried out a number of upper bound and lower bound calculation for the stability of slopes, walls, and foundations for undrained loading. In th chapter we will demonstrate similar calculations for drained loading.

We may recall that the distinction between drained and undrained loading wa concerned solely with the rate of loading compared with the rate of consolidation Thus for undrained loading the loading is very fast compared with the rate of con solidation and it is assumed that volumetric strains are zero; for this case por pressures will not, in general, be in equilibrium, but since the undrained analysi is carried out in terms of total stresses it is not required to know the magnitude o these pore pressures.

For drained loading, on the other hand, the rate of loading is very slow com pared with the rate of consolidation and it is assumed that *excess* pore pressure at zero. Drained stability analyses must be carried out in terms of effective, no total, stresses and hence it is required to know the magnitudes of the pore pressure everywhere throughout the soil. There are in general two cases which may occur First, if the water is everywhere stationary and there is no seepage flow then por pressures are simply hydrostatic and are found from

$$u = \gamma_w h \tag{6.1}$$

where h is the height to the water table. Second, if there is steady state seepage flow, pore pressures must be found by constructing a flownet and the pore pressure at a point is given by

$$u = \gamma_w (P - z) \tag{6.2}$$

where P is the potential and z is the elevation of the point above the arbitrary datum for potential. In either case of no seepage or of steady state seepage it is a relatively simple task to calculate the magnitudes of the pore pressures throughout the soil.

The change of effective stress in the soil caused by drag of the flowing water on the soil grains is given by Atkinson and Bransby (1978, pp. 94–5) as

$$\frac{d\sigma_s'}{ds} = \gamma_w i_s \tag{6.3}$$

where σ_s' is the effective stress due solely to the seepage, s is a distance along a low line measured positively in the direction of the flow and $i_s = -\,\mathrm{d}p/\mathrm{d}s$ is the hydraulic gradient. The seepage stress acts in the direction of flow and hence the magnitude and direction of the seepage stress at any point in a soil mass may be found from a flownet.

For drained loading the failure criterion corresponding to the critical state in terms of effective stress is

$$\tau'_n = \sigma'_n \tan \phi'_{cs} \qquad (6.4)$$

where ϕ'_{cs} is the critical state angle of friction as discussed in Sec. 2.3, the value of ϕ'_{cs} for a given soil may be assumed to be the same for triaxial compression, triaxial extension, and for plane strain and hence ϕ'_{cs} may be taken to be a soil constant. Thus values for ϕ'_{cs} for design may be found from the results of triaxial or shear box tests. If a site investigation reveals the presence of residual slip planes which may be reactivated then it may be necessary to replace ϕ'_{cs} with ϕ'_r, the residual friction angle. We will not discuss the methods for determining ϕ'_{cs} or ϕ'_r here and we will assume that, in some way, the appropriate friction angle of the soil has been found as a result of site investigations and laboratory testing.

As before, throughout this chapter it is assumed that the soil is isotropic and homogeneous. It will be stated whether the soil is dry or saturated but in either case its unit weight is γ. Each structure considered is regarded as being long normal to the page and so deformations and collapse occur in plane strain.

As soil strains at its critical state, volumetric strains are by definition zero and the value of the angle of dilation ψ must be zero also. Thus, as discussed in Sec. 2.8, the failure envelopes given by Eq. (6.4) do not serve as plastic potentials and the flow rule $\psi = 0 \neq \phi'_{cs}$ does not satisfy the normality condition. In order to proceed with upper and lower bound calculations for drained loading of soil structures we *assume* that the normality condition is satisfied and that $\psi = \phi'_{cs}$. The consequences of making this assumption, as discussed in Sec. 4.5, are that an upper bound calculated with $\psi = \phi'_{cs}$ is a true upper bound for soil but a lower bound calculated with $\psi = \phi'_{cs}$ may not be a true lower bound.

6.2 BOUND CALCULATIONS FOR DRAINED LOADING

The procedure for calculating upper and lower bounds for drained loading are similar to those used for undrained loading and described in the previous chapter. For an upper bound we are required to construct a compatible mechanism of plastic collapse and, for an increment of collapse, to equate the increment δE of work done by the external loads to the increment δW of work done by the internal stresses. For drained loading, a mechanism of plastic collapse may consist only of straight lines or logarithmic spirals, as discussed in Sec. 4.6. Any compatible mechanism of plastic collapse will do, but one which is close to the true collapse mechanism will give an upper bound close to the true value. We will assume that, a collapse, displacements due to continuous strain are negligible with displacements due to discontinuous slipping, and we consider only the case of plan strain. As shown in Sec. 2.8, the vector of relative displacement across a slip plan for drained loading makes an angle ψ with the direction of the slip plane, an displacement diagrams may be constructed as described in Sec. 4.8.

For perfectly plastic soil which satisfies the normality condition for draine loading, the increment of work δW done by all internal stresses is zero, as show in Sec. 4.7, and so, for every case of drained loading,

$$\delta W = 0 \tag{6.5}$$

From Sec. 4.7 the increment of work δE done by the external loads and stresse and by the body weight forces is given by

$$\delta E = \sum \delta \mathbf{w} \cdot \mathbf{F} + \int_A \delta \mathbf{w} \cdot (\mathbf{p} - u)\, dA + \int_V \delta \mathbf{w} \cdot (\gamma - \gamma_w)\, dV \tag{6.6}$$

where $\mathbf{F}$ are boundary forces, $\mathbf{p}$ are total stresses, u are water pressures acting on boundary areas A, γ is the unit weight of a volume V of soil, γ_w is the unit weight of water and $\delta \mathbf{w}$ are increments of displacement. Note that in Eq. (6.6) which is analogous to Eq. (5.4) for undrained loading, all the terms contain the scalar or dot product of vectors of force and displacement. As before, a displacement diagram may be used to obtain the components of the increments of displacement in the directions of the appropriate forces. For dry soil we simply put $u = \gamma_w = 0$ into Eq. (6.6), and γ is then the unit weight of the dry soil.

For a lower bound calculation we are required to find an equilibrium state of stress which nowhere exceeds the drained failure criterion and which is also in equilibrium with the external lower bound loads. The equilibrium state of stress may vary smoothly from place to place or there may be stress discontinuities. For a smoothly varying state of stress, from Eqs. (4.50) and (4.51),

$$\frac{\partial \sigma_z'}{\partial z} + \frac{\partial \tau_{xz}'}{\partial x} = \gamma - \frac{\partial u}{\partial z} \tag{6.7}$$

$$\frac{\partial \sigma_z'}{\partial x} + \frac{\partial \tau_{zx}'}{\partial z} = -\frac{\partial u}{\partial x} \tag{6.8}$$

where the z axis is positive downwards, so that the vertical effective stress σ_z' increases with depth. The change $\delta s'$ of the state of stress across a single discontinuity is given by

$$\delta s' = \pm 2s' \frac{\sin \delta\theta \sin \rho'}{\cos (\delta\theta - \rho')} \tag{6.9}$$

where the angle of shearing resistance ρ' mobilized on the plane of the discontinuity is given by

$$\sin \rho' = \cos \delta\theta \sin \phi'_{cs} \tag{6.10}$$

and where $\delta\theta$ is the rotation of the direction of the major principal effective stress across the discontinuity. The change of the state of stress through a fan of discontinuities is given by

$$\frac{ds'}{d\theta} = \pm 2s' \tan \phi'_{cs} \tag{6.11}$$

where $d\theta$ is the small rotation of the direction of the major principal effective stress through a small sector of the fan. In Eqs. (6.9) and (6.11) the positive signs apply for β discontinuities and the negative signs for α discontinuities, while the angle $\delta\theta$ is positive for counterclockwise rotations.

6.3 STABILITY OF SLOPES IN DRY SOIL

We begin by examining the case of a vertical slope cut into dry soil, as shown in Fig. 6.1. The unit weight of the dry soil is γ and its critical state angle of friction is ϕ'_{cs}. It is required to calculate the critical height H_c at which the slope collapses and the problem is similar to that discussed in Sec. 5.3 for the case of quick undrained excavation of a slope in saturated soil

1. Upper bound for a vertical slope in dry soil

Figure 6.2(a) shows a mechanism of plastic collapse consisting of a single straight slip plane at an arbitary angle 45° to the vertical and Fig. 6.2(b) shows the corresponding displacement diagram for an increment of displacement δw which makes an angle ψ with the slip plane where $\psi = \phi'_{cs}$ for a material which satisfies

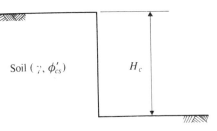

Soil (γ, ϕ'_{cs}) H_c

Figure 6.1 Simple vertical cut in soil.

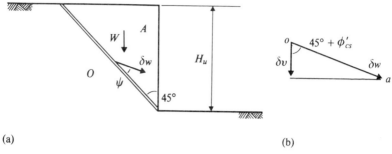

(a)   (b)

Figure 6.2 Mechanism of plastic collapse for a vertical cut slope.

the normality condition. The increment of work done by the internal stresses for drained loading is given by Eq. (6.5):

$$\delta W = 0 \qquad [6.5]$$

The only external loads are those due to body weight forces and hence, for dry soil, from Eq. (6.5) and from the geometry of Fig. 6.2, the increment of work done by the external loads is given by

$$\delta E = \int_V \delta w \cdot \gamma \, dV = \tfrac{1}{2} \gamma H_u^2 \, \delta v \qquad (6.12)$$

where H_u is an upper bound for the height at which the slope collapses. Hence equating $\delta W = \delta E$, we have

$$H_u = 0 \qquad (6.13)$$

Since Eq. (6.13) is an upper bound solution and, since negative values for the height of a cut slope have no meaning, the true height of a vertical cut slope in dry cohesionless soil is given by

$$H_c = 0 \qquad (6.14)$$

and thus *it is impossible to cut a vertical slope in dry cohesionless soil*. We might have anticipated this result from our experience of pouring dry sand from a bucket or pouring dry salt from a spoon; in both cases the dry 'soil' forms an angled slope and it is impossible to form a vertical cut. For drained loading, therefore, the appropriate problem is to examine the maximum slope angle for which soil remains stable.

Figure 6.3 shows part of an infinitely long slope in dry soil whose unit weight is γ and whose critical state angle of friction is ϕ'_{cs}. It is required to calculate the critical angle i_c at which the slope becomes unstable. Although the slope is assumed to be infinitely long failure takes place by the surface sliding parallel with the slope and the solution is relevant for real slopes, which must have a top and a bottom. The solution is applicable equally for slopes which are formed by excavation and for slopes which are formed by pouring soil into a heap.

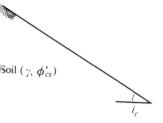

Soil (γ, ϕ'_{cs})

i_c

Figure 6.3 Infinite slope in dry soil.

Upper bound for an infinite slope in dry soil

Figure 6.4(a) shows a mechanism of plastic collapse for an infinitely long slope whose angle to the horizontal is an upper bound i_u. The mechanism is a single slip plane at a depth z measured vertically below the surface, and for convenience we consider a block of soil length l measured down the slope. For an infinitely long slope the forces on any such block are identical to those on any other similar block and hence the forces F_1 and F_2 which act on the vertical sides are equal and opposite. The displacement diagram for an increment of displacement δW is shown in Fig. 6.4(b), where the direction of the increment of displacement makes an angle $\psi = \phi'_{cs}$ to the slip plane.

For drained loading the increment of work done by the internal stresses for an increment of plastic collapse is

$$\delta W = 0 \qquad [6.5]$$

and, noting that $F_1 = F_2$, the increment of work done by the external loads for dry soil is

$$\delta E = \delta v \gamma V \qquad (6.15)$$

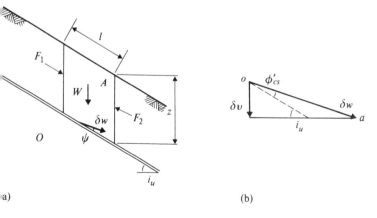

(a)   (b)

Figure 6.4 Mechanism of plastic collapse for an infinite slope in dry soil.

where $V = zl \cos i_u$ is the volume of the block. Hence, equating $\delta E = \delta W$, an upp
bound is given by

$$\delta v \, \gamma V = 0 \tag{6.1}$$

Now, since the volume V is non-zero, the upper bound is given by $\delta v = 0$ an
hence, from the geometry of Fig. 6.4(b), an upper bound for the critical slo
angle is given by

$$i_u = \phi_{cs}' \tag{6.1}$$

i.e. the increment of displacement δw is horizontal. The same result may be obtaine
by writing Eq. (6.16) in vector form as

$$\delta \mathbf{w} \cdot \mathbf{W} = 0 \tag{6.18}$$

where $\mathbf{W}$ is the vector of the body weight and its direction is vertical. The scalar
dot product of two non-zero vectors is zero when they are orthogonal and henc
the result follows from the geometry of Fig. 6.4(b).

3. Lower bound for an infinite slope in dry soil

Figure 6.5(a) shows an infinite slope whose angle with the horizontal is a low
bound i_l and we seek an equilibrium state of stress which nowhere exceeds th
drained failure criterion given by Eq. (6.4). Figure 6.5(a) shows a block of soi
length l, measured down the slope and depth z measured vertically; the forces o
the faces of the block are shown and, as before, the forces F_1 and F_2 are equa
and opposite for an infinite slope. Thus, resolving normal to and parallel with th
base AB the normal and shear forces N and T are

$$N = W \cos i_l = \gamma z l \cos^2 i_l \tag{6.19}$$

$$T = W \sin i_l = \gamma z l \sin i_l \cos i_l \tag{6.20}$$

For dry soil, where pore pressures are zero and total and effective stresses are equa
the effective normal and shear stresses on the plane AB are given by

$$\sigma_n' = \gamma z \cos^2 i_l \tag{6.21}$$

$$\tau_n' = \gamma z \sin i_l \cos i_l \tag{6.22}$$

and hence

$$\tau_n' = \sigma_n' \tan i_l \tag{6.23}$$

which is valid for all planes such as AB at any depth.

From Eq. (6.4) the limiting values of τ_n' and σ_n' are given by

$$\tau_n' = \sigma_n' \tan \phi_{cs}' \tag{6.24}$$

and hence a lower bound for the limiting slope angle is given by

$$i_l = \phi_{cs}' \tag{6.25}$$

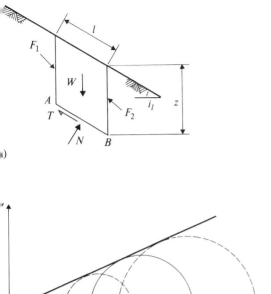

Figure 6.5 Equilibrium state of stress for an infinite slope in dry soil.

The Mohr's circle of effective stress for the state of stress in an element on AB is shown in Fig. 6.5(b); the circles shown with broken lines correspond to the states of stress in elements above and below AB. All the Mohr's circles just touch the drained failure envelope given by Eq. (6.3). The shear stresses τ_n' on the planes parallel with the slope are clockwise and so plot negatively in Fig. 6.5(b). The pole of the Mohr's circle is at P and hence we may calculate the stresses on any other plane in the slope using the construction described in Sec. 1.4; in particular, the normal and shear stresses on vertical planes are equal in magnitude to those on planes parallel to the slope.

From Eqs (6.17) and (6.27) the upper and lower bounds are equal and hence the critical slope angle for dry soil is

$$i_c = \phi_{cs}' \tag{6.26}$$

Since the bounds are equal, the solution is exact and the mechanism of plast
collapse shown in Fig. 6.4 corresponds to the state of stress shown in Fig. 6.
There is of course no point in seeking better bounds for an infinite slope.

The limiting angle i_c for a long slope is applicable to any slope in dry cohesio
less soil, whether it is excavated or built up. Thus soil poured from a point w
form a conical heap whose sides make the critical angle i_c to the horizontal an
such conical heaps may often be seen near sand and gravel workings where min
material is poured from a conveyor. Making use of Eq. (6.26), an estimate of tl
critical state angle of friction for a soil may be obtained by constructing a lor
slope which is just at its critical angle.

6.4 DRAINED STABILITY OF A SMOOTH WALL

The stability of a wall for drained loading is similar to the case for undrained load
ing discussed in Sec. 5.4. Figure 6.6(a) shows a smooth, rigid wall, height H, retai
ing dry soil whose unit weight is γ and whose critical state angle of friction is ϕ
and, as before, strong rock occurs at the base of the wall, so that slip mechanism
cannot pass below the wall and we need not examine states of stress in the roc
The wall is smooth so that shear stresses between it and the soil are zero.

The total horizontal force on the wall is P per unit length normal to the page
applied so that the wall moves horizontally without any rotation and without an
vertical displacement. The variation of P with horizontal displacement $\pm \delta h$
sketched in Fig. 6.6(b). As was the case for undrained loading, the maximum forc
P_p as the wall moves towards the soil is known as the *passive force* and the min
mum force P_a as the wall moves away from the soil is known as the *active forc*
these are associated with passive and active normal stresses between the soil and th
wall. For drained loading of soil, vertical slopes are impossible, as shown in th
previous section, and hence there cannot be tension cracks for either active c
passive loading.

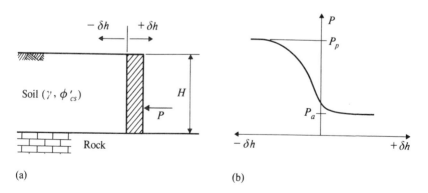

Figure 6.6 Displacement and failure of a retaining wall.

Upper bound for the active case

e begin by considering the active force P_a for which collapse occurs as the wall oves away from the soil. Figure 6.7(a) shows a mechanism of plastic collapse with single slip plane at an angle $(45° - \frac{1}{2}\phi'_{cs})^\dagger$ to the vertical and Fig. 6.7(b) is the splacement diagram for an increment of displacement δw at an angle $\psi = \phi'_{cs}$ to e slip plane. From geometry of Fig. 6.7(a) the volume V of the sliding wedge or unit thickness normal to the page) is given by

$$V = \tfrac{1}{2}\gamma H^2 \tan(45° - \tfrac{1}{2}\phi'_{cs}) \tag{6.27}$$

id, from the geometry of Fig. 6.7(b), the horizontal and vertical components of ꙃ are related by

$$\delta v = \delta h \tan(45° - \tfrac{1}{2}\phi'_{cs}) \tag{6.28}$$

ɔr dry soil $u = \gamma_w = 0$ and from Eqs. (6.5) and (6.6)

$$\delta W = 0 \tag{6.5}$$

$$\delta E = -P_{au}\,\delta h + \gamma V\,\delta v \tag{6.29}$$

ence, equating $\delta W = \delta E$ and making use of Eqs. (6.27) and (2.28), an upper ɔund for the active force is given by

$$P_{au} = \tfrac{1}{2}\gamma H^2 \tan^2(45° - \tfrac{1}{2}\phi'_{cs}) \tag{6.30}$$

his is an upper bound, and the wall must fail by moving away from the soil if the ᴄtive force falls below the value P_{au} given by Eq. (6.30). Again, as for undrained ᴀding, we must be careful to note that although P_{au} is an upper bound, collapse

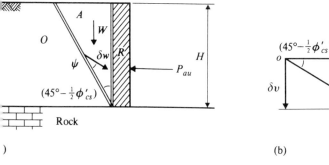

)   (b)

ɪgure 6.7 Mechanism of plastic collapse for a retaining wall: active case.

---

† It turns out that this choice for the angle of the slip plane gives the lowest possible upper ꙃund and it was made from prior knowledge. The method of calculation is similar for any ᴀsonable choice of angle but for other slip planes the calculated upper bounds will be further ɔm the true solution.

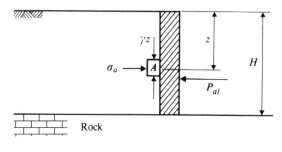

(a)

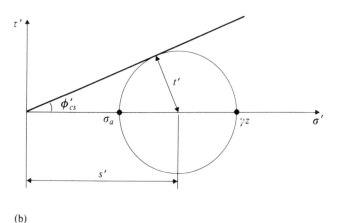

(b)

Figure 6.8 Equilibrium state of stress for a retaining wall: active case.

must occur if P_a is equal to or less than P_{au}; hence P_{au} given by Eq. (6.30) represents a *lower* limit to P_{ac}, the true active force at collapse.

2. Lower bound for the active case

Figure 6.8(a) shows a state of stress in which shear stresses on horizontal and vertical planes are zero, which clearly satisfies conditions at the soil surface and at the smooth wall. Hence, putting $\tau'_{xz} = \tau'_{zx} = 0$ and $u = 0$ for dry soil into Eqs (6.7) and (6.8), and integrating with the limits $\sigma'_z = 0$ at the surface and $\sigma'_x = \sigma_a$ at the wall, the stresses throughout the soil are given by

$$\sigma'_z = \gamma z \qquad \sigma'_x = \sigma_a \qquad (6.31)$$

where σ_a is the active pressure and total and effective stresses are equal. These are principal stresses and, for active loading, $\sigma'_z = \sigma'_1$ and $\sigma'_x = \sigma'_3$.

The Mohr's circle of stress for the element A in Fig. 6.8(a) is shown in Fig

3(b) and the circle does not cross the drained failure envelope. From the geo-
try of Fig. 6.8(b), or from Eq. (6.4), making use of Eqs. (1.24) and (1.25), we
ve

$$\sigma_a = \gamma z \, \frac{1 - \sin \phi'_{cs}}{1 + \sin \phi'_{cs}} = \gamma z \tan^2 (45° - \tfrac{1}{2}\phi'_{cs}) \tag{6.32}$$

e state of stress in Fig. 6.8(a) is in equilibrium and does not exceed the drained
lure criterion. Hence, a lower bound for the active force is given by

$$P_{al} = \int_0^H \sigma_a \, dz = \tfrac{1}{2}\gamma H^2 \tan^2 (45° - \tfrac{1}{2}\phi'_{cs}) \tag{6.33}$$

is is a lower bound and the wall cannot fail by moving away from the soil unless
e active force falls below the value of P_{al} given by Eq. (6.35). We must be careful
note that, although P_{al} is a lower bound, collapse cannot occur if the active
rce is equal to or greater than the value of P_{al} given by Eq. (6.33); hence P_{al}
presents an *upper* limit to P_{ac}, the true active force at collapse. This lower bound
lculation for the active pressure on a smooth wall for drained loading, and the
rresponding calculation for the passive pressure, are essentially the same as those
rried out by Rankine (1857), although of course the bound theorems were not
own then. Nor was the principle of effective stress, and Rankine's original calc-
ations were therefore strictly applicable only for dry soil. Comparing Eqs. (6.30)
d (6.33), we have $P_{au} = P_{al}$, and hence an exact solution for the active force at
llapse is

$$P_{ac} = \tfrac{1}{2}\gamma H^2 \tan^2 (45° - \tfrac{1}{2}\phi'_{cs}) \tag{6.34}$$

d the mechanism of collapse shown in Fig. 6.7(a) must correspond to the state
stress shown in Fig. 6.8(a).

Upper bound for the passive case

e now consider the passive force P_p for which collapse occurs as the wall moves
wards the soil. Figure 6.9(a) shows a mechanism of plastic collapse consisting of
single straight slip plane at an angle $(45° + \tfrac{1}{2}\phi'_{cs})$ to the vertical and the displace-
ent diagram for an increment δw of displacement is shown in Fig. 6.9(b). Pro-
eding as before,

$$\delta W = 0 \tag{6.5}$$

$$\delta E = P_{pu} \, \delta h - \tfrac{1}{2}\gamma H^2 \tan (45° + \tfrac{1}{2}\phi'_{cs}) \, \delta v \tag{6.35}$$

here P_{pu} is an upper bound for the passive force. Hence, equating $\delta W = \delta E$, and
om the geometry of Fig. 6.9(b), we have

$$P_{pu} = \tfrac{1}{2}\gamma H^2 \tan^2 (45° + \tfrac{1}{2}\phi'_{cs}) \tag{6.36}$$

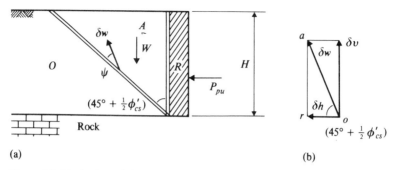

Figure 6.9 Mechanism of plastic collapse for retaining wall: passive case.

4. Lower bound for the passive case

Figure 6.10(a) shows a state of stress in which shear stresses on vertical and ho
zontal planes are zero, which clearly satisfies conditions at the soil surface and
the smooth wall. Hence, putting $\tau'_{xz} = \tau'_{zx} = 0$ and $u = 0$ for dry soil into E
(6.7) and (6.8), and integrating with the limits $\sigma'_z = 0$ at the surface and $\sigma'_x = \sigma_p$
the wall, the stresses throughout the soil are given by

$$\sigma'_z = \gamma z \qquad \sigma'_x = \sigma_p \qquad (6.3$$

where σ_p is the passive pressure and total and effective stresses are equal. The sta
of stress shown in Fig. 6.10(a) is similar to that shown in Fig. 6.8(a) except th
$\sigma'_z = \sigma'_3$ and $\sigma'_x = \sigma'_1$. The Mohr's circle for the element A in Fig. 6.10(a) is sho
in Fig. 6.10(b) and the circle does not cross the drained failure envelope. From t
geometry of Fig. 6.10(b) or otherwise,

$$\sigma_p = \gamma z \, \frac{1 + \sin \phi'_{cs}}{1 - \sin \phi'_{cs}} = \gamma z \tan^2 (45° + \tfrac{1}{2}\phi'_{cs}) \qquad (6.3$$

The state of stress in Fig. 6.10(a) is in equilibrium and does not exceed the drain
failure criterion. Thus, a lower bound for the passive force is given by

$$P_{pl} = \int_0^H \sigma_p \, dz = \tfrac{1}{2}\gamma H^2 \tan^2 (45° + \tfrac{1}{2}\phi'_{cs}) \qquad (6.3$$

Comparing Eqs (6.38) and (6.41) we have $P_{pu} = P_{pl}$ and hence the exact val
of the passive force at collapse is

$$P_{pc} = \tfrac{1}{2}\gamma H^2 \tan^2 (45° + \tfrac{1}{2}\phi'_{cs}) \qquad (6.4$$

and the mechanism of collapse shown in Fig. 6.9(a) corresponds to the state
stress shown in Fig. 6.10(a).

For calculations of earth pressure it is convenient to define a coefficient
earth pressure as

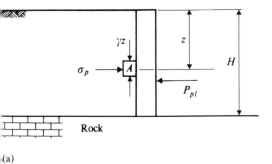

(a)

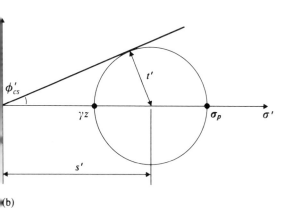

(b)

Figure 6.10 Equilibrium state of stress for a retaining wall: passive case.

$$K = \frac{\sigma_h'}{\sigma_v'} \tag{6.41}$$

We have already discussed the special case of K_0, the *coefficient of earth pressure at rest* which applies for zero horizontal strain. We may also define a *coefficient of active earth pressure*:

$$K_a = \frac{\sigma_a'}{\sigma_v'} = \tan^2 (45° - \tfrac{1}{2}\phi_{cs}') \tag{6.42}$$

and a *coefficient of passive earth pressure*:

$$K_p = \frac{\sigma_p'}{\sigma_v'} = \tan^2 (45° + \tfrac{1}{2}\phi_{cs}') \tag{6.43}$$

It should be noted that values of K_a and K_p given by $\tan^2 (45° \pm \tfrac{1}{2}\phi_{cs}')$ are valid only for the smooth wall supporting dry soil with a horizontal surface as shown in Fig. 6.6(a); for other cases, values of K_a and K_p will be different.

6.5 DRAINED STABILITY OF A FOUNDATION

The problem of the stability of a foundation for drained loading is similar to th
for the undrained case discussed in Sec. 5.5. Figure 6.11(a) shows a section of
long foundation, width B, at the surface of a soil whose unit weight is γ and who
critical state angle of friction is ϕ'_{cs}. Loads F per unit length normal to the pa
cause a total bearing pressure $q = F/B$, which is assumed to be uniform, and a u
form constant total stress p is applied to the soil surface outside the area of t
foundation.[†] For a constant value of surface pressure p, the relationship betwe
settlement ρ and bearing pressure is approximately as shown in Fig. 6.11(b); t
collapse pressure $q_c = F_c/B$ is known as the bearing capacity of the foundation.
this section we suppose that the load F is increased very slowly so the loading
drained and q_c is known as the drained bearing capacity of the foundation. T
drained bearing capacity will almost certainly differ from the undrained beari
capacity of the same foundation discussed in Sec. 5.5.

For the case of drained loading of a foundation it is convenient to separa
the contributions made to the bearing capacity by the unit weight of the soil an
by any surface pressures. First we will consider the bearing capacity of a foundati

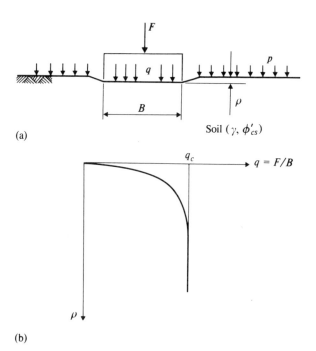

(a)

(b)

Figure 6.11 Settlement and collapse of a foundation: drained loading

† See footnote on p. 164.

a weightless dry soil for which $\gamma = \gamma_w = u = 0$, where the stability of the found-ion is due solely to a total stress p applied to the soil surface outside the area of e foundation. We will consider a number of different mechanisms of collapse and umber of states of stress in order to illustrate several different calculations.

Upper bound for a foundation

gure 6.12(a) shows a mechanism of plastic collapse similar to that shown in Fig. 17, and Fig. 6.12(b) shows the displacement diagram for an increment of dis-acement δw_f of the foundation. The increments of relative displacement across

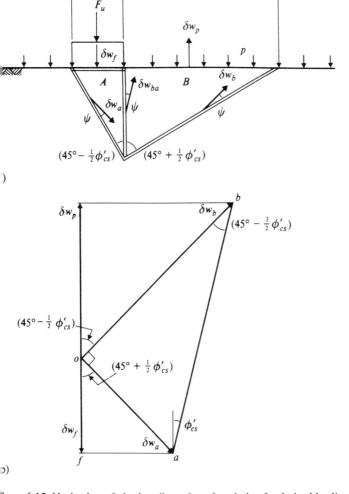

Figure 6.12 Mechanism of plastic collapse for a foundation for drained loading.

each slip plane make angles $\psi = \phi'_{cs}$ with the appropriate slip planes. The choices the angles $(45° \pm \frac{1}{2}\phi'_{cs})$ defining the slip planes were influenced by the resu obtained in the previous section for the active and passive forces on a retaining wa but of course the slip planes may be put at any angles which produce a compatib mechanism of plastic collapse. From the geometry of Fig. 6.12(a) the dimensi C is given by

$$C = B \tan^2 (45° + \tfrac{1}{2}\phi'_{cs}) \qquad (6.4$$

and from the geometry of Fig. 6.12(b) the vertical components of the surfa displacements are given by

$$\delta w_p = \delta w_f \tan (45° + \tfrac{1}{2}\phi'_{cs}) \tan (45° + \tfrac{3}{2}\phi'_{cs}) \qquad (6.4.$$

For dry and weightless soil, $u = \gamma = 0$, and from Eqs. (6.5) and (6.6)

$$\delta W = 0 \qquad [6.5]$$

and

$$\delta E = F_u\, \delta w_f - pC\, \delta w_p \qquad (6.4\text{\textbullet}$$

Hence, equating δW and δE and making use of Eqs. (6.44) and (6.45) we obta an upper bound for the collapse load:

$$F_u = pB \tan^3 (45° + \tfrac{1}{2}\phi'_{cs}) \tan (45° + \tfrac{3}{2}\phi'_{cs}) \qquad (6.4^*$$

2. Lower bound for a foundation

Figure 6.13(a) shows a state of stress with two discontinuities similar to that show in Fig. 5.17(a) for undrained loading. The discontinuity on the right is an α di continuity and that on the left is a β discontinuity and the state of stress is sym metrical about the centreline of the foundation. Shear stresses on horizontal an vertical planes are zero and, for weightless soil, the vertical stresses in regions and III are

$$\sigma'_x = p \qquad (6.48$$

the vertical stresses in regions II and IV are

$$\sigma'_z = q_1 \qquad (6.49$$

and these are principal stresses.

Mohr's circles of effective stress for elements A and B are shown in Fig. 6.13(t and, for weightless soil, these circles represent the stresses throughout the regions and II. Both Mohr's circles just touch the drained failure envelope and they satisf conditions of equilibrium across the α discontinuity where the point a in Fig 6.13(b) represents the state of stress on the discontinuity. From the geometry c Fig. 6.13(b), we have

$$\frac{q_1}{\sigma'_a} = \frac{\sigma'_a}{p} = \frac{1 + \sin \phi'_{cs}}{1 - \sin \phi'_{cs}} \qquad (6.50$$

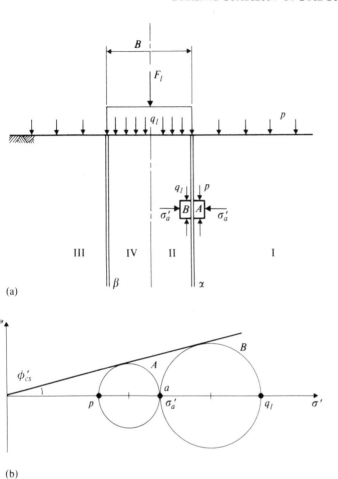

(a)

(b)

Figure 6.13 Equilibrium state of stress for a foundation for drained loading.

and hence

$$F_l = pB \tan^4 (45° + \tfrac{1}{2}\phi'_{cs}) \tag{6.51}$$

The state of stress in Fig. 6.13(a) is everywhere in equilibrium and nowhere exceeds the drained failure criterion, and hence F_l given by Eq. (6.49) is a lower bound for the collapse of the foundation.

From Eqs. (6.47) and (6.51) the collapse load F_c is given by

$$pB \tan^3 (45° + \tfrac{1}{2}\phi'_{cs}) \tan (45° + \tfrac{3}{2}\phi'_{cs}) \geqslant F_c \geqslant pB \tan^4 (45° + \tfrac{1}{2}\phi'_{cs}) \tag{6.52}$$

3. Upper bound for a foundation

Another mechanism of plastic collapse is shown in Fig. 6.14(a). It is similar to the

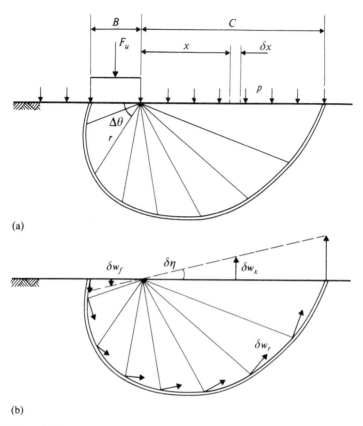

(a)

(b)

Figure 6.14 Mechanism of plastic collapse for a foundation for drained loading.

circular arc shown in Fig. 5.16 for undrained loading except that, for drained load
ing, the slip surface is a logarithmic spiral given by Eq. (4.28). In Fig. 6.14(a) the
foundation rotates about one edge instead of remaining horizontal as in Fig. 6.12(a)
but both mechanisms are equally allowable. From Eq. (4.28), with $\psi = \phi'_{cs}$, radii
of the spiral are given by

$$r = B \exp (\Delta\theta \tan \phi'_{cs}) \tag{6.53}$$

and hence the dimension C in Fig. 6.14(a) is given by

$$C = B \exp (\pi \tan \phi'_{cs}) \tag{6.54}$$

For an increment of rotation $\delta\eta$, all increments of displacement are normal to the
radii of the spiral and are given by

$$\delta w_r = r \, \delta\eta \tag{6.55}$$

where δw_r is the increment of displacement of a point within the mechanism at a dius r from the origin of the spiral. For dry weightless soil $u = \gamma = 0$ and from qs. (6.5) and (6.6)

$$\delta W = 0 \qquad [6.5]$$

nd

$$\delta E = F_u \, \delta w_f - \int_0^C p \, \delta w_x \, dx \qquad (6.56)$$

here F_u is an upper bound for the collapse load of the foundation. Hence equating $\delta W = \delta E$ and making use of Eq. (6.55), we have

$$F_u \cdot \tfrac{1}{2} B \, \delta \eta = \int_0^C p \, \delta \eta \, x \, dx = \tfrac{1}{2} p C^2 \, \delta \eta \qquad (6.57)$$

nd, from Eq. (6.56)

$$F_u = pB \exp \left(2\pi \tan \phi_{cs}'\right) \qquad (6.58)$$

4. Lower bound for a foundation

Figure 6.15(a) shows a state of stress with four discontinuities similar to that shown n Fig. 5.19(a) for undrained loading. The discontinuities to the right of the centreine are α discontinuities and those to the left are β discontinuities. Shear stresses on horizontal and vertical planes in regions I and III are zero, and for weightless dry soil the vertical stress in region I is

$$\sigma_z' = p \qquad (6.59)$$

the vertical stress in region III is

$$\sigma_z' = q_l \qquad (6.60)$$

and these are principal stresses. The positions of the discontinuities in Fig. 6.15(a) may be found from the analysis in Sec. (4.11) with $n = 2$. The total rotation of the direction of the major principal stress from region I to region III is $\Delta\theta = 90°$, and hence from Eq. (4.72) we have $\delta\theta = 45°$ for each discontinuity. From Eq. (4.57) we have

$$P = 90 - \delta\theta = 45° \qquad (6.61)$$

and hence the angle of shearing resistance ρ' mobilized on each of the discontinuities, given by Eq. (4.59) is

$$\sin \rho' = \sin P \sin \phi_{cs}' = \frac{1}{\sqrt{2}} \sin \phi_{cs}' \qquad (6.62)$$

Thus, from Eqs. (4.70), the angles between the directions of the major principal stresses and the normals to the discontinuities are given by

$$\theta_a = 45° + \rho'/2 - \delta\theta/2 \qquad (6.63)$$

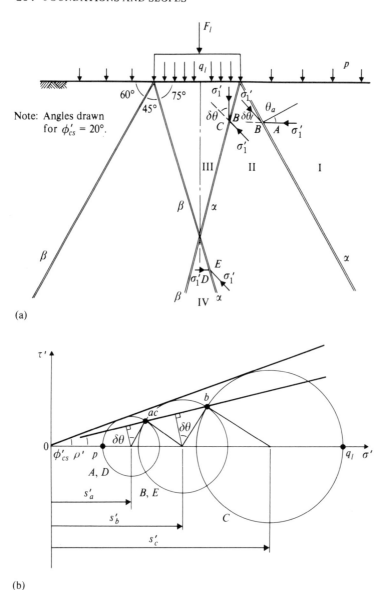

(a)

(b)

Figure 6.15 Equlibrium state of stress for a foundation for drained loading.

$$\theta_b = 45° + \rho'/2 + \delta\theta/2 \qquad (6.64)$$

Taking an arbitrary value of $\phi'_{cs} = 20°$, we have $\rho' \approx 14°$ and hence $\theta_a \approx 30°$ and $\theta_b \approx 75°$ and the angles of the discontinuities are as shown in Fig. 6.15(a). Mohr's circles of effective stress for the elements A to E are shown in Fig. 6.15(b). Each just touches the drained failure envelope and the circles satisfy conditions of quilibrium across α discontinuities for rotations $\delta\theta = 45°$ of the directions of the major principal stress. The points a to c represent the normal and shear stresses n the discontinuities and in each case the mobilized angle of shearing resistance is '. From Eq. (4.63) the centres of adjacent Mohr's circles are related by

$$\frac{s_b'}{s_a'} = \frac{s_c'}{s_b'} = \frac{\sin (P + \rho')}{\sin (P - \rho')} \tag{6.65}$$

'here $P = 45°$ and ρ' is given by Eq. (6.62). Hence, noting that $\sin P = \cos P = /\sqrt{2}$ we have

$$\frac{s_c'}{s_a'} = \left[\frac{\sin (P + \rho')}{\sin (P - \rho')} \right]^2 = \tan^2(45° + \rho') \tag{6.66}$$

'rom the geometry of a Mohr's circle

$$\frac{s_a'}{p} = \frac{1}{1 - \sin \phi_{cs}'} \qquad \frac{s_c'}{q_l} = \frac{1}{1 + \sin \phi_{cs}'} \tag{6.67}$$

nd hence

$$\frac{q_l}{p} = \frac{s_c'}{s_a'} \tan^2 (45° + \tfrac{1}{2}\phi_{cs}') \tag{6.68}$$

Thus, from Eqs (6.68) and (6.66), a lower bound for the collapse load is given by

$$F_l = pB \tan^2 (45° + \rho') \tan^2 (45° + \tfrac{1}{2}\phi_{cs}') \tag{6.69}$$

vhere

$$\sin \rho' = \frac{1}{\sqrt{2}} \sin \phi_{cs}' \tag{6.64}$$

It is of course possible to eliminate ρ' between Eqs. (6.62) and (6.69) but the resulting expression is inconvenient.

From Eqs. (6.58) and (6.69) the collapse load F_c is given by

$$pB \exp (2\pi \tan \phi_{cs}') \geqslant F_c \geqslant pB \tan^2 (45° + \rho') \tan^2 (45° + \tfrac{1}{2}\phi_{cs}') \tag{6.70}$$

It is not immediately obvious whether the bounds given by Eq. (6.70) are any better than those given by Eq. (6.52). In order to investigate this point, both sets of bounds are plotted against ϕ_{cs}' in Fig. 6.16, where it is at once apparent that the upper and lower bounds given by Eq. (6.70) fall within, and are thus better than, those given by Eq. (6.52).

5. Upper bound for a foundation

Figure 6.17(a) shows a mechanism of plastic collapse similar to that shown in Fig. 5.20 except that, for drained loading, the slip fan is bounded by a logarithmic spiral. Figure 6.17(b) shows the corresponding displacement diagram for an increment δw_f of settlement of the foundation. For a fan angle $\theta_f = 90°$ as shown in Fig. 6.17(a) we have, from Eqs (4.43) and (4.44),

$$r_b = r_a \exp (\tfrac{1}{2}\pi \tan \phi_{cs}') \tag{6.71}$$

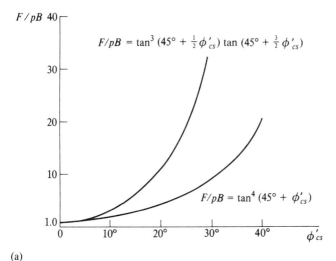

(a)

(b)

Figure 6.16 Upper and lower bounds for a foundation for drained loading. (a) From Eq. (6.52) (b) From Eq. (6.70).

$$\delta w_b = \delta w_a \exp \left(\tfrac{1}{2}\pi \tan \phi'_{cs}\right) \tag{6.72}$$

We should note that, unlike the mechanism shown in Fig. 6.14, the radii of the fan in Fig. 6.17(a) do not rotate but instead suffer increments of displacement as shown in Fig. 4.20(b). From the geometry of Figs. 6.17(a) and (b), and making use of Eqs. (6.71) and (6.72), we have

$$C = B \tan \left(45° + \tfrac{1}{2}\phi'_{cs}\right) \exp \left(\tfrac{1}{2}\pi \tan \phi'_{cs}\right) \tag{6.73}$$

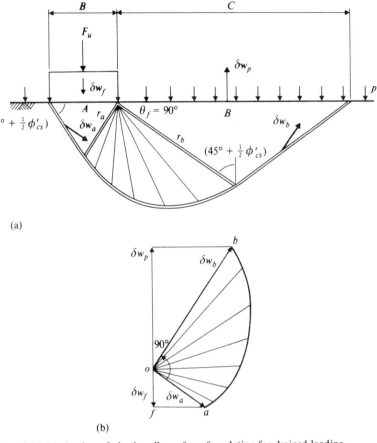

(a)

(b)

Figure 6.17 Mechanism of plastic collapse for a foundation for drained loading.

$$\delta w_p = \delta w_f \tan (45° + \tfrac{1}{2}\phi'_{cs}) \exp (\tfrac{1}{2}\pi \tan \phi'_{cs}) \qquad (6.74)$$

For dry weightless soil, $u = \gamma = 0$ and from Eqs (6.5) and (6.6)

$$\delta W = 0 \qquad [6.5]$$

and

$$\delta E = F_u \, \delta w_f - pC \, \delta w_p \qquad (6.75)$$

where F_u is an upper bound for the collapse load of the foundation. Hence, equating $\delta E = \delta W$ and making use of Eqs. (6.73) and (6.74), we have

$$F_u = pB \tan^2 (45° + \tfrac{1}{2}\phi'_{cs}) \exp (\pi \tan \phi'_{cs}) \qquad (6.76)$$

6. Lower bound for a foundation

Figure 6.18(a) shows a state of stress similar to that shown in Fig. 5.21(a), with two fans marked II and IV. Fan II consists of α discontinuities and fan IV consists

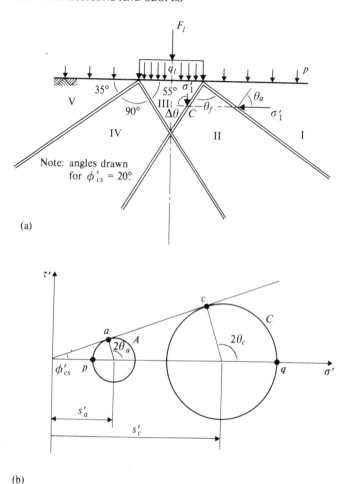

(a)

(b)

Figure 6.18 Equilibrium state of stress for a foundation for drained loading.

of β discontinuities and the state of stress is symmetrical about the centreline of the foundation. Shear stresses on horizontal and vertical planes are zero in regions I and III and, for weightless soil, the vertical stress in region I is

$$\sigma_z' = p \tag{6.77}$$

and the vertical stress in region III is

$$\sigma_z' = q_l \tag{6.78}$$

and these are principal stresses. The position of the fan in Fig. 6.18(a) may be found from the analysis in Sec. 4.11. The total rotation of the direction of the major principal stress from region I to region III is $\Delta\theta = 90°$ and hence the fan gle is $\theta_f = 90°$. The angles between the directions of the major principal stresses d the normals to the outer discontinuities of the fan are given by

$$\theta_b = \theta_a = 45° + \tfrac{1}{2}\phi'_{cs} \tag{6.79}$$

aking an arbitary value of $\phi'_{cs} = 20°$, the outer discontinuities of the fan are at 5° and 55° to the horizontal, as shown in Fig. 6.18(b). Mohr's circles of effective ress for elements at A and C in Fig. 6.18(a) are shown in Fig. 6.18(b). Each just uches the drained failure envelope and the points a and c represent the states f stress on the discontinuities a and c in Fig. 6.18(a) which bound the fan. There an infinity of Mohr's circles between the limiting circles A and C, each coresponding to the states of stress in elements along radii in the stress fan. From Eq. (4.73) ith $\Delta\theta = 90°$, the centres of the Mohr's circles are related by

$$\frac{s'_c}{s'_a} = \exp(\pi \tan \phi'_{cs}) \tag{6.80}$$

nd from Eq. (6.68) we have

$$\frac{q_l}{p} = \frac{s'_c}{s'_a} \tan^2(45° + \tfrac{1}{2}\phi'_{cs}) \tag{6.81}$$

hus, from Eqs. (6.80) and (6.81) a lower bound for the collapse load is given by

$$F_l = pB \tan^2(45° + \tfrac{1}{2}\phi'_{cs}) \exp(\pi \tan \phi'_{cs}) \tag{6.82}$$

t must be noted that in this analysis we have not examined the state of stress in egion VI in Fig. 6.18(a), where the stress fans II and IV overlap, and therefore we annot yet be certain that F_l given by Eq. (6.82) is a true lower bound. The problem is similar to that considered in Sec. 5.5 for a foundation for undrained loading nd again a complete analysis which examines the state of stress in region VI is engthy. An analysis which examines the state of stress everywhere below a foundation for drained loading but which uses a different approach to that used here is given by Chen (1975, Chapter 6) and this analysis gives a lower bound which is he same as that given by Eq. (6.82).

From Eqs (6.76) and (6.82) we have $F_u = F_l$ and hence the collapse load of he foundation is given by

$$F_c = pB \tan^2(45° + \tfrac{1}{2}\phi'_{cs}) \exp(\pi \tan \phi'_{cs}) \tag{6.83}$$

nd the mechanism of plastic collapse as shown in Fig. 6.17(a) corresponds to the state of stress shown in Fig. 6.18(a).

7. Bearing capacity factors for foundations on weightless soil

It is convenient to define a *bearing capacity factor* as

$$J = \frac{F_c}{pB} \tag{6.84}$$

and hence, for dry weightless soil

$$J = \tan^2 (45° + \tfrac{1}{2}\phi'_{cs}) \exp(\pi \tan \phi'_{cs}) \tag{6.8}$$

The value of J given by Eq. (6.85) is shown plotted against ϕ'_{cs} in Fig. 6.19. If w compare Figs. 6.14 and 6.19, the exact solution given by Eq. (6.83) falls betwee the upper and lower bounds given by Eqs. (6.52) and (6.70).

We now turn our attention to the case where the soil is not assumed to I weightless, and investigate the collapse of a foundation on dry soil whose un weight is $\gamma > 0$ and for which the surface pressure is $p = 0$.

8. Lower bound for a foundation

Figure 6.20(a) shows a state of stress with two discontinuities similar to that show in Fig. 6.13. Shear stresses on horizontal and vertical planes are zero and henc from Eqs. (6.7) and (6.8), the vertical stresses in regions I and III are

$$\sigma'_z = \gamma z \tag{6.86}$$

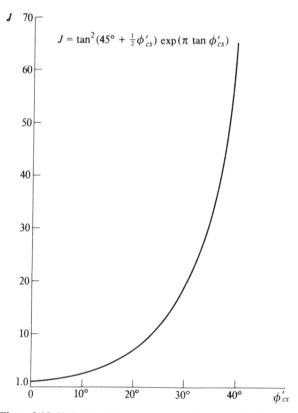

Figure 6.19 Variation of bearing capacity factor J with ϕ'_{cs} from Eq. (6.85).

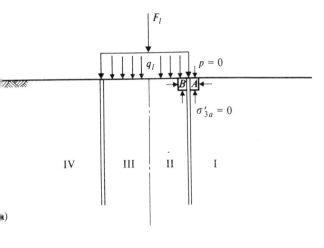

a)

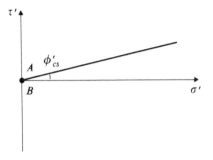

b)

Figure 6.20 Equilibrium state of stress for a foundation for drained loading.

and the vertical stresses in regions II and IV are

$$\sigma_z' = q_1 + \gamma z \tag{6.87}$$

The Mohr's circle of effective stress for the element A in Fig. 6.20(a) can only be the point A in Fig. 6.20(b) since, for $z = 0$, we have $\sigma_z' = 0$ from Eq. (6.86) and, similarly, the Mohr's circle of effective stress for the element B in Fig. 6.20(a) can only be the same point A in Fig. 6.20(b). Thus from Eq. (6.87) we have $q_1 = 0$, and, for drained loading of a foundation at the surface of a soil for which $p = 0$, the best lower bound solution available is given by

$$F_1 = 0 \tag{6.88}$$

This is a disappointing result but it *is* a lower bound and the true collapse load F_c should be greater than zero. In practice, a foundation placed at the surface of dry soil immediately settles a small distance ρ. Hence at the level of the base of the

foundation the vertical stress is $p = \gamma\rho$ and the appropriate lower bound calculatic
is that given by Eq. (6.82).

9. Upper bound for a foundation

In order to calculate an upper bound for a foundation on dry soil it would be log
cal to choose the mechanism shown in Fig. 6.18(a), which gave an exact solutio
for the case when $p > 0$ and $\gamma = 0$. For the case when $p = 0$ and $\gamma > 0$ and for dr
soil for which $u = 0$, we have, from Eqs. (6.5) and (6.6),

$$\delta W = 0 \qquad\qquad [6.5]$$

$$\delta E = F_u \, \delta w_f + \int_V \delta \mathbf{w}_\gamma \cdot \gamma \, dV \qquad\qquad (6.89$$

where the integral is taken for both triangular wedges and for the slip fan. Wit
the mechanism of collapse shown in Fig. 6.17(a) the integral in Eq. (6.89) is alge
braically lengthy and it is slightly simpler, and perfectly adequate for illustrativ
purposes, to take the rotational mechanism shown in Fig. 6.21(a).

Fig. 6.21(b) shows a sector of the mechanism whose weight is $W = \frac{1}{2}\gamma r^2 \, \delta$
acting at a distance $\frac{2}{3}r$ from the centre of rotation at O. For an increment of rotatio
$\delta\eta$, the increment of displacement $\delta w_\gamma = \frac{2}{3}r \, \delta\eta$ and is normal to the radius. Hence
from Eq. (6.89) we have

$$\delta E = F_u \tfrac{1}{2} B \, \delta\eta + \int_0^\pi \tfrac{2}{3} r \, \delta\eta \cos\theta \, \tfrac{1}{2}\gamma r^2 \, d\theta \qquad\qquad (6.90$$

where, making use of Eq. (4.28), with $\psi = \phi'_{cs}$, we obtain

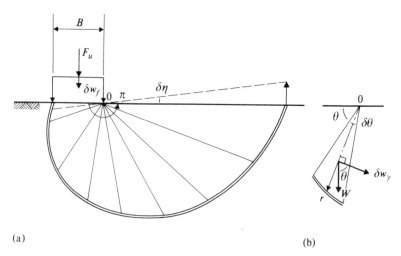

(a)   (b)

Figure 6.21 Mechanism of plastic collapse for a foundation for drained loading.

$$r = B \exp (\theta \tan \phi'_{cs}) \tag{6.91}$$

ence, equating $\delta W = \delta E$, we find that an upper bound for the collapse load is ven by

$$F_u = \tfrac{1}{2}\gamma B^2 G_u \tag{6.92}$$

here

$$G_u = -\tfrac{4}{3} \int_0^\pi \exp (3\theta \tan \phi'_{cs}) \cos \theta \, d\theta \tag{6.93}^\dagger$$

nd

$$G_u = \frac{4 \tan \phi'_{cs}}{1 + 9 \tan^2 \phi'_{cs}} [1 + \exp (3\pi \tan \phi'_{cs})] \tag{6.94}$$

0. Bearing capacity factors for soil with unit weight $\gamma > 0$

t is convenient to define a bearing capacity factor as

$$G = \frac{F_c}{\tfrac{1}{2}\gamma B^2} \tag{6.95}$$

nd thus we have an upper bound G_u given by Eq. (6.94) and a lower bound $G_l =$ given by Eq. (6.88). The values of G_u and G_l given by Eqs. (6.94) and (6.88) are hown plotted against ϕ'_{cs} in Fig. 6.22. The upper and lower bounds for the bearing apacity factor G given by Eqs. (6.88) and (6.94) and shown in Fig. 6.22 are lisappointing compared with the exact soultion found for the bearing capacity actor J given by Eq. (6.85). There is no possibility of increasing the value of G_l bove zero for the case when $p = 0$ without violating the failure conditions in the oil beneath the edge of the foundation; but, by examining different mechanisms of plastic collapse, we may reduce the values of G_u and so obtain better upper ounds. We will not pursue these calculations further here and we will be content

---

$\dagger$ The integral in Eq. (6.93) may be evaluated by integrating by parts, twice; hence

$$I = \int \exp (3\theta \tan \phi'_{cs}) \cos \theta \, d\theta$$

$$= \frac{\cos \theta}{3 \tan \phi'_{cs}} \exp (3\theta \tan \phi'_{cs}) + \frac{1}{3 \tan \phi'_{cs}} \int \exp (3\theta \tan \phi'_{cs}) \sin \theta \, d\theta$$

$$= \frac{\cos \theta}{3 \tan \phi'_{cs}} \exp (3\theta \tan \phi'_{cs}) + \frac{1}{3 \tan \phi'_{cs}} \left[\frac{\sin \theta}{3 \tan \phi'_{cs}} \exp (3\theta \tan \phi'_{cs}) - \frac{I}{3 \tan \phi'_{cs}} \right]$$

$$= \frac{1}{1 + 9 \tan^2 \phi'_{cs}} [\exp (3\theta \tan \phi'_{cs}) \{3 \tan \phi'_{cs} \cos \theta + \sin \theta \}]$$

and, with the limits $\theta = 0 \to \pi$,

$$I = - \frac{3 \tan \phi'_{cs}}{1 + 9 \tan^2 \phi'_{cs}} [1 + \exp (3\pi \tan \phi'_{cs})]$$

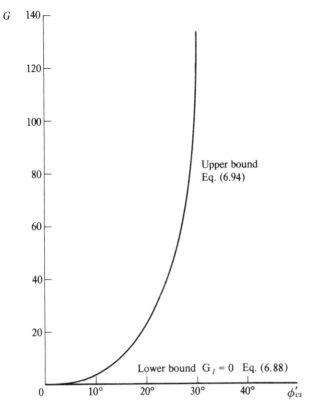

Figure 6.22 Variation of bearing capacity factor G with ϕ'_{cs}.

with having demonstrated all the relevant procedures for calculating upper and lower bounds for the failure of shallow foundations on dry soil.

Although it is of course not strictly correct to use superposition here the bearing capacity of a foundation on a soil with self weight $\gamma > 0$ and surface pressures $p > 0$ is usually estimated by summing the collapse loads given by Eqs. (6.84) and (6.95) as

$$F_c = \tfrac{1}{2}\gamma B^2 G + pBJ \qquad (6.96)$$

where G and J are bearing capacity factors. For plane strain, J is given by Eq. (6.85) and the value of G lies between the lower bound $G_l = 0$ and the upper bound G_u given by Eq. (6.94). We have now obtained the general form of the bearing capacity equation given by Terzaghi (1943, Chapter VIII) and by most texts on soil mechanics and foundation engineering. We must be careful to appreciate that Eq. (6.96) was obtained for drained loading of *dry* soil and it is not applicable for any other condition. For undrained loading of saturated soil the appropriate bearing capacity equation is Eq. (5.97) while for drained loading of saturated soil Eq. (6.96) must be modified to account for the effects of pore pressures. The values of G and J given by Eqs. (6.85) and (6.94) are for plane strain loading of a foundation placed

the surface, and different values will be required for square, circular, or rec-
ngular foundations and for those buried below the soil surface.

.6 BOUND CALCULATIONS FOR SATURATED SOIL

o far, in calculating the stability of slopes, walls, and foundations for drained
ading, we have considered only dry soil and we will now investigate how these
alculations may be modified for saturated soil to account for the presence of pore
ressures. As noted in Sec. 6.1, there are two cases to be considered. There is one
ase in which the water is stationary and pore pressures are everywhere hydro-
atic and there is another case where there is steady state seepage so that pore
ressures may be found by constructing a flownet. Both cases are fully drained,
nce pore pressures do not change with time and excess pore pressures are zero,
ut in either case we must be able to calculate the pore pressures everywhere
hroughout the soil and so proceed with calculations in terms of effective stress.

. Stability of a foundation on saturated soil

'igure 6.23 shows a foundation of width B, depth D, and weight W_f founded on
he bed of a river or lake or on the sea bottom, where the depth of water is H_w.
The load F is applied slowly until collapse occurs at a load F_c, when pore pressures
re everywhere hydrostatic, as shown by the level of water in a typical standpipe
Fig. 6.23).

For an upper bound calculation for drained loading of saturated soil, we make
se of Eqs. (6.5) and (6.6). Since the water remains stationary for drained loading,
o work is done by the water pressures. The external loads are the upper bound
ollapse load F_u, the submerged weight of the foundation $(W_f - \gamma_w H_w B)$, and
orces due to the *total* stress p acting on the surface, as shown in Fig. 6.23. We must
e very careful here to note that the total stress p is the sum of the applied stress
nd the free water pressure so that if there is no applied stress we have $p = \gamma_w H_w$.
'roceeding as in the previous section, we have

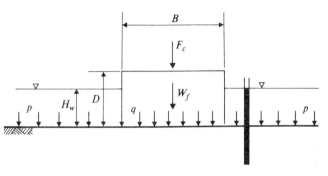

Figure 6.23 Foundation on saturated soil for drained loading.

$$F_u + (W_f - \gamma_w H_w B) = \tfrac{1}{2}(\gamma - \gamma_w)B^2 G_u + (p - \gamma_w H_w)BJ \qquad (6.9?$$

where G_u is the upper bound bearing capacity factor given by Eq. (6.94) and J the bearing capacity factor given by Eq. (6.85).

For a lower bound calculation we must determine the effective stresses q' an p' on the soil surface beneath and outside the foundation. Beneath the foundatic the total stress q is given by

$$q = \frac{1}{B}[F_l + (W_f - \gamma_w H_w B)] + \gamma_w H_w = \frac{1}{B}[F_c + W_f] \qquad (6.98$$

and hence the effective stress is

$$q' = \frac{1}{B}(F_l + W_f) - \gamma_w H_w \qquad (6.9?$$

The *total* stress applied to the soil surface outside the foundation is p and henc the effective stress is

$$p' = p - \gamma_w H_w \qquad (6.10C$$

Thus, proceeding as in the previous section, we may write a lower bound for th collapse load:

$$F_l + W_f - \gamma_w H_w B = \tfrac{1}{2}(\gamma - \gamma_w)B^2 G_l + (p - \gamma_w H_w)BJ \qquad (6.101$$

where the bearing capacity factor J is given by Eq. (6.85) and the lower boun bearing capacity factor is $G_l = 0$.

From Eqs. (6.97) and (6.101), the collapse load is given by

$$F_c + W_f = \tfrac{1}{2}(\gamma - \gamma_w)B^2 G + (p - \gamma_w H_w)BJ + \gamma_w H_w B \qquad (6.102$$

where G and J are the bearing capacity factors in terms of effective stresses obtaine in the previous section. If the foundation is hollow so that its weight is negligibl we have

$$F_c = \tfrac{1}{2}(\gamma - \gamma_w)B^2 G + (p - \gamma_w H_w)BJ + \gamma_w H_w B \qquad (6.103$$

and if the soil is very weak so that both bearing capacity factors G and J are zer we have

$$F_c = \gamma_w H_w B \qquad (6.104$$

Equation (6.104) is of course simply a statement of the principle of Archimedes that the upthrust on a submerged body is equal to the weight of fluid displaced.

2. Stability of a submerged infinite slope

Figure 6.24 shows a portion of an infinite slope of saturated soil completely sub merged below water. The slope is constructed slowly corresponding to drained loading, and the pore pressures are everywhere hydrostatic. Thus the *potential* o the pore water defined by Eq. (6.2) in Sec. 6.1, and shown by the levels of wate

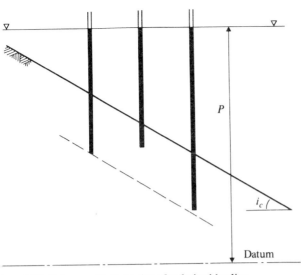

Figure 6.24 Submerged infinite slope for drained loading.

typical standpipes, is everywhere constant and so there is no seepage flow and no seepage pressures.

The calculations for an upper bound for the limiting slope angle i_c for the submerged slope shown in Fig. 6.24 follow closely those in Sec. 6.3, with $(\gamma - \gamma_w)$ instead of γ in Eq. (6.15). Thus, with reference to the mechanism of plastic collapse and the displacement diagram shown in Fig. 6.4, we have

$$\delta W = 0 \qquad [6.5]$$

$$\delta E = \delta v (\gamma - \gamma_w) V \qquad (6.105)$$

here $V = zl \cos i_u$ is the volume of the sliding block. Hence, equating $\delta W = \delta E$ and proceeding as before, we find that an upper bound for the critical slope angle is given by

$$i_u = \phi_{cs}' \qquad (6.106)$$

The calculations for a lower bound for the limiting angle of the submerged slope also follow closely those in Sec. 6.3. The state of effective stress for saturated soil is given by Eqs. (6.7) and (6.8) and hence, with reference to Fig. 6.5, the effective normal and shear stresses on planes parallel with the slope are given by Eqs. (6.21) and (6.22), with $(\gamma - \gamma_w)$ instead of γ. Thus, for the submerged slope shown in Fig. 6.24, the effective stresses on planes parallel with the slope at a depth z are

$$\sigma_n' = (\gamma - \gamma_w) z \cos^2 i_l \qquad (6.107)$$

$$\tau_n' = (\gamma - \gamma_w) z \sin i_l \cos i_l \qquad (6.108)$$

and hence

$$\tau_n' = \sigma_n' \tan i_l \tag{6.10}$$

The state of stress does not exceed the failure criterion for drained loading giv
by Eq. (6.4) as

$$\tau_n' = \sigma_n' \tan \phi_{cs}' \tag{6.4}$$

and hence a lower bound for the limiting angle of a submerged slope is given by

$$i_l = \phi_{cs}' \tag{6.11}$$

The above analysis is valid for any depth z and for any point within the soil and
the state of stress is in equilibrium and does not exceed the drained failure criteri
anywhere. The Mohr's circles for the states of effective stress at different dept
are similar to those shown in Fig. 6.5(b), with stresses given by Eqs. (6.107) a
(6.108).

From Eqs. (6.106) and (6.110), the upper and lower bounds are equal, a
hence the critical slope angle for a submerged infinite slope for drained loading is

$$i_c = \phi_{cs}' \tag{6.11}$$

This is exactly the solution obtained in Sec. (6.3) for the limiting slope angle of a
infinite slope in dry soil; thus the presence of the water makes no difference to th
stability of an infinite slope, provided that the potential of the water is everywhe
the same in the saturated soil.

3. Stability of an infinite slope with steady state seepage

A second case of an infinite slope in saturated soil, but where the surface is expose
to the atmosphere, is shown in Fig. 6.25. The levels of water in standpipes at
and at C coincide with the soil surface so the potentials at A and at C are differe
and consequently there must be steady state seepage flow of water through th
soil giving rise to seepage stresses.

Figure 6.25 shows a portion of a square flownet for steady state seepage i
which the flow lines are parallel with the slope and equipotentials are normal t
this slope. The level of water in the standpipe at B on the same equipotential as tha
through A rises to the same height as the water in the standpipe at A and hence th
pore pressure at B at a depth z below the surface is

$$u = \gamma_w h = \gamma_w z \cos^2 i_c \tag{6.112}$$

and Eq. (6.112) is valid for any point in the soil at a depth z below the surface. A
water seeps through the soil the effective stress σ_s' due solely to the drag on the so
grains caused by the flow of water past them is given by Eq. (6.3) as

$$\frac{d\sigma_s'}{ds} = \gamma_w i_s \tag{6.3}$$

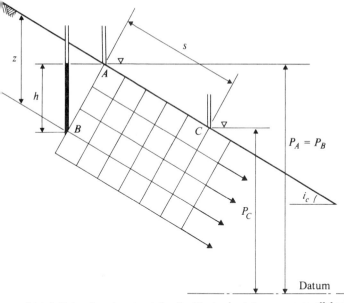

gure 6.25 Infinite slope in saturated soil with steady state seepage parallel with the slope.

here $i_s = -\,\mathrm{d}P/\mathrm{d}s$ is the hydraulic gradient and s is measured in the direction of ıe flow. Considering the flow between the equipotentials through A and C in Fig. .25, we have

$$i_s = -\frac{\mathrm{d}P}{\mathrm{d}s} = \sin i_c \qquad (6.113)$$

ıd hence the seepage stress on a block of soil length s measured down the slope given by

$$\sigma'_s = \gamma_w s \sin i_c \qquad (6.114)$$

he seepage forces act down the slope thus making the slope less stable and we xpect to find that the critical slope angle i_c will be less than the value ϕ'_{cs} for dry ɔil or for a submerged slope.

. Upper bound for an infinite slope with steady state seepage

igure 6.26(a) shows a mechanism of plastic collapse, consisting of a single straight .ip plane parallel with the slope and at a depth z, similar to that shown in Fig. 6.4 ɔr dry soil, while Fig. 6.26(b) shows the corresponding displacement diagram for ı increment of displacement δw at an angle $\psi = \phi'_{cs}$ to the slip plane. In Fig. .26(a) the force S is due to seepage stresses and, from Eq. (6.114), is given by

$$S = \sigma'_s z \cos i_u = \gamma_w z l \sin i_u \cos i_u \qquad (6.115)$$

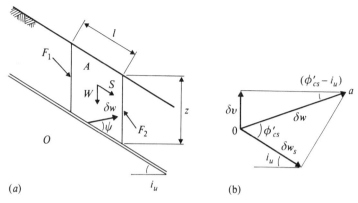

Figure 6.26 Mechanism of plastic collapse for an infinite slope for drained loading with steady state seepage parallel with the slope.

where i_u is an upper bound for the limiting slope angle. As before, the forces F_1 and F_2 on the vertical sides of a sliding block are equal and opposite for an infinite slope and thus from Eqs. (6.5) and (6.6) the increments of work done by the internal stresses and by the external loads and stresses are

$$\delta W = 0 \qquad [6.5]$$

$$\delta E = -\int_V \delta v(\gamma - \gamma_w)\, dV + S\, \delta w_s \qquad (6.116)$$

where $V = zl \cos i_u$ is the volume of the sliding block in Fig. 6.26(a) and δv and δw_s are components of the increment of displacement shown in Fig. 6.26(b) and given by

$$\delta v = \delta w \sin (\phi'_{cs} - i_u) \qquad (6.117)$$

$$\delta w_s = \delta w \cos \phi'_{cs} \qquad (6.118)$$

Thus, equating $\delta W = \delta E$ and making use of Eqs. (6.117) and (6.118), we have

$$\delta v(\gamma - \gamma_w)zl \cos i_u = \delta w_s \gamma_w zl \sin i_u \cos i_u \qquad (6.119)$$

and,

$$(\gamma - \gamma_w) \sin (\phi'_{cs} - i_u) = \gamma_w \sin i_u \cos \phi'_{cs} \qquad (6.120)$$

Hence, expanding $\sin (\phi'_{cs} - i_u)$ and rearranging we obtain

$$\tan i_u = \frac{\gamma - \gamma_w}{\gamma} \tan \phi'_{cs} \qquad (6.121)$$

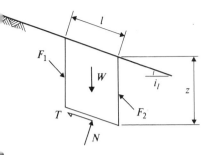

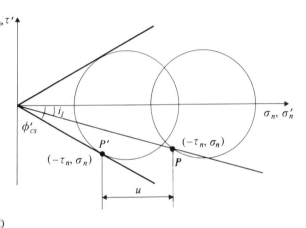

)
gure 6.27 Equilibrium state of stress for an infinite slope for drained loading with steady
te seepage parallel with the surface.

. **Lower bound for an infinite slope with steady state seepage**

igure 6.27(a) shows a block of soil depth z and length l in an infinite slope whose
ope angle i_l is a lower bound for the limiting angle. As before, the forces F_1 and
$_2$ are equal and opposite for an infinite slope and the total normal and shear
resses on the plane AB are given by

$$\sigma_n = \gamma z \cos^2 i_l \tag{6.122}$$

$$\tau_n = \gamma z \sin i_l \cos i_l \tag{6.123}$$

ow, from Eq. (6.112) the pore pressure at a depth z in saturated soil for steady
ate seepage is

$$u = \gamma_w h = \gamma_w z \cos^2 i_l \tag{6.112}$$

d hence the effective normal and shear stresses on AB are

$$\sigma'_n = (\gamma - \gamma_w)z \cos^2 i_l \tag{6.12}$$

and hence

$$\tau'_n = \gamma z \sin i_l \cos i_l \tag{6.12}$$

$$\tau'_n = \left(\frac{\gamma}{\gamma - \gamma_w}\right) \sigma'_n \tan i_l \tag{6.12}$$

The state of stress does not exceed the drained failure criterion given by Eq. (6.4)

$$\tau'_n = \sigma'_n \tan \phi'_{cs} \tag{6.4}$$

and hence a lower bound for the limiting angle of an infinite slope in saturat soil is given by

$$\tan i_l = \left(\frac{\gamma - \gamma_w}{\gamma}\right) \tan \phi'_{cs} \tag{6.12}$$

The Mohr's circles of total and effective stress in an element on AB in Fig. 6.27(are shown in Fig. 6.27(b). The Mohr's circle of effective stress just touches t drained failure envelope given by Eq. (6.4) and the Mohr's circle of total stress shifted to the right by a distance equal to the magnitude of the pore pressure u. T poles of the circles are at P' and P, and hence we may determine the total an effective stress on any plane through the soil using the methods described in Sec. 1

From Eqs. (6.121) and (6.127), the upper and lower bounds are equal an hence the critical slope angle for an infinite slope in saturated soil with steady sta seepage parallel with the surface is given by

$$\tan i_c = \left(\frac{\gamma - \gamma_w}{\gamma}\right) \tan \phi'_{cs} \tag{6.12}$$

For most practical cases $\gamma \approx 2\gamma_w$ and hence $i_c \approx \frac{1}{2}\phi'_{cs}$. Since the upper and low bounds are equal the mechanism of plastic collapse shown in Fig. 6.26(a) mu correspond to the state of stress shown in Fig. 6.27(a).

6.7 DRAINED STABILITY OF A ROUGH RETAINING WALL

In Section 6.4 we examined the stability of a retaining wall which was assumed be smooth, so that shear stresses between it and the soil were zero. Now we examin the case where the wall is rough and where, for drained loading, the effective she stresses between the wall and the soil τ'_w are given by

$$\tau'_w = \sigma'_a \tan \phi'_w \qquad \text{or} \qquad \tau'_w = \sigma'_p \tan \phi'_w \tag{6.129}$$

In Eq. (6.129) σ'_a and σ'_p are the effective normal active and passive stresses betwee the soil and the wall and ϕ'_w is an angle of wall friction where, of course, $\phi'_w \leqslant \phi'_c$ In practice, a value for ϕ'_w may be estimated by conducting a drained shear bo test in which the lower half of the shear box contains the material of the wall. Fo simplicity, we will consider the case of a wall retaining dry soil so that pore pressur

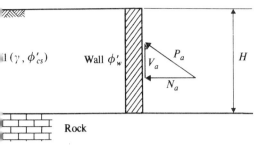

ure 6.28 Loads on a rough retaining wall for drained loading: active case.

zero and total and effective stresses are equal, but the analyses may be extended
cover the cases of saturated soil with or without steady state seepage by using
e methods outlined in the previous section.

For the present we will consider the active case shown in Fig. 6.28. As the wall
oves away the soil tends to slump downwards and the shear stresses τ'_w act up-
irds on the soil. The active force P_a has a component N_a normal to the wall and a
mponent V_a acting upwards as shown in Fig. 6.28 where, for dry soil,

$$V_a = N_a \tan \phi'_w \qquad (6.130)$$

is simplest to calculate the normal component of the active force N_a and then to
lculate the active force P_a from

$$P_a = N_a \sec \phi'_w \qquad (6.131)$$

Upper bound for a rough wall

gure 6.29(a) shows a mechanism of plastic collapse similar to that shown in Fig.
9(a) and Fig. 6.29(b) shows the corresponding displacement diagram for an
crement of displacement δw across the slip plane. The vector of relative displace-
ent at the wall, δw_w in Fig. 6.29 makes an angle ψ_w to the wall and in order
the normality condition at the wall to be satisfied we require $\psi_w = \phi'_w$. Thus,
theory, the soil and wall separate which, as noted by Heyman (1972), is clearly
ireasonable. However, Collins (1973) shows that if we assume $\psi_w = \phi'_w$, so that
e vector of relative displacement between the soil and the wall makes an angle
$_v = \phi'_w$ to the wall, the upper bound calculated is a true upper bound solution.
or the case where the wall is roughened with soil attached to it so that $\phi'_w = \phi'_{cs}$,
e slipping near the wall takes place through the soil rather than between the soil
d the wall, and for this case we take $\psi_w = \phi'_{cs}$. The calculation for an upper
ound N_{au} for the normal component of the active force follows closely that given
Sec. 6.4 for a smooth wall. The wall is assumed to move horizontally and with-
t rotation and so the external force V_{au} does no work. Hence from Eqs. (6.5)
d (6.6), we have, for dry soil,

$$\delta W = 0 \qquad [6.5]$$

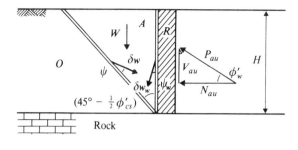

(a)

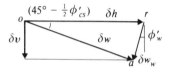

(b)

Figure 6.29 Mechanism of plastic collapse for a rough retaining wall for drained loading: act[t] case.

$$\delta E = -N_{au}\,\delta h + \gamma V\,\delta v \qquad (6.13[)]$$

and, equating $\delta W = \delta E$, an upper bound for the normal component of the acti[ve] force is given by

$$N_{au} = \tfrac{1}{2}\gamma H^2\,(45° - \tfrac{1}{2}\phi'_{cs})\,\delta v/\delta h \qquad (6.13[)]$$

From the geometry of Fig. 6.29(b), δv and δh are related by ϕ'_{cs} and ϕ'_w, and hen[ce] we may obtain an expression for N_{au}. The expression is algebraically lengthy a[nd] we will not give the working here.

2. Lower bound for a rough wall.

Figure 6.30(a) shows an equilibrium state of stress consisting of regions I and [II] separated by a single stress discontinuity. It is similar to that shown in Fig. 5.26([a)] for undrained loading, except of course that there are no tension cracks for draine[d] loading. The Mohr's circle of total and effective stress for the state of stress in a[n] element A at a depth z in region II is shown in Fig. 6.30(b). The circle just touch[es] the drained failure envelope given by Eq. (6.4) and the stresses (τ'_w, σ'_a) on verti[cal] planes define the position of the circle and its pole at P_a. The broken line is parall[el] with the major principal plane in region II and, since the major principal plane [in] region I is horizontal, the angle $\delta\theta$ gives the rotation of the direction of the maj[or] principal stress between the two regions.

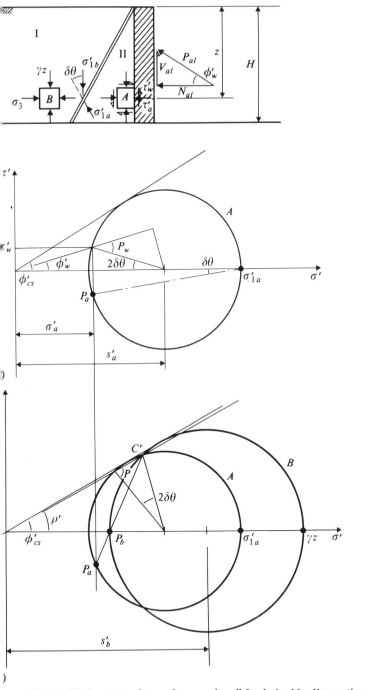

Figure 6.30 Equilibrium state of stress for a rough wall for drained loading: active case.

The Mohr's circles of stress for the states of stress in the elements A and B shown in Fig. 6.30(c), where the circle A is the same as that in Fig. 6.30(b) and t circle B is the same as that in Fig. 6.8(b) for a smooth wall. The circles intersect C', which represents the stresses on the discontinuity, and P_a and P_b are the po of the respective circles. From the geometry of Fig. 6.30(b) and (c), a lower bou for the active pressure σ_a' may be found in terms of γz, ϕ_{cs}', and ϕ_w', making use the angles P and P_w. The solution is relatively simple but the expression for σ_a' algebraically lengthy and we will not give the working here. For dry soil, p pressures are zero and a lower bound for the normal component of the active for on the wall is given by

$$N_{al} = \int_0^H \sigma_a \, dz = \int_0^H \sigma_a' \, dz \tag{6.13}$$

Thus, from the bound theorems, the normal component N_{ac} of the active for P_{ac} at collapse for a rough wall moving away from the soil for drained loading a for dry soil is given by

$$N_{au} \leqslant N_{ac} \leqslant N_{al} \tag{6.13}$$

where N_{au} and N_{al} are upper and lower bounds. We should note that, as was t case for a smooth wall, the upper bound solution gives a *lower* limit for N_{ac} wh the lower bound gives an *upper* limit. Upper and lower bounds for the vertic component of the active force at collapse are given, from Eq. (6.130), as

$$V_{au} = N_{au} \tan \phi_w' \tag{6.13}$$

$$V_{al} = N_{al} \tan \phi_w' \tag{6.13}$$

Similar calculations may be conducted to obtain upper and lower bounds for t passive forces as the wall moves towards the soil, and the calculations may l extended to include hydrostatic and steady state seepage pore pressures.

6.8 DISCUSSION

In this chapter we have examined upper and lower bound calculations for drain loading of foundations, slopes, and walls, and the problems considered were simil to those discussed in Chapter 5 for undrained loading. We have examined calc lations for smooth and rough walls, for dry soil and for saturated soil with a without steady state seepage. However, all the methods in the chapter are appli able only for drained loading for which pore pressures can be found throughout t soil. Although the examples considered were relatively simple, the methods a equally applicable to more general cases.

:FERENCES

:inson, J. H. and P. L. Bransby (1978), *The Mechanics of Soils*, McGraw-Hill, London.
en, W. F. (1975), *Limit Analysis and Soil Plasticity*, Elsevier, New York.
llins, I. F. (1973), 'A note on the interpretation of Coulomb's analysis of the thrust in a rough wall in terms of the limit theorems of plasticity theory', *Geotechnique*, **23**, 442–7.
yman, J. (1972), *Coulomb's Memoir on Statics*, Cambridge University Press, Cambridge.
nkine, W. J. M. (1857), 'On the stability of loose earth', *Phil Trans. R. Soc.*, **147**, 9–28.
rzaghi, K. (1943), *Theoretical Soil Mechanics*, Wiley, New York.

ORKED EXAMPLES

5.1 Stability of a Loaded Slope

slope with angle i and height H is cut in dry soil above strong rock. The critical te angle of friction of the soil is $\phi'_{cs} = 30°$ and its unit weight is taken as zero. A iform normal stress q is applied to the soil surface and a uniform normal stress p : q) is applied to the slope. Obtain upper and lower bounds for the stress q for iven value of p.

Figure E6.1(a) shows a mechanism of plastic collapse for drained loading nsisting of two wedges separated by a slip fan of fan angle $\Delta\theta$ and Fig. E6.1(b) a displacement diagram for an increment of displacement δw_q of the surface. e slip fan and the displacement diagram both contain logarithmic spirals and nce, from Eqs. (4.43) and (4.44), with $\psi = \phi'_{cs}$, we have

$$\frac{R_b}{R_a} = \frac{\delta w_b}{\delta w_a} = \exp\left(\Delta\theta \tan \phi'_{cs}\right)$$

om the geometry of Fig. E6.1(a), the fan angle is $\Delta\theta = (90° - i)$. Since the soil assumed to be weightless, the only external loads are P due to the stresses on the ipe and an upper bound Q_u due to the upper bound stresses q_u on the surface, d their displacements are δw_p and δw_q respectively. For a slice 1 m thick we have

$$p = \int_A p \, dA = \frac{pH}{\sin i}$$

$$Q_u = \int_A q_u \, dA = \frac{q_u H}{\sin i \exp\left(\Delta\theta \tan \phi'_{cs}\right) \tan\left(45° + \frac{1}{2}\phi'_{cs}\right)}$$

$$\frac{\delta w_p}{\delta w_q} = \exp\left(\Delta\theta \tan \phi'_{cs}\right) \tan\left(45° + \frac{1}{2}\phi'_{cs}\right)$$

d, from Eq. (6.6), with $u = \gamma_w = 0$ for dry soil,

$$\delta E = \int_A \delta w_q \, q_u \, dA - \int_A \delta w_p \, p \, dA$$

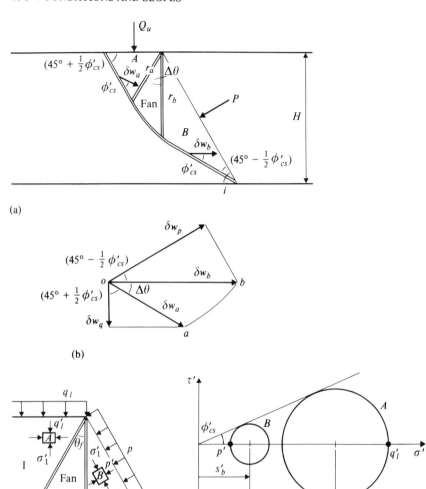

Figure E6.1

For drained laoding $\delta W = 0$ and hence, equating $\delta E = \delta W$, and with $\Delta\theta = \tfrac{1}{2}\pi -$
we have

$$q_u = p \exp [(\pi - 2i) \tan \phi'_{cs}] \tan^2 (45° + \tfrac{1}{2}\phi'_{cs})$$

Figure E6.1(c) shows a state of stress, with regions I and II separated by a str
fan with a fan angle $\theta_f = (90° - i)$. In region I shear stresses on horizontal a
vertical planes are zero, and in region II shear stresses on planes normal to a
parallel with the slope are zero. Figure E6.1(d) shows the Mohr's circles of effecti

esses for elements A and B in regions I and II respectively, and the directions the major principal stresses are shown in Fig. E6.1(c). The change of stress rough a stress fan for drained loading is given by Eq. (6.11) as

$$\frac{ds'}{d\theta} = 2s' \tan \phi'_{cs}$$

d hence

$$\frac{s'_a}{s'_b} = \exp\left[(\pi - 2i) \tan \phi'_{cs}\right]$$

om the geometry of Fig. E6.1(d)

$$s'_b = \frac{p'}{1 - \sin \phi'_{cs}} \qquad s'_a = \frac{q'_u}{1 + \sin \phi'_{cs}}$$

d, since total and effective stresses are equal for dry soil,

$$q_u = p \exp\left[(\pi - 2i) \tan \phi'_{cs}\right] \tan^2 \left(45° + \tfrac{1}{2}\phi'_{cs}\right)$$

ius the upper bound for the collapse mechanism shown in Fig. E6.1(a) and the wer bound for the state of stress shown in Fig. E6.1(c) are equal, and both equal e exact solution.

6.2 Loads on Trench Struts

trench is excavated to a depth of 5 m through soil with critical state friction ıgle $\phi'_{cs} = 30°$; the dry unit weight is $\gamma = 15$ kN/m^3 and the saturated unit weight $\gamma = 20$ kN/m^3. Strong rock occurs at the base of the trench, there is a thin gravel ·ain above the rock. The sides of the trench are stabilized by smooth, rigid sheet ·les held apart by struts at intervals of 1 m normal to the page and placed so that ıe sheet piles do not rotate. Calculate upper and lower bounds for the strut loads ·quired to maintain the stability of the trench (1) for dry soil when there is a niform surcharge of 80 kN/m^2 at the surface and (2) when heavy rain saturates ıe soil and there is steady state seepage from the surface to the gravel drain.

(1) For dry soil, Fig. E6.2(a) shows a mechanism of plastic collapse with a ıngle straight slip plane at an angle $(45° - \tfrac{1}{2}\phi'_{cs}) = 30°$ to the vertical and Fig. 6.2(b) is a displacement diagram for an increment of displacement δw at an angle $_{cs} = 30°$ to the slip plane. The external forces are the weight W of the sliding lock, the surcharge stress and an upper bound P_u for the strut load. For a slice m thick normal to the page we have, from Eq. (6.6), with $u = \gamma_w = 0$ for dry ɔil,

$$\delta E = \int_V \delta v \, \gamma \, dV + \int_A \delta v \, q \, dA - P_u \, \delta h$$

·here

$$\delta v = \tfrac{1}{2}\delta w \qquad \delta h = \frac{\sqrt{3}}{2}\delta w$$

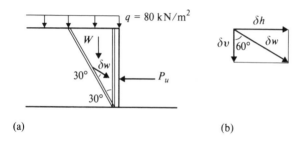

(a)   (b)

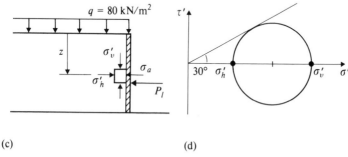

(c)   (d)

Figure E6.2

$$\int_V \gamma \, dV = \tfrac{1}{2} \times 15 \times 5^2 \tan 30° = \frac{188}{\sqrt{3}} \text{ kN/m}$$

$$\int_A q \, dA = 80 \times 5 \tan 30° = \frac{400}{\sqrt{3}} \text{ kN/m}$$

and

$$\delta E = \frac{1}{2\sqrt{3}}[588 - 3P_u] \, \delta w$$

For drained loading we have $\delta W = 0$ and hence, equation $\delta E = \delta w$,

$$\underline{P_u = 196 \text{ kN}}$$

Figure E6.2(c) shows a state of stress in which shear stresses on horizonta
and vertical planes are zero and Fig. E6.2(d) shows the Mohr's circles of effectiv
stress for an element at a depth z below the surface. For dry soil, total and effectiv
stresses are equal and $\sigma_a = \sigma_h'$ where, from Fig. E6.2(d),

$$\sigma_h' = \sigma_v' \tan^2 (45° - \tfrac{1}{2}\phi_{cs}') = \tfrac{1}{3}\sigma_v'$$

$$\sigma_v' = q + \gamma z = (80 + 15z)$$

and

$$\sigma_a = \sigma_h' = (26.7 + 5z)$$

A lower bound for the strut load P_l is given by

$$P_l = \int_0^H \sigma_a \, dz = \int_0^5 (26.7 + 5z) \, dz$$

$$= [26.7z + 2.5z^2]_0^5$$

$$P_l = 196 \text{ kN}$$

us the upper bound for the collapse mechanism in Fig. E6.2(a) and the lower
und for the state of stress in Fig. E6.2(c) are equal and so both must equal the
act solution. Hence, to maintain the stability of the trench, the capacity of the
uts must exceed 196 kN.

(2) Figure E6.3(a) shows a flownet for steady state seepage from the surface to
e gravel drain for which pore pressures are everywhere zero. Figure E6.3(b) shows
mechanism of plastic collapse which is the same as that shown in Fig. E6.2(a),
d the corresponding displacement diagram is the same as that shown in Fig.
.2(b). The external forces are now the weight of the sliding block of soil, an
per bound P_u for the strut load, and a force S due to the vertical seepage stresses.
r a slice 1 m normal to the page we have, from Eq. (6.6),

$$\delta E = \int_V \delta v \, \gamma \, dV + S \, \delta v - P_u \, \delta h$$

here

$$\delta v = \tfrac{1}{2}\delta w \qquad \delta h = \frac{\sqrt{3}}{2}\delta w$$

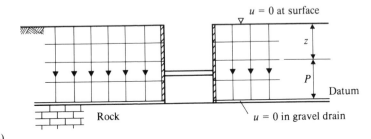

)

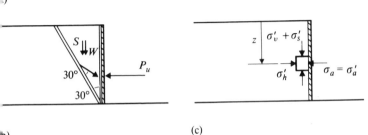

b)   (c)

igure E6.3

From the flownet shown in Fig. E6.3(a) the pore pressure is everywhere zero a
hence

$$\int_V \gamma \, dV = \tfrac{1}{2} \times 20 \times 5^2 \tan 30° = 144 \text{ kN/m}$$

Taking the datum for potential at the base of the trench, the potential at a dep
z is P as shown in Fig. E6.3(a). Thus, the hydraulic gradient is

$$i = -\frac{dP}{ds} = 1$$

and, from Eq. (6.3), the vertical seepage stress σ_s' is given by

$$\frac{d\sigma_s'}{ds} = \gamma_w$$

Since the seepage is vertical, the seepage stress acts like a body force by apparent
increasing the unit weight of the soil. Hence

$$S = \int_V \gamma_w \, dV = \tfrac{1}{2} \times 9.81 \times 5^2 \tan 30° = 71 \text{ kN/m}$$

Thus we have

$$\delta E = \left[\tfrac{1}{2} \times 215 - \frac{\sqrt{3}}{2} P_u \right] \delta w$$

For drained loading $\delta W = 0$, and hence, equating $\delta E = \delta W$, we have

$$\underline{P_u = 124 \text{ kN}}$$

Figure E6.3(c) shows a state of stress similar to that shown in Fig. E6.2(c
except that the seepage stress σ_s' must be added to the vertical effective stres
Noting that pore pressures are zero, we have

$$\sigma_v' + \sigma_s' = \gamma z + \gamma_w z = 29.81z \text{ kN/m}^2$$

and, as before,

$$\sigma_a = \sigma_h' = \sigma_v' \tan^2 (45° - \tfrac{1}{2}\phi_{cs}') = \tfrac{1}{3} \sigma_v'$$

and

$$\sigma_a = \tfrac{1}{3} \times 29.81z = 9.94z \text{ kN/m}^2$$

a lower bound for the strut load P_l is given by

$$P_l = \int_0^H \sigma_a \, dz = \int_0^5 9.94z \, dz$$

$$\underline{P_l = 124 \text{ kN}}$$

Again the upper bound and the lower bound are equal and so both must equal th
exact solution.

.3 Force on a Bulldozer Blade

bulldozer blade 1 m high and 3 m wide pushes dry soil across the top of a strong
:k and the blade does not rotate. The soil has a critical state friction angle $\phi'_{cs} =$
° and unit weight 15 kN/m³ and the friction angle between the soil and the
de is $\phi'_w = 15°$. Calculate upper and lower bounds for the force P which the
dozer must apply to its blade. (It may be assumed that the problem is plane
ain and any three-dimensional effects at the ends of the blade may be neglected.)

Figure E6.4(a) shows a mechanism of plastic collapse with a single straight
p plane at an angle $(45° + \frac{1}{2}\phi'_{cs}) = 60°$ to the vertical; Fig. E6.4(b) is a displace-
ent diagram for an increment of displacement δw of the sliding block. The
lative displacement across the slip plane makes an angle $\phi'_{cs} = 30°$ to the slip
ine and the relative displacement between the soil and the blade is taken at an
gle $\phi'_w = 15°$ to the wall. The external forces are the weight W of the block of
il, the shear force V between the soil and the blade, and an upper bound N_u
r the horizontal component of the force applied by the bulldozer but, as the blade
oves horizontally, the vertical force V does no work. For a slice 1 m thick normal
the page we have, from Eq. (6.6), with $u = \gamma_w = 0$ for dry soil,

$$\delta E = -\int_V \delta v \gamma \, dV + N_u \, \delta h$$

here

$$\delta h = \delta v(\tan 30° - \tan 15°) = 0.31 \, \delta v$$

$$\int_V \gamma \, dV = \frac{1}{2} \times 15 \times \tan 60° = 13.0 \text{ kN/m}$$

nd

$$\delta E = (-13.0 + 0.31 \, N_u) \, \delta v$$

'or drained loading we have $\delta W = 0$ and hence, equating $\delta E = \delta W$, we have

$$N_u = 42 \text{ kN/m}$$

n upper bound P_u for the force applied by the bulldozer to its blade is given by

$$P_u = N_u \sec \phi'_w$$

nd hence, noting that the blade is 3 m wide normal to the page, we have

$$P_u = 3 \times 42 \sec 15°$$

$$\underline{P_u = 130 \text{ kN}}$$

Figure E6.4(c) shows a state of stress containing a single β discontinuity separating
egions I and II and, for dry soil, total and effective stresses are equal. In region I,
hear stresses on horizontal and vertical planes are zero and the Mohr's circle of
effective stress for an element A at a depth z is shown in Fig. E6.4(d). The pole of
the circle is at P_a and

$$\sigma'_v = \gamma z = 15z \qquad \sigma'_h = \sigma'_1$$

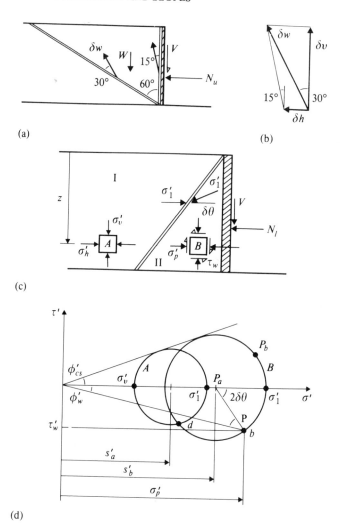

(a)

(b)

(c)

(d)

Figure E6.4

In region II shear stresses on horizontal and vertical planes are given by

$$\tau_w' = \sigma_n' \tan \phi_w'$$

and the Mohr's circle of effective stress for an element B at depth z is shown i
Fig. E6.4(d); the pole is at P_b, the point b gives the stresses on the face of the
blade, and the point d gives the stresses on the discontinuity.

From Eq. (4.59) the angle P in Fig. E6.4(d) is given by

$$\sin P = \frac{\sin \phi'_w}{\sin \phi'_{cs}} = \frac{\sin 15°}{\sin 30°}$$

$$P = 31°$$

⸀e angle between the direction of the major principal stress and the horizontal in ⸀ion II is $\delta\theta$ and, from the geometry of Fig. E6.4(d),

$$2\delta\theta = P + \phi'_w = 31° + 15°$$

$$\delta\theta = 23°$$

⸀e distance between the centres of the Mohr's circles, corresponding to the change ⸀ stress across the discontinuity, is given by Eq. (4.64)

$$\frac{s'_b}{s'_a} = \frac{\cos(\delta\theta - \rho')}{\cos(\delta\theta + \rho')}$$

⸀here ρ', the angle of shearing resistance mobilized on the discontinuity, is given ⸀ Eq. (4.60) as

$$\sin \rho' = \cos \delta\theta \sin \phi'_{cs} = \cos 23° \sin 30°$$

$$\rho' = 27.4°$$

⸀ence

$$\frac{s'_b}{s'_a} = \frac{\cos(-4.4°)}{\cos 50.4°} = 1.56$$

⸀here

$$s'_a = \sigma'_v/(1 - \sin \phi'_{cs}) = 15z/(1 - \sin 30°)$$

$$s'_a = 30z \text{ kN/m}^2$$

⸀d

$$s'_b = 1.56 \times 30z = 47z \text{ kN/m}^2$$

⸀rom the geometry of Fig. E6.4(d), the normal stress $\sigma'_p = \sigma_p$ between the blade ⸀d soil is given by

$$\sigma'_p = s'_b(1 + \sin \phi'_{cs} \cos 2\delta\theta)$$

$$= 47(1 + \sin 30° \cos 46°)z$$

$$\sigma_p = 63.3z$$

⸀ lower bound for the normal force N_l is given by

$$N_l = \int_0^H \sigma_p \, dz = \int_0^1 63.3z \, dz$$

$$N_l = 31.7 \text{ kN/m}$$

⸀ lower bound P_l for the force applied by the bulldozer to its blade is given by

$$P_l = N_l \sec \phi'_w$$

⸀nd hence, noting that the blade is 3 m wide normal to the page, we have

$$P_l = 3 \times 31.7 \sec 15°$$

$$\underline{P_l = 98 \text{ kN}}$$

Thus we have bounds $P_u = 130$ kN and $P_l = 98$ kN, which are not equal but whi̇
are relatively close to one another. These bounds may be improved by making u̇
of stress fans and slip fans.

SEVEN

ASSOCIATED FIELDS AND
SLIP LINE METHODS

.1 INTRODUCTION

the previous two chapters we obtained upper and lower bounds for the stability
various soil structures for undrained loading and for drained loading. In some
ses we found upper bounds which equalled the corresponding lower bounds, but
others we could only obtain unequal bounds. When the upper and lower bounds
e equal both must also equal an exact solution and the mechanism of plastic
ollapse used to obtain the upper bound corresponds to the state of stress used
obtain the lower bound. Thus, if we are able to calculate equilibrium states of
ress, which correspond to particular mechanisms of plastic collapse, we may
alculate exact solutions for the stability of soil structures.

In this chapter we will consider some of the methods available for calculating
ese exact solutions and, as before, we will consider only homogeneous and
otropic soil. The soil may be either saturated or dry and, as usual, we will need
distinguish between drained and undrained loading. The soil is assumed to be
erfectly plastic, so that the normality condition is satisfied and the flow rule is
ssociated, and this provides the relationship which allows a state of stress to be
ssociated with a mechanism of collapse.

Hitherto we have considered discontinuous slipping on *slip planes* but, for
lane strain, planes project as lines and hence slip planes project as *slip lines*. In
his chapter, following conventional usage in plasticity theory, we will talk about
lip lines rather than slip planes, but for plane strain they are the same.

7.2 RELATIONSHIP BETWEEN STRESS AND STRAIN IN A
PERFECTLY PLASTIC MATERIAL AT FAILURE

Figure 7.1(a) shows the principal effective stresses σ_1' and σ_3' at a point in the
$x:z$ plane at a state of drained failure at the critical state and Fig. 7.1(b) shows
the corresponding Mohr's circle of effective stress: as usual in this book the z
axis is drawn vertically downwards so that z and σ_z increase with depth. The
direction of the major principal effective stress makes an angle η with the vertical

247

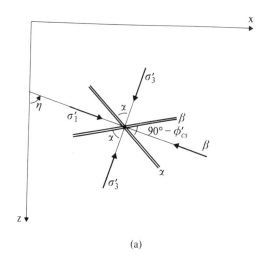

(a)

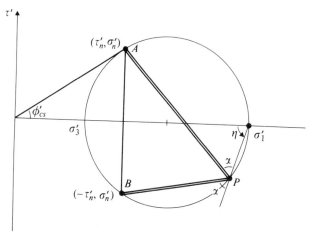

Figure 7.1 Stress characteristics for drained loading.

z axis and the pole of the Mohr's circle is at P. Hence we can locate the planes α and β in Fig. 7.1(a) on which the stresses are those at A and B in Fig. 7.1(b), where the Mohr's circle touches the drained failure envelope given by

$$\tau'_n = \sigma'_n \tan \phi'_{cs} \tag{7.1}$$

The α and β planes in Fig. 7.1(a) are known as *stress characteristics* and we will need to distinguish between the α characteristic associated with positive (counterclockwise) shear stresses and the β characteristic associated with negative (clockwise) shear stresses. It should be noted that a stress characteristic is not the same as a ess discontinuity discussed in Sec. 4.10, but discontinuities and characteristics incide in the special case when the normal and shear stresses on a stress discontinuity satisfy the drained failure criterion given by Eq. (7.1). From the geomtry Fig. 7.1, and as shown in Sec. 1.4, the angle α between each stress characteristic d the major principal plane is given by

$$\alpha = (45° + \tfrac{1}{2}\phi'_{cs}) \tag{7.2}$$

nce, stress characteristics intersect at $(90° - \phi'_{cs})$ and this angle is bisected by e direction of σ'_1, which makes an angle η with the z axis. Figure 7.1(a) shows pair of stress characteristics for a single point in the $x:z$ plane. Clearly, there will similar characteristics for every point for which the Mohr's circle touches the ained failure envelope, and thus we can construct families of α and β characteristics throughout a region of failing soil. These characteristics may be straight or ey may be curved, but members of the α and β families will everywhere intersect $(90° - \phi'_{cs})$ and they will form a mesh throughout the region of failing soil.

Figure 7.2(a) represents an increment of strain for a point in the $x:z$ plane d Fig. 7.2(b) shows the corresponding Mohr's circle of strain; these correspond drained loading with an increment of negative volumetric strain. As shown in ec. 1.3, the increment of strain, and the Mohr's circle, may be characterized by angle of dilation ψ as shown in Fig. 7.2(b) and given by

$$\frac{\delta\epsilon_n}{\delta\gamma_n} = \tan\psi \tag{7.3}$$

here $\delta\epsilon_n$ and $\delta\gamma_n$ are the increments of normal and shear strain corresponding the points A and B in Fig. 7.2(b). The pole of the Mohr's circle is at P and ence we can locate the planes α and β in Fig. 7.2(a) for which the increments of train are those at A and B. The broken lines in Fig. 7.2(b) are the normals to the and β planes and hence the strains in the directions of the α and β planes are zero. he α and β planes in Fig. 7.2(a) are known as *strain increment characteristics*[†] nd we will need to distinguish between the α characteristic associated with positive counterclockwise) shear strain and the β characteristic associated with negative clockwise) shear strain. From the geometry of Fig. 7.2, the angle β between each train increment characteristic and the major principal plane is

$$\beta = (45° + \tfrac{1}{2}\psi) \tag{7.4}$$

Ience strain increment characteristics intersect at $(90° - \psi)$, and this angle is isected by the direction of $\delta\epsilon_1$, which makes an angle η with the z axis. Figure .2(a) shows a pair of characteristics for a single point in the $x:z$ plane. Clearly, here will be similar characteristics for every point which suffers an increment of strain, and thus we can find families of α and β characteristics throughout a

---

[†] Strain increment characteristics are sometimes known also as velocity characteristics, for n increment of displacement may be interpreted as a velocity; they are also known as zero xtension lines to identify them as directions of zero strain increment.

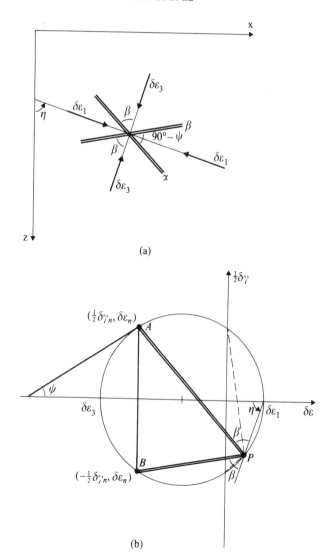

Figure 7.2 Strain increment characteristics for drained loading.

region of straining soil. Strain increment characteristics may be straight or they may be curved, but members of the α and β families will everywhere intersect at $(90° - \psi)$.

Figures 7.1 and 7.2 are for drained loading and Figs 7.3 and 7.4 show the corresponding states of total stress and strain increment for undrained loading. The Mohr's circle of total stress touches the undrained failure envelope given by

$$\tau_n = c_u \tag{7.5}$$

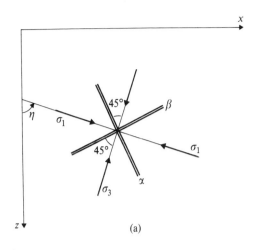

(a)

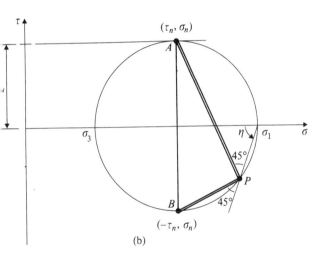

(b)

Figure 7.3 Stress characteristics for undrained loading.

and hence $\phi_u = 0$, while for undrained loading $\delta\epsilon_v = 0$ and so $\psi = 0$. The angles of the characteristics may be found by putting $\phi'_{cs} = \psi = 0$ in Eqs (7.2) and (7.4) and thus α and β characteristics of stress and of strain increment intersect at $90°$.

We assume that under all circumstances the coaxiality condition holds and that the axes of principal stress and of principal strain increment coincide; thus the angles η in Figs 7.1 and 7.2 are the same, and similarly, in Figs 7.3 and 7.4. Furthermore, for a soil which is assumed to be perfectly plastic, elastic components of strain are zero, the normality condition holds, and so the flow rule is associated. Then, for drained loading, we have

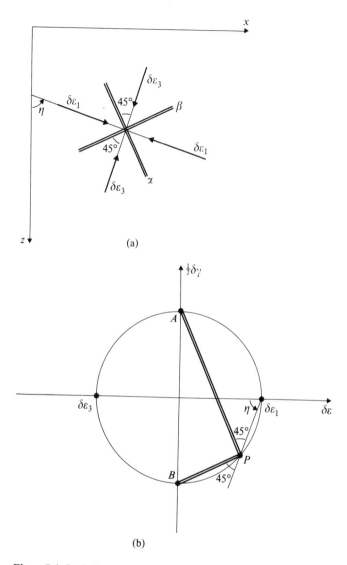

Figure 7.4 Strain increment characteristics for undrained loading.

and hence
$$\psi = \psi_p = \phi'_{cs} \tag{7.6}$$
$$\alpha = \beta = (45° + \tfrac{1}{2}\phi'_{cs}) \tag{7.7}$$

Similarly, for undrained loading, where both elastic and plastic volumetric strain increments are zero at failure, we have

and hence
$$\psi = \psi_p = \phi_u = 0 \tag{7.8}$$
$$\alpha = \beta = 45° \tag{7.9}$$

hus, for soil which is assumed to have an associated flow rule and which is failing
the critical state, *characteristics of stress and of strain increment coincide*.

.3 STRESS FIELD CALCULATIONS FOR UNDRAINED LOADING

'irst we consider the state of stress in a region of soil which is everywhere at
ailure, so that the stresses satisfy the conditions of equilibrium and the failure
riterion for undrained loading. The calculations will consider only the states of
tress within the failing region and nothing will be said at this stage about the
eformations. For undrained loading of saturated soil, where there is no volume
hange during loading, conditions of equilibrium are given by Eqs (4.48) and
4.49) in terms of total stress as

$$\frac{\partial \sigma_z}{\partial z} + \frac{\partial \tau_{xz}}{\partial x} = \gamma \tag{7.10}$$

$$\frac{\partial \sigma_x}{\partial x} + \frac{\partial \tau_{zx}}{\partial z} = 0 \tag{7.11}$$

nd the failure criterion for undrained loading of soil in plane strain is given by

$$t = \tfrac{1}{2}(\sigma_1 - \sigma_3) = c_u \tag{7.12}$$

Figure 7.5(a) shows total normal stresses at a point in the $x:z$ plane and
Fig. 7.5(b) shows the corresponding Mohr's circle of total stress: the state of
tress is at failure and hence the Mohr's circle just touches the undrained failure
envelope given by Eq. (7.12). From the geometry of Fig. 7.5 we have

$$\sigma_x = s + c_u \cos (180° - 2\eta) = s - c_u \cos 2\eta \tag{7.13}$$

$$\sigma_z = s - c_u \cos (180° - 2\eta) = s + c_u \cos 2\eta \tag{7.14}$$

$$\tau_{zx} = \tau_{xz} = c_u \sin (180° - 2\eta) = c_u \sin 2\eta \tag{7.15}$$

Differentiating Eqs (7.13) to (7.15) partially with respect to x and z, and substituting into Eqs (7.10) and (7.11), we obtain

$$\frac{\partial s}{\partial z} - 2c_u \sin 2\eta \frac{\partial \eta}{\partial z} + 2c_u \cos 2\eta \frac{\partial \eta}{\partial x} = \gamma \tag{7.16}$$

$$\frac{\partial s}{\partial x} + 2c_u \cos 2\eta \frac{\partial \eta}{\partial z} + 2c_u \sin 2\eta \frac{\partial \eta}{\partial x} = 0 \tag{7.17}$$

Equations (7.16) and (7.17) are a pair of simultaneous partial differential equations
in s and η. If these can be solved with the appropriate boundary conditions then,
making use of Eqs (7.13) to (7.15), we may calculate the magnitudes and directions of the total stresses throughout a region of failing soil.

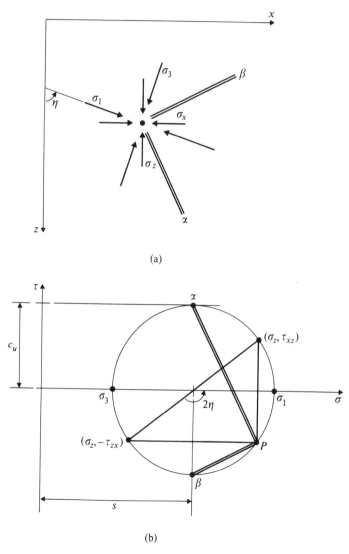

(a)

(b)

Figure 7.5 State of stress at a point for undrained loading.

Without going into the mathematics,[†] we can say that most partial differential equations belong to one of three special classes known as elliptic, parabolic, and hyperbolic, and different solution procedures are appropriate for each class of equation. For example, the Laplace equation which governs the steady state seepage of water through soil and the distribution of stress throughout an *elastic* body is

[†] Partial differential equations are dealt with in most undergraduate texts on mathematics for engineers and also in specialised texts e.g. Garabedian (1964).

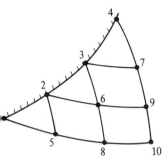

Figure 7.6 Characteristics moving away from a boundary.

lliptic, while the one-dimensional consolidation equation is parabolic and Eqs (7.16) and (7.17) which govern the distribution of stress throughout a *plastic* body are hyperbolic. The appropriate procedure for the solution of hyperbolic partial differential equations is the method of characteristics.[†] The crux of the method is that there are lines throughout the region along which certain *total*, rather than *partial*, differentials can be found; these special lines are called *characteristics* and calculations may proceed outwards from some known boundary, as we calculate the directions of the characteristics and evaluate the total differentials along them. For two simultaneous partial differential equations we expect there to be two intersecting families of characteristics. Hence, for example, Fig. 7.6 shows a boundary 1–4 along which conditions are specified. The lines 1–5 and 2–5 are characteristics and, since their directions are known, the point 5 may be located and the conditions at point 5 calculated from those at the points 1 and 2. Similarly, the points 6 to 10 may be located and the conditions at them determined as the solutions 'march' away from the boundary. It should be noted, however, that we are unable to extend the solution outside the region bounded by the characteristics 1–10 and 4–10.

For the hyperbolic equations (7.16) and (7.17) governing the distribution of stress throughout a region of failing soil for undrained loading, the characteristics are given by

$$\frac{dx}{dz} = \tan{(\eta \mp 45°)} \qquad (7.18)$$

Equation 7.18 defines two families of characteristics which intersect at $90°$ and the direction of σ_1 bisects the angle between the characteristics. Thus characteristics for undrained loading which arise as a consequence of the mathematics of hyperbolic equations coincide with the stress characteristics for undrained loading shown in Fig. 7.3. As usual, we must distinguish between members of the two families of characteristics. Comparing Eq. (7.18) and Fig. 7.3, the α characteristics are associated with the upper (negative) sign in Eq. (7.18) and the β characteristics are associated

[†] Full details of the method of characteristics are given by Abbott (1966).

with the lower (positive) sign. Along the characteristics given by Eq. (7.18), tot differentials are

$$ds = \pm 2c_u \, d\eta + \gamma \, dz \qquad (7.1\text{?})$$

where the upper (positive) sign gives the change of stress along an α characterist and the lower (negative) sign gives the change of stress along a β characteristic.[†]

Equations (7.18) and (7.19) are four equations with four unknowns (i.e $x, z, s,$ and η) but each of Eqs (7.19) must be applied along the appropriate charac teristic given by Eq. (7.18). Thus, given values of $x, z, s,$ and η at two points suc as 1 and 2 in Fig. 7.6, we may calculate values of $x, z, s,$ and η at point 5 at th intersection of the characteristics from the points 1 and 2. Repeating the process the values at the point 6 are found from those given for the points 2 and 3 an the solution 'marches' away from the boundary.

7.4 STRESS FIELD CALCULATIONS FOR DRAINED LOADING

For drained loading, the conditions of equilibrium are given by Eqs (4.50) and (4.51) in terms of effective stress as

$$\frac{\partial \sigma_z'}{\partial z} + \frac{\partial \tau_{xz}'}{\partial x} = \gamma - \frac{\partial u}{\partial z} \qquad (7.20)$$

$$\frac{\partial \sigma_x'}{\partial x} + \frac{\partial \tau_{zx}'}{\partial z} = -\frac{\partial u}{\partial x} \qquad (7.21)$$

and for dry soil we put $u = 0$. The failure criterion for drained loading of soil in plane strain is given by

$$t' = s' \sin \phi_{cs}' \qquad (7.22)$$

Figure 7.7(a) shows the effective normal stresses at a point in the $x:z$ plane and Fig. 7.7(b) shows the corresponding Mohr's circle of effective stress: the state of stress is at failure and hence the Mohr's circle just touches the drained failure envelope given by Eq. (7.22). From the geometry of Fig. 7.7 we have

$$\sigma_x' = s' + t' \cos(180° - 2\eta) = s'(1 - \sin \phi_{cs}' \cos 2\eta) \qquad (7.23)$$

$$\sigma_z' = s' - t' \cos(180° - 2\eta) = s'(1 + \sin \phi_{cs}' \cos 2\eta) \qquad (7.24)$$

$$\tau_{xz}' = \tau_{zx}' = t' \sin(180° - 2\eta) = s' \sin \phi_{cs}' \sin 2\eta \qquad (7.25)$$

Now, differentiating Eqs (7.23) to (7.25) partially with respect to z and x, and substituting into Eqs (7.20) and (7.21), we obtain

[†] A similar expression, given by Eq. (4.79), was obtained in Chapter 4 for the change of stress across a stress fan. In Eq. (4.79) the positive sign is taken for the change of stress *across* a fan of β discontinuities, while in Eq. (7.19) the positive sign is taken for the change of stress *along* an α characteristic.

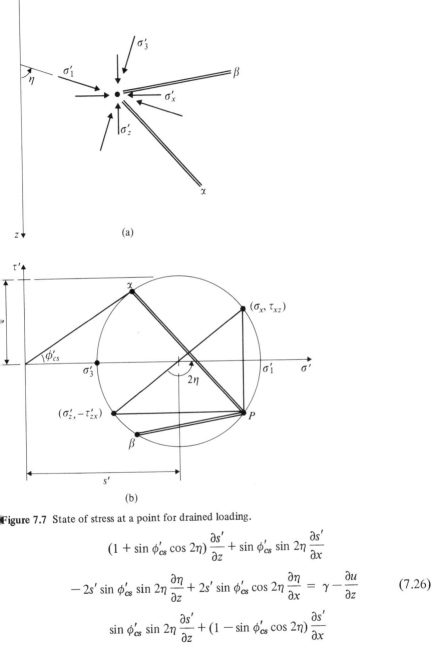

Figure 7.7 State of stress at a point for drained loading.

$$(1 + \sin \phi'_{cs} \cos 2\eta) \frac{\partial s'}{\partial z} + \sin \phi'_{cs} \sin 2\eta \frac{\partial s'}{\partial x}$$

$$- 2s' \sin \phi'_{cs} \sin 2\eta \frac{\partial \eta}{\partial z} + 2s' \sin \phi'_{cs} \cos 2\eta \frac{\partial \eta}{\partial x} = \gamma - \frac{\partial u}{\partial z} \qquad (7.26)$$

$$\sin \phi'_{cs} \sin 2\eta \frac{\partial s'}{\partial z} + (1 - \sin \phi'_{cs} \cos 2\eta) \frac{\partial s'}{\partial x}$$

$$+ 2s' \sin \phi'_{cs} \cos 2\eta \frac{\partial \eta}{\partial z} + 2s' \sin \phi'_{cs} \sin 2\eta \frac{\partial \eta}{\partial x} = - \frac{\partial u}{\partial x} \qquad (7.27)$$

Equations (7.26) and (7.27) are a pair of simultaneous partial differential equations in s' and η. If these can be solved with the appropriate boundary conditions then making use of Eqs (7.23) and (7.25), we may calculate the magnitudes and directions of the effective stresses throughout a region of failing soil.

Equations (7.26) and (7.27), like Eqs (7.16) and (7.17) are hyperbolic and their characteristics are given by

$$\frac{dx}{dz} = \tan\left[\eta \mp (45° - \tfrac{1}{2}\phi'_{cs})\right] \qquad (7.28)$$

Equation (7.28) defines two families of characteristics which intersect at $(90° - \phi'_{cs})$ and the direction of σ'_1 bisects the angle between the characteristics. Thus the characteristics for drained loading which arise as a consequence of the mathematics of hyperbolic equations coincide with the stress characteristics for drained loading shown in Fig. 7.1. As before, α characteristics are associated with the upper (negative) sign in Eq. (7.28) and β characteristics are associated with the lower (positive) sign. Along the characteristics given by Eq. (7.28) total differentials are

$$ds' = \pm 2s' \tan \phi'_{cs} \, d\eta + \gamma[dz \pm \tan \phi'_{cs} \, dx] \qquad (7.29)$$

where the upper (positive) signs give the changes of stress along an α characteristic and the lower (negative) signs give the change of stress along a β characteristic.

Equations (7.28) and (7.29) are four equations with four unknowns (i.e. x, z, s', and η) and, as before, solutions may be found by 'marching' along characteristics from a known boundary. A particular method of solution for drained loading used by Sokolovskii (1965)[†] consists of writing the differential equations in finite difference form, and, since s' appears on the right hand side of Eq. (7.29), employing iterative procedures.

The stresses given by Eqs (7.16) and (7.17) for undrained loading and by Eqs (7.26) and (7.27) for drained loading satisfy the conditions of equilibrium, together with the appropriate failure criterion everywhere within a region of soil limited by the outermost characteristics. They may therefore be thought of as partial lower bounds, but for a complete lower bound it is necessary to examine the states of stress in the regions outside the characteristic mesh, although this may not always be possible.

7.5 DISPLACEMENT FIELD CALCULATIONS

In the previous section we examined solutions which considered only stresses and which satisfied conditions of equilibrium and failure. Similar solutions may be found which examine displacements and which satisfy conditions of compatibility. These displacement calculations assume that all the deformations take place within a region of failing soil, where the value of the angle of dilation ψ is constant

---

[†] Sokolovskii (1965) makes a number of substitutions which simplify Eqs (7.26) and (7.27).

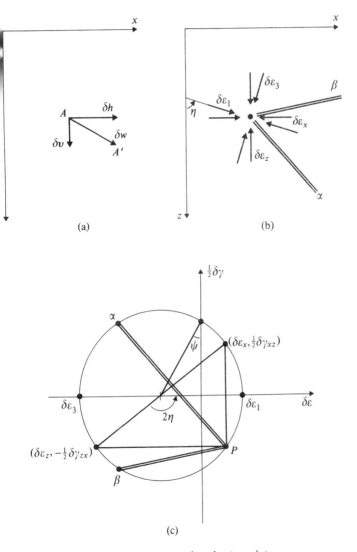

Figure 7.8 Increments of displacement and strain at a point.

and that soil outside this region is stationary. For drained loading, the value of ψ assumes a positive or negative value for dilating or compressing soil respectively and for undrained loading of saturated soil $\psi = 0$.

Figure 7.8(a) shows a plane section which suffers an increment of strain such that a point initially at A moves to A'. The displacement δw has components δv and δh as shown and, as defined in Sec. 2.3, the increments of strain are given by

$$\delta \epsilon_x = -\frac{\partial(\delta h)}{\partial x} \qquad (7.30)$$

$$\delta \epsilon_z = -\frac{\partial(\delta v)}{\partial z} \qquad (7.31)$$

$$\partial \gamma_{xz} = \partial \gamma_{zx} = -\left(\frac{\partial(\delta v)}{\partial x} + \frac{\partial(\delta h)}{\partial z}\right) \qquad (7.32)$$

Figure 7.8(b) shows the increments of normal strain at the point A and Fig. 7.8(c) shows the corresponding Mohr's circle of strain increment for $\psi > 0$.

Conditions of compatibility are satisfied if the increments of strain satisfy the geometry of the Mohr's circle. Hence, from Fig. 7.8,

$$(\delta \epsilon_x - \delta \epsilon_z) = (\tfrac{1}{2}\delta \gamma_{xz} + \tfrac{1}{2}\delta \gamma_{zx}) \cot(180° - 2\eta) \qquad (7.33)$$

$$\tfrac{1}{2}(\delta \epsilon_x + \delta \epsilon_z) = -\tfrac{1}{2}\delta \gamma_{xz} \sin \psi \operatorname{cosec}(180° - 2\eta) \qquad (7.34)$$

and, from Eqs (7.30) to (7.34), we have

$$\frac{\partial(\delta h)}{\partial x} - \frac{\partial(\delta v)}{\partial z} + \cot 2\eta \left[\frac{\partial(\delta v)}{\partial x} + \frac{\partial(\delta h)}{\partial z}\right] = 0 \qquad (7.35)$$

$$\frac{\partial(\delta h)}{\partial x} + \frac{\partial(\delta v)}{\partial z} + \sin \psi \operatorname{cosec} 2\eta \left[\frac{\partial(\delta v)}{\partial x} + \frac{\partial(\delta h)}{\partial z}\right] = 0 \qquad (7.36)$$

Equations (7.35) and (7.36) are a pair of simultaneous partial differential equations with unknowns δh, δv, and η. They are hyperbolic, like Eqs (7.16) and (7.17) and Eqs (7.26) and (7.27), and the characteristics are given by

$$\frac{dx}{dz} = \tan[\eta \mp (45° - \tfrac{1}{2}\psi)] \qquad (7.37)$$

Equation (7.37) defines two families of characteristics which intersect at $(90° - \psi)$ where the direction of $\delta \epsilon_1$ bisects the angle between the characteristics. Thus, characteristics which arise as a consequence of hyperbolic equations coincide with the strain increment characteristics shown in Figs 7.2 and 7.4. As before, α characteristics are associated with the upper (negative) sign in Eq. (7.37) and β characteristics are associated with the lower (positive) sign.

Equations (7.35) to (7.37) are four simultaneous equations in five unknowns (i.e., δv, δh, η, x, and z) and they cannot be solved without additional information. If the coaxiality condition (Sec. 1.5) is valid for soil and so the directions of σ_1 (or σ_1') and $\delta \epsilon_1$ coincide, the angle η is the same for stresses and displacements. Thus values of η found for a stress characteristic mesh may be used to calculate displacements and Eqs (7.35) to (7.37) contain only the unknowns δv, δh, x, and z.

As before, total differentials can be found along the characteristics. Figure 7.9

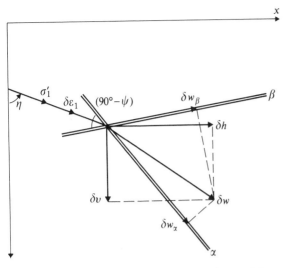

Figure 7.9 Components of displacement along characteristics.

shows a displacement δw with horizontal and vertical components δh and δv, as in Fig. 7.8(a). The components of δw along the characteristics are δw_α and δw_β, and these are related by[†]

$$d(\delta w_\alpha) + (\delta w_\alpha \tan \psi - \delta w_\beta \sec \psi)\, d\eta = 0 \qquad (7.38)$$

$$d(\delta w_\beta) - (\delta w_\beta \tan \psi - \delta w_\alpha \sec \psi)\, d\eta = 0 \qquad (7.39)$$

Equations (7.38) and (7.39) may be solved by 'marching' away from a known boundary along characteristics previously found from a stress field calculation. Having calculated the components δw_α and δw_β, and knowing the value of η, it is a relatively simple matter to calculate the magnitude and direction of δw at each node in the characteristic mesh. Hence we may calculate the horizontal and vertical components δh and δv, respectively, and the strains from Eqs (7.30) to (7.32).

7.6 ASSOCIATED FIELDS CALCULATIONS

In Secs 7.3 and 7.4 we made use of the conditions of equilibrium, together with a criterion of failure to calculate stress fields, and in Sec. 7.5 we made use of the compatibility conditions, together with the associated flow rule, to calculate strain or displacement fields. The complete set of calculations for stresses and strains are known as *associated field calculations*, for the stress characteristic mesh is the same

[†] An analysis is given by Shield (1953), but, in obtaining Eqs (7.38) and (7.39) from this analysis, care must be taken to identify the appropriate characteristics and the directions of the displacements.

as the strain increment characteristic mesh for a material with an associated flo
rule, and hence the two characteristic meshes may be associated one with the othe
Associated field calculations satisfy all the conditions of equilibrium and compa
bility and the requirements of the material properties for a soil with an associate
flow rule which is at a state of failure everywhere within the characteristic mes
and they are therefore exact solutions.

We have only considered the case for which the flow rule is associated an
the soil is everywhere at failure, so the stress and strain increment characterist
meshes are the same, but it is possible to extend the method to the case where th
soil is not everywhere at failure and the flow rule is not associated. In this case th
stress and strain increment characteristic meshes will not be the same, but the
may still be related one to the other by the particular flow rule. These extende
associated fields calculations are beyond the scope of this book and are describe
by, for example, Atkinson and Potts (1975) and Potts (1976).

These calculations have assumed that the strains were continuous and we hav
not, so far, considered states of discontinuous slipping for which there will b
slip lines through the soil. If the deformations are due only to discontinuou
slipping and the material outside the slip planes is assumed to be rigid then, a
shown in Sec. 1.3, slip lines must be lines of zero normal strain and hence the
must coincide with the strain increment characteristics. For this case the restriction
imposed on the shapes of slip planes discussed in Sec. 4.6 apply also to the shape
of the characteristics and hence characteristics must be straight lines or circular arc
for undrained loading or straight lines or logarithmic spirals for drained loadin;
If, however, there are continuous strains, whether or not there is simultaneou
discontinuous slipping, these restrictions do not apply and slip lines, and characte
istics, may follow other curves.

7.7 SLIP LINE SKETCHING FOR UNDRAINED LOADING

For the general case where continuous strains occur, characteristics may be any
curved shape and they have to be calculated as part of the solution. For the cas
where there are no continuous strains and all the deformations are due to dis
continuous slipping, characteristics coincide with slip lines which may only be
straight lines and circular arcs or logarithmic spirals for undrained and drainec
loading respectively. With these strong restrictions on the permissible shapes of the
slip lines, it is often possible to *sketch* a characteristic mesh, thus simplifying the
solution. The technique of sketching a slip line mesh to solve problems of stability
is similar to the technique of sketching flow nets to solve problems of steady state
seepage (e.g. Atkinson and Bransby, 1978, Chapter 4): all that is required in each
case is that the meshes satisfy certain geometrical conditions.

For undrained loading, and in the absence of continuous strains, slip lines must

straight lines or circular arcs, they must intersect at 90°, and the direction of
the major principal stress must bisect the angle between intersecting slip lines. It
is usually fairly simple to sketch a permissible slip line mesh and α and β slip lines
may be distinguished by inspection.

Figure 7.10 shows an element of a slip line mesh for undrained loading, con-
sisting of α slip lines pr and qs and β slip lines pq and rs, which are circular arcs
and which everywhere intersect at 90°. Changes of stress along the slip lines are
given by Eqs (7.19)

$$ds = \pm 2c_u \, d\eta + \gamma \, dz \qquad [7.19]$$

taking the upper (positive) sign for an α slip line and the lower (negative) sign
for a β slip line. If c_u and γ are constants Eq. (7.19) may be integrated to give

$$\Delta s = \pm 2c_u \, \Delta\eta + \gamma \Delta z \qquad (7.40)$$

which gives the change of stress Δs along a slip line in terms of the change of
direction $\Delta\eta$ of the major principal stress and the change of elevation Δz. Since
the direction of σ_1 makes a constant angle of 45° to each slip line, the angle $\Delta\eta$
gives also the change of direction of both slip lines.

The change of stress from p to s in Fig. 7.10 must be the same along the
slip lines pqs and prs, and hence

$$(s_s - s_p) = (s_q - s_p) + (s_s - s_q) = (s_r - s_p) + (s_s - s_r) \qquad (7.41)$$

From Eq. (7.40), along the appropriate slip lines we have

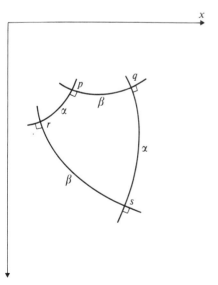

Figure 7.10 Element of a slip line mesh for undrained loading.

$$(s_q - s_p) = -2c_u(\eta_q - \eta_p) + \gamma(z_q - z_p)$$

$$(s_s - s_q) = +2c_u(\eta_s - \eta_q) + \gamma(z_s - z_q)$$

$$(s_r - s_p) = +2c_u(\eta_r - \eta_p) + \gamma(z_r - z_p)$$

$$(s_s - s_r) = -2c_u(\eta_s - \eta_r) + \gamma(z_s - z_r) \tag{7.42}$$

and, from Eq. (7.41),

or

$$(\eta_q - \eta_p) = (\eta_s - \eta_r) \tag{7.43}$$

$$(\eta_r - \eta_p) = (\eta_s - \eta_q) \tag{7.44}$$

Equations (7.43) and (7.44) are an additional geometrical condition which mu be satisfied for a permissible slip line mesh. Put into words, this states that th change of inclination of all slip lines of one family between their intersections wit any two slip lines of the other family is the same and this is known as *Hencky first theorem*. In particular, if (say) an α slip line is straight between two β sli lines then all α slip lines are straight between the same two β slip lines.

7.8 SLIP LINE SOLUTIONS FOR UNDRAINED LOADING

1. Foundation

Figure 7.11(a) shows a section of a long smooth foundation, width B, at the surfac of a soil whose unit weight is γ and those undrained shear strength is c_u. The tot stress at the soil surface outside the foundation is $p^{\dagger}$ and it is required to calcu late the load F_c which, when applied quickly, will cause undrained collapse o the foundation. Figure 7.11(b) shows a slip line mesh consisting of α and β sli lines which are straight lines and arcs of circles, which everywhere interse at 90° and which satisfy Eqs (7.43) and (7.44). Vertical and horizontal tot stresses beneath the foundation and beneath the soil surface are principal stresse and hence the slip lines are inclined at 45° to the horizontal at the soil surfac as shown. The slip line mesh shown in Fig. 7.11(b) may be drawn simply b sketching in the same way that a flow net may be sketched to obtain a solutio for a problem of steady state seepage. It may be compared to the mechanism o plastic collapse shown in Fig. 5.22(a) and the state of stress shown in Fig. 5.23(a which gave identical upper and lower bounds for the undrained failure of foundation.

We consider the states of stress along the β slip line $ADCEB$ in Fig. 7.11(b Noting that principal stresses at A and B are horizontal and vertical, and makin use of the Mohr's circle constructions shown in Fig. 7.11(c), we see that the state of stress at A and B at failure are

$$s_A = \frac{F_c}{B} - c_u \tag{7.45}$$

$$s_B = p + c_u \tag{7.46}$$

† See footnote on p. 164.

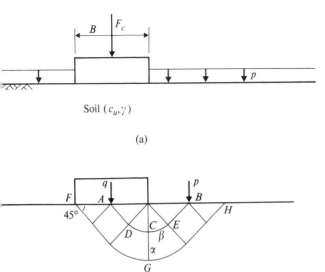

(a)

(b)

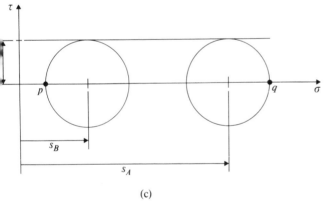

(c)

Figure 7.11 Slip line mesh for a foundation for undrained loading.

The change of stress from s_A to s_B along the slip line $ADCEB$ is given by Eq. (7.40), with the negative sign for a β slip line. From the geometry of Fig. 7.11(b), we have $\Delta\eta = \frac{1}{2}\pi$ and $\Delta z = 0$. Hence

$$s_B - s_A = -\pi c_u \qquad (7.47)$$

and, from Eqs. (7.45) and (7.46),

$$F_c = (2 + \pi)c_u B + pB \qquad (7.48)$$

which is the same as the solution found in Sec. 5.5 for which the upper and low bounds were equal. We might note that in Eq. (7.48) there is no contribution the bearing capacity made by the unit weight of the soil γ, since the increase s along AD is balanced by an equal decrease of s along EB. The calculations for t slip line ACB are valid also for the slip line FGH, and indeed the state of stress ma be found for any point in the mesh. The obvious advantage of the slip line meth is that we have been able to proceed directly to an exact solution without havi to investigate several different mechanisms of plastic collapse and several differe states of stress to find equal upper and lower bounds. We should note, howeve that in the slip line solution we have not examined the state of stress in the regic of soil outside the slip line mesh, and consequently we cannot be absolutely certa that the solution is a lower bound, although for most cases this is not a serio objection.

2. Smooth retaining wall

Figure 7.12(a) shows a section of a long, smooth, rigid wall, height H, retaining so whose unit weight is γ and whose undrained shear strength is c_u. Strong rock occu below the wall so that the slip line mesh will not extend below the base of the wall

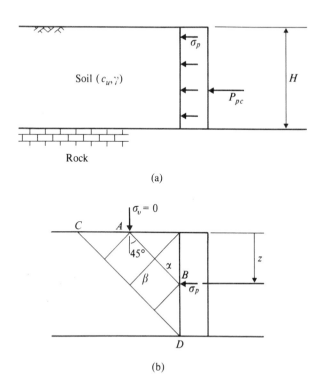

Figure 7.12 Slip line mesh for a smooth wall for undrained passive loading.

s required to calculate the passive force P_{pc} at collapse as the wall moves towards
soil without rotation. The total passive stress between the soil and the wall at a
th z is σ_p and hence

$$P_{pc} = \int_0^H \sigma_p \, dz \qquad (7.49)$$

Figure 7.12(b) shows a sketched slip line mesh for undrained loading, consist-
of straight α and β slip lines which everywhere intersect at $90°$ and which satisfy
s (7.43) and (7.44). The vertical stress at the surface $\sigma_v = 0$ and the horizontal
ess at the wall σ_p are principal stresses, and hence both sets of slip lines intersect
surface and the wall at $45°$ as shown.

We now consider the state of stress along the straight α slip line AB in
. 7.12(b) where the point B is at a depth z below the surface. Making use of
Mohr's circle construction like that shown in Fig. 7.11(c), we find the states
stress at A and B at failure to be

$$s_A = c_u \qquad (7.50)$$

$$s_B = \sigma_p - c_u \qquad (7.51)$$

e change of stress from s_A to s_B along the slip line AB is given by Eq. (7.40)
h $\Delta\eta = 0$ and $\Delta z = z$ as

$$s_B - s_A = \gamma z \qquad (7.52)$$

nce, from Eqs (7.50) to (7.52),

$$\sigma_p = \gamma z + 2c_u \qquad (7.53)$$

d from Eq. (7.49)

$$P_{pc} = \tfrac{1}{2}\gamma H^2 + 2c_u H \qquad (7.54)$$

ich is the same as the solution found in Sec. 5.4 for which the upper and lower
unds were equal. The calculations for the slip line AB are valid also for the slip
e CD and the state of stress may be found for any point in the mesh.

Rough retaining wall

e case for a rough wall is shown in Fig. 7.13. At failure, the shear stress between
soil and the wall is c_w, where, of course, $c_w \leqslant c_u$ and c_w acts downwards
the soil as the soil tends to move upwards with respect to the wall. The total
ssive force at collapse P_{pc} has components N_{pc} and V_{pc}, as shown in Fig. 7.13(a).
e total normal passive stress at a depth z is σ_p, and hence

$$N_{pc} = \int_0^H \sigma_p \, dz \qquad V_{pc} = c_w H \qquad (7.55)$$

the soil surface, the vertical stress $\sigma_v = 0$ is a principal stress and slip lines
ersect the soil surface at $45°$. At the wall, however, there is a shear stress c_w
d the vertical wall is not a principal plane; consequently, σ_p is not a principal
ess and slip lines do not intersect the wall at $45°$. Figure 7.13(b) shows a slip

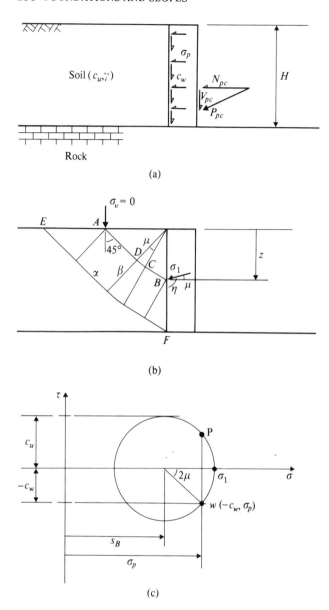

Figure 7.13 Slip line mesh for a rough wall for undrained passive loading.

line mesh for the rough wall for undrained loading, consisting of α and β slip li
which everywhere intersect at $90°$ and which satisfy Eqs (7.43) and (7.44).
vertical stress at the surface $\sigma_v = 0$ is a principal stress and both sets of slip li
are inclined at $45°$ at the surface as shown. If we make use of a Mohr's cir
construction as before, the state of stress at the point A at failure is

$$s_A = c_u \tag{7.56}$$

the point B in Fig. 7.13(b) at a depth z the direction of the major principal
ess is η from the vertical as shown and the angle between the stresses σ_1 and
is μ where $\mu = \eta - 90°$. The Mohr's circle of total stress for the point B is
wn in Fig. 7.13(c) where the point w represents the normal and shear stresses
the wall. From the geometry of Fig. 7.13(c), we have

$$\sin 2\mu = \frac{c_w}{c_u} \tag{7.57}$$

$$s_B = \sigma_p - c_u \cos 2\mu \tag{7.58}$$

m the geometry of Fig. 7.13(b), the rotation of the α slip line from D to C is
as given by Eq. (7.57). The change of stress from s_A to s_B along the α slip line
DCB is given by Eq. (7.40), with $\Delta\eta = \mu$ and $\Delta z = z$ and with the positive sign
an α slip line as

$$s_B - s_A = + 2c_u\mu + \gamma z \tag{7.59}$$

nce, from Eqs (7.56) to (7.59),

$$\sigma_p = \gamma z + c_u [1 + 2\mu + \cos 2\mu] \tag{7.60}$$

ere the angle μ is given by Eq. (7.57) in terms of the shear stress on the wall
and the undrained shear strength c_u. From Eqs (7.55) and (7.56), the hori-
ntal and vertical components of the passive force are

$$N_{pc} = \tfrac{1}{2}\gamma H^2 + c_u H[1 + 2\mu + \cos 2\mu] \tag{7.61}$$

$$V_{pc} = c_w H \tag{7.62}$$

d the total passive force P_{pc} at collapse is given by the vector sum of its
mponents. The calculations for the slip line $ADCB$ are valid also for the slip
e EF, and indeed the state of stress may be found for any point on the mesh.

9 SLIP LINE SKETCHING FOR DRAINED LOADING

r drained loading, and in the absence of continuous strains, slip lines must be
aight lines or logarithmic spiral arcs, they must intersect at $(90° - \phi'_{cs})$, and the
ection of the major principal stress bisects the angle between intersecting slip
es. Figure 7.14(a) shows an element of a slip line mesh for drained loading
nsisting of α slip lines pr and qs and β slip lines pq and rs, which are logarithmic
ral arcs and which everywhere intersect at $(90° - \phi'_{cs})$. Changes of stress along
e slip lines are given by Eqs (7.29):

$$ds' = \pm 2s' \tan \phi'_{cs} \, d\eta + \gamma [dz \pm \tan \phi'_{cs} \, dx] \tag{7.29}$$

king the upper (positive) signs for an α slip line and the lower (negative) signs

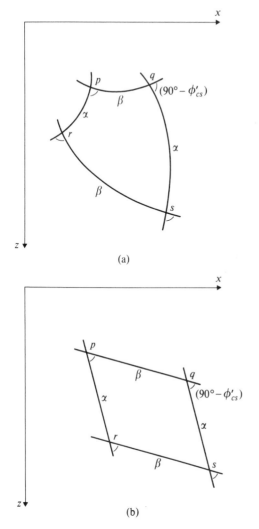

Figure 7.14 Elements of a slip line mesh for drained loading.

for a β slip line. Since s' appears on the right hand side of Eq. (7.29), it cann be simply integrated, even if ϕ'_{cs} and γ are constants.

If, however, we assume that the soil is weightless so that $\gamma = 0$ we may in grate Eq. (7.29). Thus for the slip lines shown in Fig. 7.14(a) we have

$$\ln (s'_q/s'_p) = -2 \tan \phi'_{cs}(\eta_q - \eta_p)$$

$$\ln (s'_s/s'_q) = +2 \tan \phi'_{cs}(\eta_s - \eta_q)$$

$$\ln (s'_r/s'_p) = +2 \tan \phi'_{cs}(\eta_r - \eta_p)$$

$$\ln (s'_s/s'_r) = -2 \tan \phi'_{cs}(\eta_s - \eta_r) \qquad (7.($$

ich may be compared with Eqs (7.42) for undrained loading. As before, the
ange of stress from p to s in Fig. 7.14(c) must be the same along the slip lines
s and prs, and hence

$$\left(\frac{s'_s}{s'_p}\right) = \left(\frac{s'_q}{s'_p}\right)\left(\frac{s'_s}{s'_q}\right) = \left(\frac{s'_r}{s'_p}\right)\left(\frac{s'_s}{s'_r}\right) \tag{7.64}$$

Thus, from Eqs (7.63) and (7.64), we have

$$(\eta_q - \eta_p) = (\eta_s - \eta_r) \tag{7.65}$$

$$(\eta_r - \eta_p) = (\eta_s - \eta_q) \tag{7.66}$$

quations (7.65) and (7.66) are an additional geometrical condition which must
 satisfied for a permissible slip line mesh. These are the same as Eqs (7.43) and
.44) and hence Hencky's first theorem applies equally to slip line meshes for
ndrained loading and to drained loading for weightless soil.

Alternatively, if we assume that slip lines are straight, as shown in Fig. 7.14(b),
 that $d\eta = 0$, Eq. (7.29) may be integrated. Thus, for the slip lines shown in
ig. 7.14(b), we have

$$s'_q - s'_p = \gamma(z_q - z_p) - \gamma \tan \phi'_{cs}(x_q - x_p)$$

$$s'_s - s'_q = \gamma(z_s - z_q) + \gamma \tan \phi'_{cs}(x_s - x_q)$$

$$s'_r - s'_p = \gamma(z_r - z_p) + \gamma \tan \phi'_{cs}(x_r - x_p)$$

$$s'_s - s'_r = \gamma(z_s - z_r) + \gamma \tan \phi'_{cs}(x_s - x_r) \tag{7.67}$$

s before, the change of stress from p to s in Fig. 7.14(b) must be the same along
e slip lines pqs and prs and hence

$$(s'_s - s'_p) = (s'_q - s'_p) + (s'_s - s'_q) = (s'_r - s'_p) + (s'_s - s'_p) \tag{7.68}$$

Hence, from Eqs (7.63) and (7.64) we have

$$(x_q - x_p) = (x_s - x_r) \tag{7.69}$$

r

$$(x_r - x_p) = (x_s - x_q) \tag{7.70}$$

quations (7.69) and (7.70) are automatically satisfied for the element of the slip
ne mesh in Fig. 7.14(b) for which the slip lines are straight and the angles of
ntersection are all $(90° - \phi'_{cs})$.

Thus, for drained loading, the slip line sketching method may be used for
wo special cases. For weightless soil, slip lines may be straight lines or logarithmic
piral arcs intersecting at $(90° - \phi'_{cs})$, and the mesh must satisfy the conditions
mposed by Hencky's theorem. Then, the change of stress along a slip line is
iven by

$$\ln(1 + \Delta s'/s') = \pm 2 \tan \phi'_{cs} \, \Delta \eta \tag{7.71}$$

aking the appropriate sign for α and β slip lines. For cases where the slip line mesh consists only of straight lines, it is not necessary to assume that the soil weightless, and the change of stress along a slip line is given by

$$\Delta s' = \gamma [\Delta z \pm \tan \phi'_{cs} \, \Delta x] \qquad (7.7\text{?})$$

taking the appropriate sign for α and β slip lines. The slip line sketching method not applicable, however, for drained loading of soil which is not weightless an where the slip lines are not all straight. For this case, it is difficult to sketch permissible slip line meshes which satisfy all the necessary requirements, and in addition, Eq. (7.29), giving the changes of stress along slip lines, cannot be simply integrated.

7.10 SLIP LINE SOLUTIONS FOR DRAINED LOADING

1. Smooth retaining wall

For a smooth wall a slip line mesh may be drawn which consists only of straight lines and hence we may make use of Eq. (7.72). In this section we consider the passive force on a smooth wall for drained loading of dry soil as the wall move towards the soil. The corresponding calculations for the active case, as the wall moves away from the soil, are similar. Figure 7.15(a) shows a section of a long smooth, rigid wall, height H, retaining dry soil whose unit weight is γ and whose critical state of angle of friction is ϕ'_{cs}. As before, strong rock occurs below the wall, so that the slip line mesh does not extend below the base of the wall. It is required to calculate the passive force P_{pc} at collapse as the wall moves toward the soil without rotation. The total passive stress between the soil and the wall a a depth z is σ_p, and for dry soil total and effective stresses are equal and

$$P_{pc} = \int_0^H \sigma_p \, dz = \int_0^H \sigma'_p \, dz \qquad (7.73)$$

Figure 7.15(b) shows a slip line mesh for drained loading consisting of straight α and β slip lines which everywhere intersect at $(90° - \phi'_{cs})$. The vertical stress at the surface $\sigma'_v = 0$ and the horizontal stress at the wall σ'_p are principal stresses and hence α slip lines intersect the vertical wall at $(45° + \frac{1}{2}\phi'_{cs})$, as shown.

We consider the states of stress along the straight α slip line AB in Fig. 7.15(b) where the point B is at a depth z below the surface. Making use of the Mohr' circle construction shown in Fig. 7.15(c), we have

$$s'_B = \frac{\sigma'_p}{1 + \sin \phi'_{cs}} \qquad (7.74)$$

and, noting that at A, $\sigma'_v = 0$, we have

$$s'_A = 0 \qquad (7.75)$$

The change of stress from s'_A to s'_B along the straight α slip line AB is given by

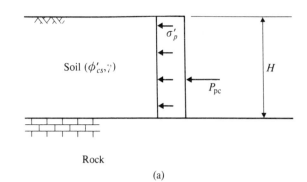

(a)

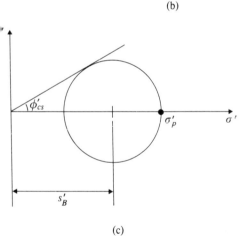

(b)

(c)

Figure 7.15 Slip line mesh for a smooth wall for drained passive loading.

Eq. (7.72), with $\Delta z = z$, $\Delta x = z \tan (45 + \frac{1}{2}\phi'_{cs})$, and, taking the positive sign for an α slip line, as

$$s'_B - s'_A = \gamma z + \gamma z \tan \phi'_{cs} \tan (45° + \frac{1}{2}\phi'_{cs}) \qquad (7.76)$$

Hence, from Eqs (7.74) to (7.76),

$$\sigma_p' = \gamma z(1 + \sin \phi_{cs}')[1 + \tan \phi_{cs}' \tan (45° + \tfrac{1}{2}\phi_{cs}')] \tag{7.7}$$

and, noting that

$$\tan^2 (45° + \tfrac{1}{2}\phi_{cs}') = \frac{1 + \sin \phi_{cs}'}{1 - \sin \phi_{cs}'} = \frac{\cos^2 \phi_{cs}'}{(1 - \sin \phi_{cs}')^2}$$

we have

$$\sigma_p' = \gamma z \tan^2 (45° + \tfrac{1}{2}\phi_{cs}') \tag{7.7}$$

From Eqs (7.73) and (7.78),

$$P_{pc} = \tfrac{1}{2}\gamma H^2 \tan^2 (45° + \tfrac{1}{2}\phi_{cs}') \tag{7.7}$$

which is the same as the solution found in Sec. 6.4 for which the upper and low bounds were equal. The calculations for the slip line AB are valid also for the sl line CD and the state of stress may be found for any point in the mesh.

2. Foundation

Figure 7.16(a) shows a section of a long, smooth foundation, width B, at the surfac of a soil whose critical state angle of friction is ϕ_{cs}' and whose unit weight is take to be zero. The total stress applied to the soil surface outside the foundation is and it is required to calculate the load F_c which, when applied slowly, will cau drained collapse of the foundation. At the soil surface pore pressures are zero ai hence $p' = p$ and the bearing pressure of the foundation is $q' = q$. Figure 7.16(l shows a slip line mesh consisting of α and β slip lines which are straight lines ar logarithmic spirals which everywhere intersect at $(90° - \phi_{cs}')$ and which satis Eqs (7.65) and (7.66). Vertical and horizontal total and effective stresses at the sc surface are principal stresses and the slip lines are inclined at $(45° \pm \tfrac{1}{2}\phi_{cs}')$ to tl soil surface as shown. Making use of the Mohr's circles shown in Fig. 7.16(c), v find that the states of stress at A and at B are

$$\frac{F_c}{B} = s_A'(1 + \sin \phi_{cs}') \tag{7.80}$$

$$p = s_B'(1 - \sin \phi_{cs}') \tag{7.8}$$

The change of stress from s_A' to s_B' along the slip line $ADCEB$ is given by Eq.(7.71 with the negative sign for a β slip line. From the geometry of Fig. 7.16(b) we ha $\Delta\eta = \tfrac{1}{2}\pi$, and hence

$$\ln \left(\frac{s_B'}{s_A'}\right) = -\pi \tan \phi_{cs}' \tag{7.8}$$

and, from Eqs (7.80) to (7.82),

$$F_c = pB \tan^2 (45° + \tfrac{1}{2}\phi_{cs}') \exp (\pi \tan \phi_{cs}') \tag{7.8}$$

which is the same as the solution for drained loading of a foundation on weightle soil found in Sec. 6.5 for which the upper and lower bounds were equal.

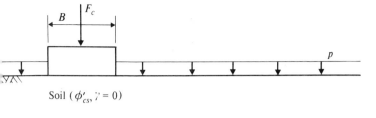

(a)

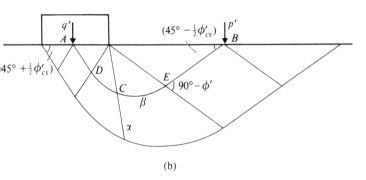

(b)

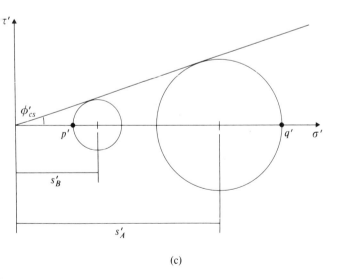

(c)

Figure 7.16 Slip line mesh for a foundation for drained loading.

3. Rough retaining wall

Figure 7.17(a) shows a section of a long, rough, rigid wall, height H, retaining s⊂ whose critical state angle of friction is ϕ'_{cs}. As before, strong rock occurs belo the wall, so that the slip line mesh will not extend below the base of the wa For the case of a rough wall we will find that the slip line mesh consists of sectio which must be curved. Thus we must take the unit weight of the soil as zero an as in the previous section, we may make use of Eq. (7.71) to calculate the chang of stress along slip lines. A uniform total stress p is applied to the soil surface shown in Fig. 7.17(a), and it is required to calculate the passive force at collap P_{pc} as the wall moves towards the soil without rotation. The *effective* shear a⊩ normal stresses τ'_w and σ'_p on the wall at a depth z are related by

$$\tau'_w = \sigma'_p \tan \phi'_w \tag{7.8⋅}$$

where ϕ'_w is the angle of wall friction and, of course, $\phi'_w \leqslant \phi'_{cs}$: as the soil ten⋅ to move upwards with respect to the wall the shear stresses τ'_w act downward For dry soil, pore pressures are zero and all total and effective stresses are equ⋅ thus, at the surface $p' = p$ and at the wall $\tau'_w = \tau_w$ and $\sigma'_p = \sigma_p$. The total passi⋅ force P_{pc} has components N_{pc} and V_{pc}, where

$$N_{pc} = \int_0^H \sigma_p \, dz = \int_0^H \sigma'_p \, dz \tag{7.8∶}$$

$$V_{pc} = \int_0^H \tau_w \, dz = \int_0^H \tau'_w \, dz \tag{7.8⋅}$$

and

$$V_{pc} = N_{pc} \tan \phi'_w \tag{7.8⋅}$$

The presence of the shear stress τ'_w on the wall means that the vertical wall is n⋅ a principal plane; consequently, σ'_p is not a principal stress and the slip lines d not intersect the wall at $(45° + \frac{1}{2}\phi'_{cs})$, as was the case for the smooth wall show in Fig. 7.15.

   Figure 7.17(b) shows a sketched slip line mesh for the rough wall for draine loading consisting of α and β slip lines, which everywhere intersect at $(90° - \phi'_{c⋅}$ and which satisfy Eqs (7.65) and (7.66). We now consider the states of stre⋅ along the α slip line $ADCB$ in Fig. 7.17(b) where the point B is at a depth z belo the surface. The vertical effective stress at the surface $\sigma'_v = p$ is a principal stre⋅ and both sets of slip lines are inclined at $(45° + \frac{1}{2}\phi'_{cs})$ at the surface, as show⋅ Making use of a Mohr's circle construction, we find that the state of stress at th point A at failure is

$$p = s'_A(1 - \sin \phi'_{cs}) \tag{7.8⋅}$$

At the point B in Fig. 7.17(b), at a depth z, the direction of the major principal stre⋅ is η, as shown, and the angle between the stresses σ'_1 and σ'_p is μ, where $\mu = \eta - 90$ The Mohr's circle of effective stress for the point B is shown in Fig. 7.17(c), whe⋅ the point w represents the normal and shear stress on the wall. From the geometr of Fig. 7.17(c), and making use of the angle P as defined in Sec. 4.10, we have

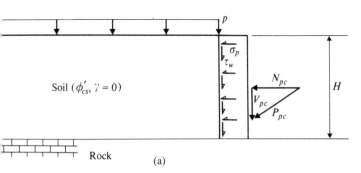

(a)

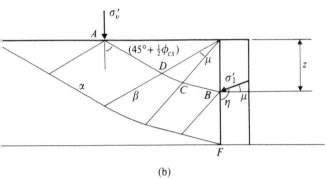

(b)

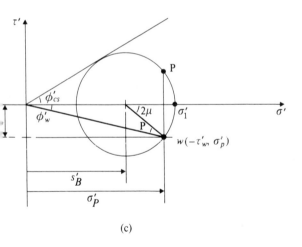

(c)

Figure 7.17 Slip line mesh for a rough wall for drained passive loading.

$$2\eta = P + \phi'_w \tag{7.89}$$

and

$$\mu = \tfrac{1}{2}P - (45° - \tfrac{1}{2}\phi'_{cs}) \tag{7.90}$$

where

$$\sin P = \frac{\sin \phi'_w}{\sin \phi'_{cs}} \tag{7.91}$$

In addition, from the geometry of Fig. 7.17(c), the state of stress at the point is given by

$$\sigma'_p = s'_B(1 + \sin \phi'_{cs} \cos 2\mu) \tag{7.9}$$

From the geometry of Fig. 7.17(b), the rotation of the α slip line from D to C μ, as given by Eqs (7.90) and (7.91).

For weightless soil, the change of stress from s'_A to s'_B is given by Eq. (7.71 with $\Delta\eta = \mu$, taking the positive sign for an α slip line, as

$$s'_B = s'_A \exp\left(2\mu \tan \phi'_{cs}\right) \tag{7.9}$$

Hence, from Eqs (7.88), (7.92), and (7.93),

$$\sigma'_p = p \, \frac{1 + \sin \phi'_{cs} \cos 2\mu}{1 - \sin \phi'_{cs}} \exp\left(2\mu \tan \phi'_{cs}\right) \tag{7.9}$$

and, from Eq. (7.85),

$$N_{pc} = pH \, \frac{1 + \sin \phi'_{cs} \cos 2\mu}{1 - \sin \phi'_{cs}} \exp\left(2\mu \tan \phi'_{cs}\right) \tag{7.9}$$

where the angle μ is given by Eqs (7.90) and (7.91). The vertical shear force V_{pc} given by Eq. (7.87) and hence the passive force P_{pc} at collapse is given by the vect sum of its components.

7.11 DISCUSSION

For the case of a soil which is at a state of failure everywhere within a particula region, the state of stress is governed by partial differential equations which are c the hyperbolic kind for both drained and undrained loading. Equations such a these may be solved along characteristics and these characteristics are the plane for which the Mohr's circle touches the appropriate failure envelope. Similarly, th equations governing the displacements throughout a region of failing soil ar hyperbolic and the characteristics are planes along which normal strains are zerc Thus, by associating fields of stress and displacement, we may obtain a complet solution for the stresses and displacements, or strains, throughout a region of failin soil.

For the case where there are no continuous strains, and where all deformation are due to discontinuous slipping, characteristics and slip lines coincide and the sli line mesh must satisfy a number of geometrical requirements. In the slip lin method, a mesh of slip lines satisfying these criteria is *sketched* and then stresse may be calculated along slip lines. The slip line method is applicable for all case of undrained loading but, for drained loading, it can only be applied simply t special cases for which either the soil is taken to be weightless or all the slip line are straight.

REFERENCES

Abbott, M. B. (1966), *An Introduction to the Method of Characteristics*, Thames and Hudson, London.

Atkinson, J. H. and P. L. Bransby (1978), *The Mechanics of Soils*, McGraw-Hill, London.

———— and D. M. Potts (1975), 'A note on associated fields solutions for boundary value problems in a variable ϕ-variable ν soil', *Geotechnique*, **25**, 379–384.

Garabedian, P. R. (1964), *Partial Differential Equations*, Wiley, New York.

Potts, D. M. (1976), *Behaviour of Lined and Unlined Tunnels in Sand*, Ph.D. Thesis, Cambridge University.

Shield, R. T. (1953), 'Mixed boundary value problems in soil mechanics', *Q. appl. maths*, **11**, 61–75.

Sokolovskii, V. V. (1965), *Statics of Granular Media*, Pergamon Press, Oxford.

WORKED EXAMPLES

E7.1 Stress and Displacement Fields for Undrained Loading

Figure E7.1(a) shows part of a slope with angle $30°$ in soil with undrained shear strength $c_u = 40 \, \text{kN/m}^2$ and unit weight $\gamma = 20 \, \text{kN/m}^3$. Normal stresses $\sigma_n = 50 \, \text{kN/m}^2$ and shear stresses $\tau_n = 20 \, \text{kN/m}^2$ are applied to the surface, which has an increment of displacement 0.1 m normal to the surface, as shown in Fig. E7.1(b). Taking two points on the surface 1.0 m apart, and assuming that the soil is everywhere at failure, calculate the stresses and the displacement at the intersection of the characteristics from the two points.

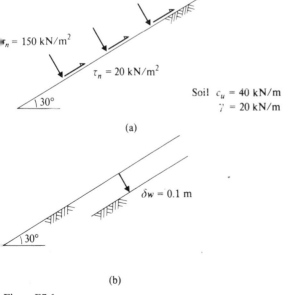

$\sigma_n = 150 \, \text{kN/m}^2$

$\tau_n = 20 \, \text{kN/m}^2$

$30°$

Soil $c_u = 40 \, \text{kN/m}$
$\gamma = 20 \, \text{kN/m}$

(a)

$\delta w = 0.1 \, \text{m}$

$30°$

(b)

Figure E7.1

Figure E7.2 shows the Mohr's circle of total stress for elements of soil at th surface. The circle just touches the undrained failure envelope, the point s gives th surface stresses (σ_n, τ_n), and the pole is at P. From the geometry of the circle, th direction of the major principal stress is given by

$$\eta = 45°$$

and

$$s = \sigma_n - c_u \cos 30° = 115 \, \text{kN/m}^2$$

Figure E7.3(a) shows points A and B which are 1.0 m apart on the surface. Th directions of the major principal stresses are $\eta_a = \eta_b = 45°$ and the directions the characteristics are given by Eq. (7.18) as

$$\frac{dx}{dz} = \tan(\eta \mp 45°)$$

taking the negative sign for the α characteristic BC and the positive sign for th β characteristic AC. The changes of stress along the characteristics are given b Eq. (7.19) as

$$ds = \pm 2c_u \, d\eta + \gamma \, dz$$

taking the positive sign for the α characteristic BC and the negative sign for th β characteristic AC. Writing these in difference form,

$$(x_c - x_a) = (z_c - z_a) \tan\left[\tfrac{1}{2}(\eta_c + \eta_a) + 45°\right]$$
$$(x_c - x_b) = (z_c - z_b) \tan\left[\tfrac{1}{2}(\eta_c + \eta_b) - 45°\right]$$
$$(s_c - s_a) = -2c_u(\eta_c - \eta_a) + \gamma(z_c - z_a)$$
$$(s_c - s_b) = 2c_u(\eta_c - \eta_b) + \gamma(z_c - z_b)$$

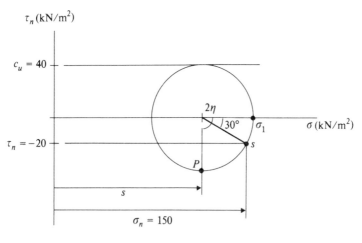

Figure E7.2

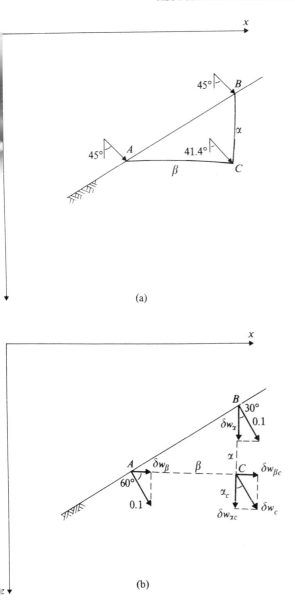

(a)

(b)

Figure E7.3

Taking the point A arbitrarily at $x = 1, z = 1$, we have

$$x_a = 1.0 \, m \qquad z_a = 1.0 \, m$$

$$x_b = 1.866 \, m \qquad z_b = 0.50 \, m$$

and

$$\eta_a = \eta_b = 45°$$

$$s_a = s_b = 115 \, kN/m^2$$

Thus we have four equations with four unknowns (i.e., x_c, z_c, η_c, and s_c) and the solution is

$$\underline{x_c = 1.850 \, m}$$

$$\underline{z_c = 1.027 \, m}$$

$$\underline{\eta_c = 0.723 = 41.4°}$$

$$\underline{s_c = 120.5 \, kN/m^2}$$

Hence we may locate the point C, as shown in Fig. E7.3(a), and the stresses may be found from the values of η_c and s_c, making use of a Mohr's circle construction like that shown in Fig. E7.2. The direction of the major principal stress at C is given by $\eta_c = 41.4°$ and hence the characteristics AC and BC are slightly curved.

Fig. E7.3(b) shows the characteristics AC and BC from Fig. E7.3(a) and the components of the surface displacement along the characteristics are given by

$$\delta w_\alpha = \delta w \cos \alpha$$

$$\delta w_\beta = \delta w \cos \beta$$

where $\alpha = 30°$ and $\beta = 60°$. Hence, for $\delta w = 0.1 \, m$, we have

$$\delta w_\alpha = 0.1 \cos 30° = 0.0866 \, m$$

$$\delta w_\beta = 0.1 \cos 60° = 0.05 \, m$$

The changes of displacement along the characteristics are given by Eqs (7.38) and (7.39) with $\psi = 0$ for undrained loading, as

$$d(\delta w_\alpha) - \delta w_\beta \, d\eta = 0$$

$$d(\delta w_\beta) + \delta w_\alpha \, d\eta = 0$$

or, written in difference form, as

$$(\delta w_{\alpha c} - \delta w_{\alpha b}) - \delta w_\beta(\eta_c - \eta_b) = 0$$

$$(\delta w_{\beta c} - \delta w_{\beta a}) + \delta w_\alpha(\eta_c - \eta_a) = 0$$

where, from the stress field calculations, $\eta_a = \eta_b = 45°$ and $\eta_c = 41.4°$. Hence, the components of the displacement at C are given by

$$\delta w_{\alpha c} = 0.0866 + 0.05(0.723 - \tfrac{1}{4}\pi) = 0.0835\,\text{m}$$

$$\delta w_{\beta c} = 0.050 - 0.0866(0.723 - \tfrac{1}{4}\pi) = 0.0554\,\text{m}$$

Thus the magnitude of the displacement at C is given by

$$\delta w_c = (\delta w_{\alpha c}^2 + \delta w_{\beta c}^2)^{1/2}$$

$$\underline{\delta w_c = 0.100\,\text{m}}$$

The direction of the displacement at C makes an angle α_c to the direction of the α characteristic where

$$\alpha_c = \tan^{-1}\frac{\delta w_{\beta c}}{\delta w_{\alpha c}} = 33.6°$$

Hence, noting that $\eta_c = 41.4°$, the angle γ between the direction of the displacement at C and the vertical is given by

$$\gamma = \eta_c - 45° + \alpha_c = 41.4° - 45° + 33.6°$$

$$\underline{\gamma = 30°}$$

7.2 Stability of a Loaded Slope for Undrained Loading

Figure E7.4 shows a slope with angle i and height H in saturated soil above strong rock. The undrained shear strength of the soil is c_u and its unit weight is γ. A uniform normal stress q is applied to the surface and a uniform normal stress p ($< q$) is applied to the slope as shown. Sketch a slip line mesh and hence calculate the surface stress at collapse q_c for a given value of p for undrained loading.

Figure E7.4 shows a slip line mesh consisting of α and β slip lines which intersect at $90°$ and satisfy Eqs (7.43) and (7.44) and which are at $45°$ to the major principal planes at the surface and at the slope. For the β slip line $ABCD$ we have, from Eq. (7.4),

$$\Delta s = -2c_u\,\Delta\eta + \gamma\,\Delta z$$

At the surface the major principal stress is vertical while at the slope the major principal stress is down the slope and at A and at D respectively we have

$$s_a = q_c - c_u \qquad s_d = p + c_u$$

From the geometry of Fig. E7.4 the counterclockwise rotation of the direction of the major principal stress from A to D is $\Delta\eta = (90° - i)$ and, from Eq. (7.40), for the β slip line $ABCD$ we have

$$s_d - s_a = -2c_u(\tfrac{1}{2}\pi - i) + \gamma z$$

where $z = \Delta z$ is the depth of the point D as shown in Fig. E7.4. Hence we have

$$\underline{q_c = p - \gamma z + c_u(2 + \pi - 2i)}$$

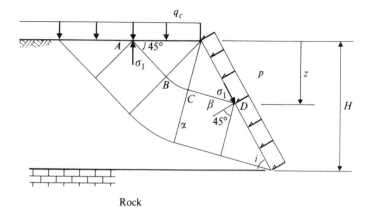

Figure E7.4

With $i = 0$ and $z = 0$, this solution reduces to that for a foundation and with $i = 90$ it reduces to that for the active pressure on a smooth wall.

E7.3 Stability of a Loaded Slope for Drained Loading

Figure E7.5 shows a slope with angle i and height H in dry soil above strong rock. The critical state angle of friction is ϕ'_{cs} and the unit weight is taken to be zero. A uniform normal stress q is applied to the surface and a uniform normal stress $p (< q)$ is applied to the slope as shown. Sketch a slip line mesh and hence calculate the surface stress at collapse q_c for a given value of p for drained loading.

Figure E7.5 shows a slip line mesh consisting of α and β slip lines which intersect at $(90° - \phi'_{cs})$ and satisfy Eqs (7.65) and (7.66) and which make angles $\alpha = (45° + \frac{1}{2}\phi'_{cs})$ to the major principal planes at the surface and at the slope as shown. For the β slip line $ABCD$ we have, from Eq. (7.71),

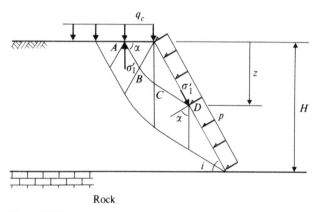

Figure E7.5

$$\ln \left(\frac{s'_d}{s'_a} \right) = -2 \tan \phi'_{cs} (\eta_d - \eta_a)$$

here $(\eta_d - \eta_a) = (90° - i)$ is the counterclockwise rotation of the direction of
the major principal stress from A to D. At the surface the major principal stress
vertical, while at the slope the major principal stress is parallel to the slope as
hown, and at A and D respectively we have, for dry soil for which total and
ffective stresses are equal,

$$s'_a = \frac{q_c}{1 + \sin \phi'_{cs}} \qquad s'_d = \frac{p}{1 - \sin \phi'_{cs}}$$

Hence we have

$$\underline{q_c = p \exp \left[(\pi - 2i) \tan \phi'_{cs} \right] \tan^2 (45 + \tfrac{1}{2} \phi'_{cs})}$$

With $i = 0$ this solution reduces to that for a foundation, and with $i = 90°$ it
educes to that for the active pressures on a smooth wall.

EIGH'

THE LIMIT EQUILIBRIUM METHOI

8.1 INTRODUCTION

The upper and lower bound method and the slip line method are founded in th
theory of plasticity and, for soils which may be assumed to be perfectly plastic a
ultimate failure at the critical state, both methods lead to solutions for the collaps
of soil structures which are theoretically correct. An alternative method fo
examining the stability of soil structures, and one commonly used by geotechnic
engineers, is the *limit equilibrium method*. This combines features of the uppe
and lower bound method, but in general it does not satisfy the requirement fo
the proofs of the bound theorems given in Chapter 4. Although there is no proo
that the limit equilibrium method leads to the correct solution for the stability
of a soil structure, experience has shown that the method gives solutions whicl
agree well with observations of the collapse of real soil structures and it i
a method of analysis which is firmly established among the techniques of geotech
nical engineering.

8.2 THE THEORY OF THE LIMIT EQUILIBRIUM METHOD

In the limit equilibrium method we construct an arbitrary mechanism of collaps
consisting of some arrangement of slip planes, and, without exceeding the appro
priate failure criterion on the slip planes, we ensure the statical equilibrium of eacl
component of the mechanism and of the complete mechanism. Then, by examinin
a number of different mechanisms, we find the critical one for which the loadin
is taken to be the limit equilibrium collapse load. Thus the limit equilibriun
method is like an upper bound calculation in that it considers a mechanism o
collapse, and it is like a lower bound calculation in that it considers conditions o
statical equilibrium.

For a limit equilibrium calculation the mechanism of collapse consists of sliɲ
planes which, for both drained and undrained loading, may be straight lines, arcs
of circles, logarithmic spirals, or any arbitarily shaped curve. The only requiremen
is that the slip planes form a mechanism, although it may be assumed that soil no
in a slip plane may suffer continuous strain to allow a mechanism to become
compatible. The equilibrium of the mechanism is found, following the usua

inciples of statics, by resolving and taking moments of *forces* acting on the
oundaries of the blocks in the mechanism and for the whole mechanism. Thus in
e limit equilibrium method we show that each component of the mechanism, as
ell as the complete mechanism, is in statical equilibrium but we do not consider
e equilibrium of the internal *stresses* in the soil.

Thus there are important differences between the limit equilibrium method and
e upper and lower bound method for the stability of soil structures. For an
opper bound calculation there are strong restrictions on the permitted shapes of the
ip planes for drained and for undrained loading, while for a limit equilibrium
alculation there are no such restrictions and a limit equilibrium mechanism may
ot be allowable for an upper bound. For a lower bound calculation we are required
o examine the states of stress *everywhere* throughout the soil, while for a limit
quilibrium calculation we examine only the overall equilibrium of blocks of soil
y ensuring that the *forces* on their boundaries are in statical equilibrium. Thus a
mit equilibrium solution may not be allowable as a lower bound.

When examining equilibrium conditions we must of course consider the forces
ue to the total stresses acting on the boundaries of the components of the mech-
nism but, as always for soils, we must distinguish carefully between drained loading
or which the ultimate or critical state strength is given in terms of effective stresses by

$$\tau'_n = \sigma'_n \tan \phi'_{cs} = (\sigma_n - u) \tan \phi'_{cs} \qquad (8.1)$$

nd undrained loading for which the soil strength is given in terms of total stresses by

$$\tau_n = c_u \qquad (8.2)$$

he limit equilibrium method may be formulated in quite general terms, from
which we may proceed to special cases. We will, however, begin by examining some
imple limit equilibrium calculations before establishing the general method.

3.3 LIMIT EQUILIBRIUM SOLUTIONS FOR RETAINING WALLS

he stability of a wall provides a convenient example to illustrate the use of the
imit equilibrium method, since a mechanism may be constructed which consists
of a single straight slip plane.

1. Undrained stability of a retaining wall – passive case

Figure 8.1(a) shows a section of a long wall, height H, retaining soil whose unit
weight is γ and whose undrained shear strength is c_u. Strong rock occurs below the
soil so that we need not consider mechanisms which pass below the level of the base
of the wall. It is required to calculate the passive force P_{pc} which causes undrained
passive failure as the wall moves towards the soil without rotation. Figure 8.1(a)
shows a collapse mechanism consisting of a single straight slip plane AB at an
angle α to the vertical. The forces acting on the wedge ABC are shown in Fig. 8.1(b)

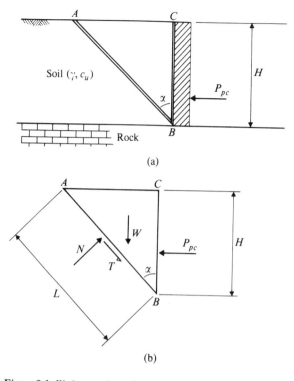

Figure 8.1 Wedge analysis for undrained loading of a wall: passive case. (a) Mechanis▪ (b) Forces on the wedge.

and they are the weight $W = \frac{1}{2}\gamma H^2 \tan \alpha$, the passive force P_{pc}, and the normal an▪ shear forces N and T across the plane AB. For the passive case, T acts down th▪ plane as the wedge moves up and to the left and, at failure,

$$T = \int_{AB} c_u \, dl = c_u L = \frac{c_u H}{\cos \alpha} \tag{8.3▪}$$

Resolving up the plane, for equilibrium,

$$P_{pc} \sin \alpha - W \cos \alpha - T = 0 \tag{8.4▪}$$

and hence

$$P_{pc} = \frac{1}{2}\gamma H^2 + \frac{c_u H}{\cos \alpha \sin \alpha} \tag{8.5▪}$$

In Eq. (8.5) the passive force P_{pc} depends on the angle α of the slip plane, and s▪ we must examine different values for α and so find the critical slip plane for whic▪ P_{pc} is a minimum. This critical slip plane may be found by trial and error, or we may proceed mathematically by differentiating Eq. (8.5) with respect to α and settin▪ $dP/d\alpha = 0$. Hence we have

$$\frac{dP}{d\alpha} = c_u H \frac{\sin^2\alpha - \cos^2\alpha}{\sin^2\alpha \cos^2\alpha} = 0 \qquad (8.6)$$

d $$\alpha = 45° \qquad (8.7)$$

.us, the critical slip plane for undrained loading is at $\alpha = 45°$ and, putting this
lue for α into Eq. (8.5), the limit equilibrium solution is given by

$$P_{pc} = \tfrac{1}{2}\gamma H^2 + 2c_u H \qquad (8.8)$$

or the active case for which collapse occurs as the wall moves away from the
.il, we may proceed in exactly the same way, noting that the shear force T acts up
.e plane AB as the wedge moves down and to the left. For the active case we
.ould also allow for the occurrence of tension cracks in the soil.

This limit equilibrium calculation for the loads on a wall is associated with the
.ame of Coulomb, and it is one of the earliest engineering calculations still in
.rrent use, although with some modifications. The active force on a wall retaining
.il was calculated by Coulomb (1776) using a method very like that given above,
.cept that he did not consider stresses and of course he did not appreciate the
.rinciple of effective stress. His calculations were carried out entirely in terms of
.e *forces* on a sliding wedge and he placed a shear force between the wedge and
.e stationary soil which was dependent on the normal force.

The calculation given above which integrates the *stresses* on the faces of the
.edge is an extension of Coulomb's original method, and the calculations given in
.e next few pages for drained loading in terms of effective stresses are an additional
.xtension of Coulomb's method. A detailed commentary on Coulomb's calculations
.or the loads on a retaining wall was given by Heyman (1972), who also traced the
.evelopments of Coulomb's method to the present. Coulomb's calculations, which
.urn out to be limit equilibrium calculations and are applicable for undrained load-
.1g of saturated soil, may be compared with Rankine's calculations, discussed in
.ec. 6.4, which are lower bounds and are applicable for drained loading of dry soil.

. Drained stability of a retaining wall: active case

'igure 8.2 shows a section of a smooth wall, height H, retaining dry soil whose unit
.veight is γ and whose critical state angle of friction is ϕ'_{cs}. As before, strong rock
.ccurs below the soil, so that slip planes do not pass below the base of the wall. It is
.equired to calculate the active force P_{ac} for which drained active failure occurs as
.he wall moves away from the soil. For drained loading, as shown in Sec. 6.3, soil
.annot exist in equilibrium with a vertical face of any height and so, for drained
.oading, it is not appropriate to consider tension cracks at the soil surface.

Figure 8.2(a) shows a mechanism of collapse consisting of a single straight slip
.lane AB at an angle α to the vertical. The forces on the wedge ABC are shown in
.ig. 8.2(b), and they are the weight $W = \tfrac{1}{2}\gamma H^2 \tan\alpha$, the active force P_{ac}, and the
.ormal and shear forces N and T across the plane AB. For the active case, T acts up
.he plane as the wedge moves down to the right and, for drained loading, T and N

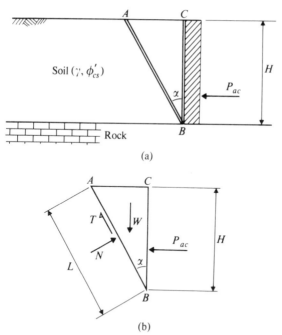

Figure 8.2 Wedge analysis for drained loading of a wall: active case. (a) Mechanism. (b) Forces on the wedge.

are related by ϕ'_{cs}. The total normal and shear forces T and N are given by integrating the total normal and shear stresses over the length AB. Hence, we have

$$T = \int_{AB} \tau_n \, dl \qquad N = \int_{AB} \sigma_n \, dl \qquad (8.9)$$

For saturated soil there is a force U on AB due to the pore pressures u, given by

$$U = \int_{AB} u \, dl \qquad (8.10)$$

Hence, from Eqs (8.9) and (8.10), making use of Eq. (8.1), we have

$$T = (N - U) \tan \phi'_{cs} \qquad (8.11)$$

and, for dry soil for which $u = 0$ everywhere,

$$T = N \tan \phi'_{cs} \qquad (8.12)$$

Resolving up and normal to the plane, for equilibrium,

$$P_{ac} \sin \alpha - W \cos \alpha + T = 0 \qquad (8.13)$$

$$P_{ac} \cos \alpha + W \sin \alpha - N = 0 \qquad (8.14)$$

and hence, using Eq. (8.12) and $W = \frac{1}{2}\gamma H^2 \tan \alpha$, we have

$$P_{ac} = \tfrac{1}{2}\gamma H^2 \tan\alpha \cot(\alpha + \phi'_{cs}) \tag{8.15}$$

oceeding as before and putting $dP/d\alpha = 0$, the active force P_{ac} is a maximum ⍵en the critical slip plane for drained loading is at $\alpha = (45° - \tfrac{1}{2}\phi'_{cs})$. Hence, putting is value for α into Eq. (8.15), the limit equilibrium active force for drained ading is given by

$$P_{ac} = \tfrac{1}{2}\gamma H^2 \tan^2(45° - \tfrac{1}{2}\phi'_{cs}) \tag{8.16}$$

⍵r the passive case we proceed exactly as above except that the shear force T acts ⍵wn the slip plane as the wedge moves up and to the left. The critical angle for ⍵e passive case is $\alpha = (45° + \tfrac{1}{2}\phi'_{cs})$ and the limit equilibrium passive force for ⍵ained loading is

$$P_{pc} = \tfrac{1}{2}\gamma H^2 \tan^2(45° + \tfrac{1}{2}\phi'_{cs}) \tag{8.17}$$

It may be noted that these limit equilibrium solutions for smooth walls for ⍵ained and for undrained loading are the same as those obtained earlier in this ⍵ok from the upper and lower bound method and from the slip line method. This ⍵reement arises because the mechanisms selected for the limit equilibrium calcu- ⍵tions happened to be the same as those found for the slip line method and also ⍵cause conditions of equilibrium of forces for the limit equilibrium method ⍵appened also to satisfy conditions for equilibrium of stress throughout the soil. ⍵his agreement between the limit equilibrium solution and the other theoretically ⍵orrect solutions is not usual, however, and normally we will obtain limit equilib- ⍵um solutions which differ from slip line or bound solutions.

⍵.4 GRAPHICAL METHODS FOR LIMIT EQUILIBRIUM ⍵ALCULATIONS

⍵n order to carry out the limit equilibrium calculations described in the previous ⍵ction, we examined the statical equilibrium of a set of forces acting on a block of ⍵oil in a mechanism by resolving the forces in one or two directions; we may locate ⍵he line of action of an unknown force by taking moments about any point, thus ⍵ollowing the familiar procedures of statics. The conditions of equilibrium for a ⍵et of forces are of course that they shall have no resultant and no couple. Instead ⍵f carrying out these calculations mathematically, we could equally well employ ⍵raphical methods. Thus a set of forces are in statical equilibrium when both their ⍵orce polygon and their funicular polygon close; closure of the force polygon ⍵nsures that the resultant force is zero, and closure of the funicular polygon ensures ⍵hat the couple is zero. It is assumed that readers are familiar with the theory and ⍵se of force and funicular polygons for the analysis of systems of forces.

Limit equilibrium calculations may be carried out using graphical methods, and ⍵n many cases these are simpler and more illustrative than the corresponding ⍵athematical methods. In most cases in geotechnical engineering it is relatively ⍵imple to construct a force polygon to examine the magnitudes of the forces but

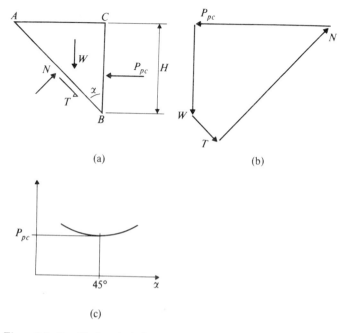

Figure 8.3 Graphical analysis for the undrained stability of the wall in Fig. 8.1. (a) Forces o the wedge. (b) Polygon of forces. (c) Location of critical slip plane.

it is much more difficult to construct a funicular polygon which examines th points of application of the forces. The problem is that, while Eqs (8.3) and (8.9 give the magnitudes of the forces T and N, nothing is said about the distribution of the shear and normal stresses τ_n and σ_n and so nothing can be said about th points of application of the forces. However in geotechnical engineering we ar concerned more with the magnitudes of the forces than with their points of appl cation and consequently we will in general need only to construct force polygor to calculate the magnitudes of the collapse loads.

1. Undrained stability of a retaining wall

Figure 8.3(a) shows the forces on the wedge ABC for undrained passive failure o the wall shown in Fig. 8.1. The directions of all the forces are known and the magnitudes of the forces $W = \frac{1}{2}\gamma H^2 \tan \alpha$ and $T = c_u H/\cos \alpha$ are known also. Thu the force polygon may be constructed as shown in Fig. 8.3(b) and the magnitude of the passive force P_{pc} is given directly. A number of similar polygons should be drawn, each for a different value of the angle α and the critical value of α, and th limit equilibrium value of P_{pc} may be found by plotting P_{pc} against α as shown i Fig. 8.3(c). For the example given in Figs 8.1 and 8.3 the critical angle is $\alpha = 45^\circ$ but this will not necessarily be the critical angle for all cases of undrained failure.

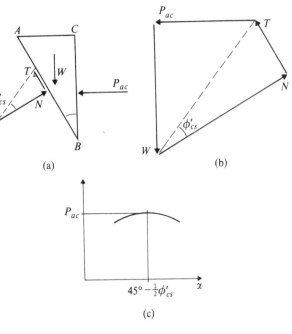

Figure 8.4 Graphical analysis for the drained stability of the wall in Fig. 8.2. (a) Forces on the wedge. (b) Force polygon. (c) Location of critical slip plane.

Drained stability of a wall retaining dry soil

Figure 8.4(a) shows the forces acting on the wedge ABC for drained active failure of the wall shown in Fig. 8.2. The directions of all forces are known, together with the magnitude of $W = \frac{1}{2}\gamma H^2 \tan \alpha$. Although the magnitudes of T and N are unknown for dry soil, they are related by Eq. (8.12):

$$T = N \tan \phi'_{cs} \qquad [8.12]$$

Thus, the force polygon may be constructed as shown in Fig. 8.4(b) and the magnitude of P_{ac} is given directly. The critical angle α and the limit equilibrium value of P_{ac} may be found by constructing a number of similar polygons for different values of α and by plotting P_{ac} against α, as shown in Fig. 8.4(c). For the example given in Figs 8.2 and 8.4, the critical angle is $\alpha = (45° - \frac{1}{2}\phi'_{cs})$ but this will not necessarily be the critical angle for all cases of drained active failure.

The advantages of these graphical calculations are that they are illustrative, relatively simple, and may easily be adapted to account for a number of factors such as irregularly shaped boundaries, free water, rough walls, and, for drained loading, pore pressures in the soil.

3. Undrained stability of a rough retaining wall

Figure 8.5 shows a general case of undrained passive loading of a wall. The w■
supports soil whose unit weight is γ, whose undrained shear strength is c_u, a■
which has a sloping surface. Strong rock occurs below the soil, so that slip plar
do not pass below the base of the wall. The uniform shear stress between t■
soil and the wall is c_w and there is a depth H_w of water to the right of the wa■
It is required to calculate the passive force P_{pc} which causes undrained passi■
failure as the wall moves towards the soil.

   Figure 8.5(a) shows a slip plane AB at an angle α to the vertical, and Fig. 8.5(■
shows the forces on the wedge ABC. The passive force P_{pc} has components N_{pc} a■
V_{pc} and the shear force V_{pc} acts downwards as the wedge ABC moves upwards a■
to the left. The total normal force applied to the soil is the sum of the normal co■
ponent N_{pc} and the force P_w due to free water pressures. The directions of all t■
forces in Fig. 8.5(b) are known and the magnitudes are known of $T = c_u$▪
$W = \gamma$ (area ABC), $V_{pc} = c_w H$, and $P_w = \frac{1}{2}\gamma_w H_w^2$. Thus the force polygon may ▮
constructed as shown in Fig. 8.5(c), and the magnitude of the passive force P▪
measured directly. The calculations should be repeated for a number of differe■
values of α to find the critical angle and the limit equilibrium value of P_{pc}.

4. Drained stability of a retaining wall with steady state seepage

Figure 8.6 shows a general case for drained active loading of a wall for which the■
is steady state seepage towards a gravel drain behind the wall. There is a drain i■
the wall and there is a depth H_w of water to the right of the wall. The wall suppor■
soil whose unit weight is γ, whose critical state angle of friction is ϕ'_{cs}, and whic■
has a sloping surface. Strong rock occurs below the soil, so that slip planes d■
not pass below the base of the wall. The wall is rough and the angle of wa■
friction is ϕ'_w. It is required to calculate the active force P_{ac} which causes draine■
active failure as the wall moves away from the soil.

   Figure 8.6(a) shows a steady state seepage flownet and a slip plane AB at a■
angle α to the vertical, and Fig. 8.6(b) shows the forces on the wedge ABC. Th■
active force P_{ac} has vertical and horizontal components and the vertical componen■
V_{ac} acts upwards as the soil moves downwards and to the right. The *total* horizont■
force N_w between the wall and the soil is given by

$$N_w = N_{ac} + P_w \tag{8.18}$$

where N_{ac} is the horizontal component of P_{ac} and $P_w = \frac{1}{2}\gamma_w H_w^2$ is the horizont■
force due to the free water pressures. The vertical component of P_{ac} is give■
simply by

$$V_{ac} = N_{ac} \tan \phi'_w = (N_w - P_w) \tan \phi'_w \tag{8.19}$$

The total shear and normal forces T and N on the slip plane are related by
Eq. (8.11):

$$T = (N - U) \tan \phi'_{cs} \tag{8.11}$$

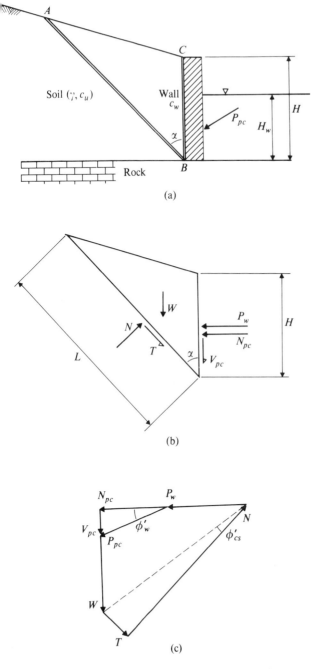

Figure 8.5 Graphical analysis for the undrained stability of a rough wall with external water pressures. (a) Mechanism. (b) Forces on the wedge. (c) Force polygon.

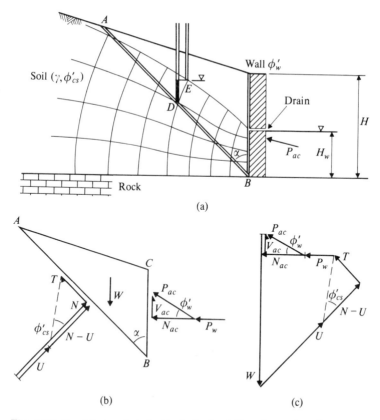

Figure 8.6 Graphical analysis for the drained stability of a rough wall with steady state seepag (a) Mechanism and flownet. (b) Forces on the wedge. (c) Force polygon.

where

$$U = \int_{AB} u \, dl \qquad [8.10]$$

and u is the pore pressure along AB. Noting that the levels of water in standpip whose tips are on the same equipotential, such as those at D and E in Fig. 8.6(a are the same, we may calculate the pore pressure u at any point on AB and thu calculate U from Eq. (8.10), using a convenient numerical integration procedu such as Simpson's rule.

Knowing the magnitudes of W, U, and P_w, we may construct the force polygo as shown in Fig. 8.6(c) and measure directly the magnitude and direction of P_{ac} As before, the calculation should be repeated for a number of different values of to find the critical angle and the limit equilibrium value of P_{pc}.

5. Stability of a slope for a mechanism with two blocks

The method is not restricted to a single wedge, and in many cases a critica mechanism may consist of a number of blocks. Thus, for the case of active failu

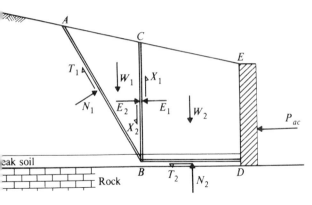

Figure 8.7 Mechanism consisting of two components.

a retaining wall where a layer of weak soil occurs near the base of the wall, as
shown in Fig. 8.7, the critical mechanism may consist of a wedge ABC and a block
CED where the slip plane BD passes through the weak soil. For this case, the
forces E_1 and E_2 and X_1 and X_2 between the blocks must be equal and opposite.
Moreover, since BC is a slip plane, the relationships between the forces X and E are
the same as those between the forces T and N; hence for undrained loading we have
$= c_u L$, and for drained loading we have $X = (E - U) \tan \phi'_{cs}$. Thus we may
calculate E_1 and X_1 by constructing a force polygon for ABC and then use $E_1 = E_2$
and $X_1 = X_2$ to construct a force polygon for $BCED$. In order to determine the
critical mechanism for two blocks, we should vary both the angle of the slip plane
B, the position of B and the inclination of the slip plane BC. The calculations may
be carried out for any number of blocks by equating the forces across the slip planes
between adjacent blocks.

8.5 THE SLIP CIRCLE METHOD FOR UNDRAINED LOADING

So far, we have considered only mechanisms which consist of straight slip planes
arranged to form wedges and blocks, but we may also consider slip planes which
are curved. The simplest curved slip plane is a circular arc and limit equilibrium
calculations involving circular arc mechanisms are known as the *slip circle method*.
Since the analysis for drained and for undrained cases are slightly different, we will
consider each separately, beginning with the undrained case.

Figure 8.8 shows a section through a long foundation, width B, at the surface of
soil with unit weight γ and undrained shear strength c_u. It is required to calculate
the load F_c per unit length of the foundation normal to the page which causes
undrained collapse. Figure 8.8 also shows a mechanism consisting of a semicircular
arc ACB, radius B, whose centre O is at the edge of the foundation. For stability,
the mechanism must be in statical equilibrium. The forces acting on the block of
soil are its weight W, the load F_c, and shear and normal forces across the arc ACB.
Since both W and all the normal forces on ACB act through O, the simplest way

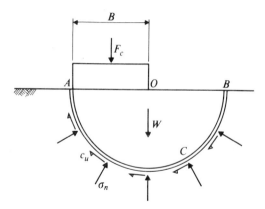

Figure 8.8 Slip circle mechanism for a foundation for undrained loading.

to examine the stability of the mechanism is to take moments about O. F
undrained loading for which $\tau_n = c_u$, the shear force T is given by

$$T = \int_{ACB} \tau_n \, dl = \pi c_u B \qquad (8.2$$

and hence, taking moments about O for equilibrium, we have

$$\tfrac{1}{2} F_c B = TB \qquad (8.2$$

or
$$F_c = 2\pi c_u B \qquad (8.2)$$

We must now investigate the statical equilibrium of different mechanisms,
consisting of circular arcs, to find the critical mechanism for which the collap
load is a minimum. Thus Fig. 8.9 shows an arbitrary circular arc mechanism
radius R which subtends an angle 2α. Proceeding as before we have, for equilibriu

$$\tfrac{1}{2} F_c B = TR \qquad (8.2)$$

where
$$T = \int_{ACB} \tau_n \, dl = 2\alpha R c_u \qquad (8.2)$$

From the geometry of Fig. 8.9 we have $R = B/(\sin \alpha)$ and hence

$$F_c = 4 c_u B \frac{\alpha}{\sin^2 \alpha} \qquad (8.2)$$

The critical slip plane may be found by trial and error or we may differentia
Eq. (8.25) with respect to α and set $dF/d\alpha = 0$. Hence we have

$$\frac{dF}{d\alpha} = 4 c_u B \frac{\sin^2 \alpha - 2\alpha \sin \alpha \cos \alpha}{\sin^4 \alpha} = 0 \qquad (8.26)$$

and
$$\alpha = 66°47' \qquad (8.27)$$

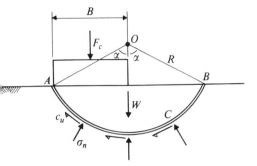

ure 8.9 Slip circle mechanism for a foundation for undrained loading.

us the critical circular slip plane is given by $\alpha = 66°47'$ in Fig. 8.9 and the limit
uilibrium collapse load is given by

$$F_c = 5.5c_uB \tag{8.28}$$

e limit equilibrium solution given by Eq. (8.28) differs from the solution
$_c = (2 + \pi)c_uB$ found from upper and lower bounds and from the slip line method
d thus the mechanism shown in Fig. 8.9 is not the true collapse mechanism.

The slip circle method may also be applied to the analysis of the undrained
ability of slopes and walls and the calculations are similar to those described for
foundation. Figure 8.10 shows a section of a slope cut into a homogeneous soil
ose unit weight is γ and whose undrained shear strength is c_u. The height of the
ope is H and its angle is i. Figure 8.10 also shows a slip circle ACB of radius R
ith its centre at O, and for stability the mechanism must be in statical equilibrium.
e forces acting on the soil block are its weight W and the shear and normal forces
and N on the arc ACB. As before, for undrained loading for which $\tau_n = c_u$, the
ear force T is given by

$$T = \int_{ACB} \tau_n \, dl = c_u L \tag{8.29}$$

here L is the length of the arc AB. Taking moments about O and noting that all
ormal forces act through O, we have, for equilibrium

$$Wx = c_u RL \tag{8.30}$$

here x is the horizontal distance from O to the line of action of W, as shown in
ig. 8.10. The position of the critical circle must usually be found by trial and
rror, by varying both the radius R of the circle and the position of its centre. Thus
e slope is just on the point of collapse if Eq. (8.30) is satisfied for the critical
echanism.

These slip circle calculations for undrained loading may be extended very simply
ɔ include loadings due to foundations or walls or to external water pressure. Thus
ig. 8.11 shows the same slope at that in Fig. 8.10, but with the addition of a load

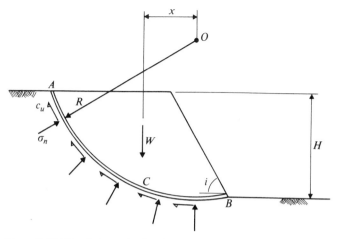

Figure 8.10 Slip circle mechanism for slope stability for undrained loading.

F at the top of the slope and with free water to a depth H_w at the toe of the slope. The water exerts a force P_w normal to the slope over the length L_w given by

$$P_w = \int_{DB} u \, dl = \tfrac{1}{2}\gamma_w H_w L_w \tag{8.3}$$

Hence, taking moments about O for equilibrium, we have

$$Wx_w + Fx_f - P_w x_u = c_u RL \tag{8.3}$$

where x_w, x_f, and x_u are measured from the centre O to the lines of action of the forces W, F, and P_w, as shown in Fig. 8.11. Again, the critical circle must be found

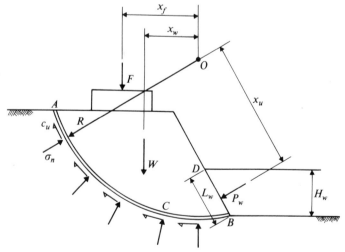

Figure 8.11 Slip circle analysis for undrained stability of a slope with external loading.

trial and error, varying both the radius R of the circle and the position of its centre. In practice, for slip circle calculations for undrained loading, it is usually simplest to prepare a scaled drawing of a section of the slope and to obtain values or W, x, and L_w by direct measurement from the scaled drawing.

6 THE SLIP CIRCLE METHOD FOR DRAINED LOADING – THE ETHOD OF SLICES

gure 8.12 shows a section of the same slope as that shown in Figs 8.10 and 8.11, it now we consider the case for drained loading. Figure 8.12(a) shows part of a etched flownet for steady state seepage towards a drain at the toe of the slope, id hence we may calculate the magnitudes of the steady state pore pressures erywhere throughout the soil. We may proceed as before to construct a circular c slip mechanism as shown in Fig. 8.12(b), and, taking moments about O, we ive, for equilibrium,

$$Wx = TR \tag{8.33}$$

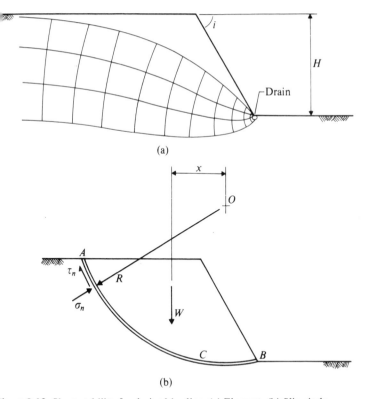

(a)

(b)

Figure 8.12 Slope stability for drained loading. (a) Flownet. (b) Slip circle.

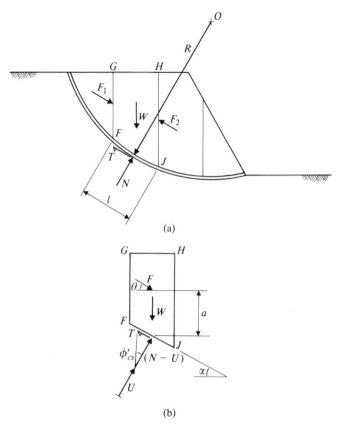

Figure 8.13 Method of slices for drained stability of a slope. (a) Arrangement of slice (b) Forces on a typical slice.

where
$$T = \int_{ACB} \tau_n \, dl \qquad (8.3$$

and, from Eq. (8.1),

$$\tau_n = \tau_n' = (\sigma_n - u) \tan \phi_{cs}' \qquad [8.1]$$

Although we may determine the values of the pore pressures u around the arc AC we cannot, at present, calculate the values of the total normal stresses σ_n. Thus th simple analysis which served for undrained loading for which $\tau_n = c_u$ is not appr priate for drained loading for which $\tau_n = (\sigma_n - u) \tan \phi_{cs}'$, and we will have **t** modify the method of analysis.

The approach adopted for the *method of slices* is to subdivide the mechanis into a number of approximately equal vertical slices, and to examine the static equilibrium of the slices and, by summation, of the whole mechanism. Figu 8.13(a) shows the mechanism of Fig. 8.12(b) divided into four slices of which typical slice *FGHJ* is shown in Fig. 8.13(b). The total forces on the slice shown Fig. 8.13(b) are its weight W, the total normal and shear forces N and T on the ba

J, and forces F_1 and F_2 from adjacent slices. The interslice forces F_1 and F_2 are not necessarily equal and opposite, and their resultant F acts at a height a above the centre of the base of the slice and at an angle θ to the horizontal. The total normal and shear forces on the base of the slice are related by Eq. (8.11)

$$T = (N - U) \tan \phi'_{cs} \qquad [8.11]$$

where, for slices which are relatively narrow, the forces may be taken as $T = \tau_n l$, $N = \sigma_n l$ and $U = ul$ where l is th length of the base FJ and it is assumed that the points of application are at the mid-point of the arc FJ. For cases where there is 8.11) is valid for each slice, and for the whole mechanism, summing for all the slices, we have

$$\sum T = \sum (N - U) \tan \phi'_{cs} \qquad (8.35)$$

The interslice forces such as F may be decomposed into horizontal and vertical components E and X, as in Fig. 8.7 and Sec. 8.4. However, in the slip circle method the boundaries between adjacent slices are not slip planes as they were in the earlier case and so nothing can be said at present about the magnitude, direction, or point of application of the force F in Fig. 8.13(b).

Consider the force on the block $FGHJ$ in Fig. 8.13(b): the magnitudes, directions, and points of application are known for W and U, the directions and points of application are known for T and N, and nothing is known about the force F. Thus there are five unknowns: T, N, F, a, and θ. We may obtain three equations by resolution of forces and by taking moments following the usual rules of statics and these, together with Eq. (8.11), lead to a possible total of four equations and each slice is statically indeterminate. In order to obtain a solution for the method of slices for drained loading, we are obliged to make at least one simplifying assumption in order to make the problem statically determinate, and there are a number of such solutions, each based on a different simplifying assumption. For the present we will consider the two commonest of these solutions.

1. The Swedish method of slices

Here it is assumed that the resultant F of the interslice forces is zero for each slice and thus F, a, and θ vanish. Each slice is then statically determinate, and from Fig. 8.14 we have

$$T = W \sin \alpha \qquad N = W \cos \alpha \qquad (8.36)$$

where α is the average inclination of the slip surface at the base of the slice. Hence we may calculate T and N for each slice and, for equilibrium,

$$\sum T = \sum (N - U) \tan \phi'_{cs} \qquad [8.35]$$

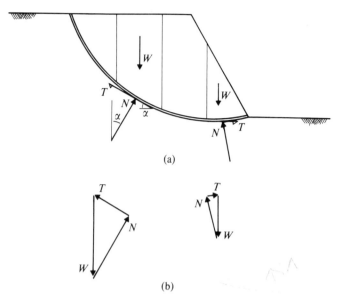

(a)

(b)

Figure 8.14 Swedish method of slices. (a) Forces on typical slices. (b) Force polygons for typical slices.

or
$$\sum W \sin \alpha = \sum (W \cos \alpha - ul) \tan \phi'_{cs} \qquad (8.37)$$

where u is the average pore pressure over the length l of the base of each slice. Instead of making use of Eqs (8.36), we may calculate T and N for each slice from force polygons, like those shown in Fig. 8.14(b), but in any event it is necessary to take account of the directions of the shear forces, as shown in Fig. 8.14. The calculations are assisted by the use of a table such as that shown in Table 8.1. As before it is necessary to examine a number of different mechanisms to locate the critical slip circle; the slope is taken to be in a state of collapse if Eqs (8.35) or (8.37) are satisfied for any mechanism.

2. The Bishop routine method (Bishop, 1955)

Here it is assumed that the resultant of the interslice forces is horizontal. Hence $\theta = 0$ as shown in Fig. 8.15 and each slice is statically determinate. Taking moments about the centre of the circle and summing for the whole mechanism, we have, for equilibrium,

$$\sum Wx = \sum TR \qquad (8.38)$$

and from Eq. (8.11), noting that $x = R \sin \alpha$ in Fig. 8.15 we have

$$\sum W \sin \alpha = \sum (N - U) \tan \phi'_{cs} \qquad (8.39)$$

Table 8.1 Scheme of calculation for the Swedish method of slices

Slice No.	Area A	Slope α	Length l	Weight $W = \gamma A$	Shear force $T = W \sin \alpha$	Normal force $N = W \cos \alpha$	Pore pressure u	$U = ul$	$(N - U) \tan \phi'_{cs}$
Totals					ΣT				$\Sigma (N - U) \tan \phi'_{cs}$

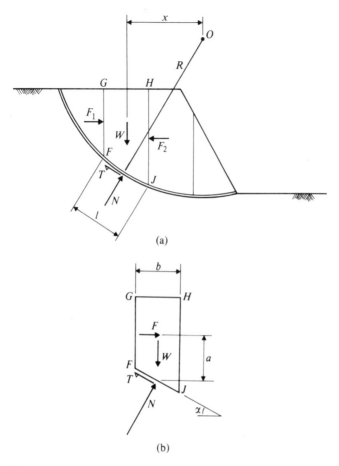

Figure 8.15 Forces on a typical slice for Bishop's routine method.

Resolving vertically for each slice, we have

$$W = N \cos \alpha + T \sin \alpha \tag{8.40}$$

and hence, making use of Eq. (8.11),

$$(N - U) = \frac{W \sec \alpha - U}{1 + \tan \alpha \tan \phi'_{cs}} \tag{8.41}$$

Substituting Eq. (8.41) in Eq. (8.39), we have, for equilibrium,

$$\sum W \sin \alpha = \sum \frac{(W \sec \alpha - U) \tan \phi'_{cs}}{1 + \tan \alpha \tan \phi'_{cs}} \tag{8.42}$$

If the width of each slice is b where $b = l \cos \alpha$ then Eq. (8.42) becomes

$$\sum W \sin \alpha = \sum \frac{(W - ub) \sec \alpha \tan \phi'_{cs}}{1 + \tan \alpha \tan \phi'_{cs}} \tag{8.43}$$

we wished, we could resolve horizontally and take moments for each slice and so calculate values for the (horizontal) interslice forces and their points of action, but there is no real need to do so. In practice, evaluation of Eq. (8.43) is simplified if use is made of a table similar to Table 8.1. As before, it is necessary to examine a number of different mechanisms to locate the critical slip circle; the slope is then taken to be in a state of collapse if Eq. (8.43) is satisfied for any mechanism.

.7 GENERAL LIMIT EQUILIBRIUM SOLUTIONS

So far we have considered mechanisms for limit equilibrium calculations which consist of straight lines or circular arcs and we have considered the stability of walls, foundations, and slopes with relatively simple boundaries. The method may, however, be applied to quite general problems, assuming mechanisms which consist of quite general curved slip surfaces (Morgenstern and Price, 1965). The approach for the general limit equilibrium method is by the method of slices described in the previous section.

Figure 8.16(a) shows a slope with a non-uniform surface and with an arbitrary mechanism and, for convenience, we define axes x and z as shown. The ground surface is given by the function $G(x)$, the slip surface by $S(x)$, and the slope of the slip surface is α, where $\tan \alpha = \mathrm{d}S/\mathrm{d}x$. The level to which water rises in a standpipe inserted into the slope with its tip at the slip surface is $P(x)$ and $P(x)$ is the potential around the slip surface; thus the pore pressures around the slip surface are given by

$$u(x) = \gamma_w[P(x) - S(x)] \tag{8.44}$$

Figure 8.16(b) shows a thin slice whose width is δx. There is an external force δQ and the weight of the slice δW is given by

$$\delta W = \gamma[G(x) - S(x)] \, \delta x \tag{8.45}$$

The total normal and shear forces on the base length δl of the slice are

$$\delta T = \tau_n \, \delta l \tag{8.46}$$

$$\delta N = \sigma_n \, \delta l \tag{8.47}$$

The forces on the slice from the adjacent slices are E and X and $(E + \delta E)$ and $(X + \delta X)$, as shown in Fig. 8.16(b). The points of application of these forces lie on a line through the slope given by $A(x)$ as shown in Fig. 8.16(a). In general the forces X and E and their line of action $A(x)$ are unknown.

Resolving vertically and horizontally and taking moments about M in Fig. 8.16(b), for the slice to be in equilibrium, we have

$$\delta Q + \delta W + \delta X - \delta T \sin \alpha - \delta N \cos \alpha = 0 \tag{8.48}$$

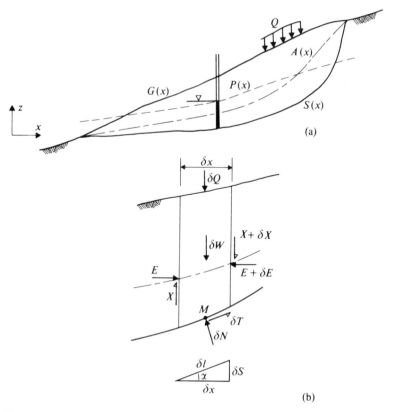

Figure 8.16 General limit equilibrium method. (a) Collapse mechanism. (b) Forces on a slice.

$$\delta E - \delta T \cos \alpha + \delta N \sin \alpha = 0 \tag{8.49}$$

$$\tfrac{1}{2}X\delta x + \tfrac{1}{2}(X + \delta X)\,\delta x + E\left[A(x) - S(x) - \frac{1}{2}\frac{\mathrm{d}A}{\mathrm{d}x}\,\delta x\right]$$

$$- (E + \delta E)\left[A(x) - S(x) + \frac{1}{2}\frac{\mathrm{d}A}{\mathrm{d}x}\,\delta x\right] = 0 \tag{8.50}$$

Hence, noting that $\sin \alpha = \delta S/\delta l$ and $\cos \alpha = \delta x/\delta l$, and making use of Eqs (8.45) to (8.47), we have

$$\delta Q + \gamma[G(x) - S(x)]\,\delta x + \delta X - \tau_n\,\delta S - \sigma_n\,\delta x = 0 \tag{8.51}$$

$$\delta E - \tau_n\,\delta x + \sigma_n\,\delta S = 0 \tag{8.52}$$

$$X\delta x - E\frac{\mathrm{d}A}{\mathrm{d}x}\,\delta x - \delta E\,A(x) + \delta E\,S(x) = 0 \tag{8.53}$$

Dividing through by δx, and in the limit as $\delta x \to 0$, Eqs (8.51) to (8.53) become

$$\frac{dQ}{dx} + \gamma[G(x) - S(x)] + \frac{dX}{dx} - \tau_n \frac{dS}{dx} - \sigma_n = 0 \tag{8.54}$$

$$\frac{dE}{dx} - \tau_n + \sigma_n \frac{dS}{dx} = 0 \tag{8.55}$$

$$X - \frac{d}{dx}[E \cdot A(x)] + S(x)\frac{dE}{dx} = 0 \tag{8.56}$$

We must also satisfy one or other of the failure criteria for soil given by Eqs (8.1) and (8.2). Hence for drained loading,

$$\tau_n = (\sigma_n - u) \tan \phi'_{cs} \tag{8.57}$$

where $u = u(x)$ is given by Eq. (8.44), while for undrained loading,

$$\tau_n = c_u \tag{8.58}$$

Equations (8.54) to (8.56) (or (8.51) to (8.53)), together with one or other of Eqs (8.57) and (8.58), govern the stability of the slope shown in Fig. 8.16; thus we may obtain four equations, but there are five unknowns (i.e., τ_n, σ_n, X, E and $A(x)$) and the solution requires at least one assumption.

We have already discussed two of these assumptions. For the Swedish method of slices it was assumed that both E and X were zero, while for the Bishop routine method it was assumed that X was zero. In the discussion of these methods in the previous section, the mechanisms were taken to be circular arcs and conditions of equilibrium were examined by taking moments about their centres; the same problems could, however, be solved using Eqs (8.51) to (8.53) or Eqs (8.54) to (8.56), with the appropriate failure criterion given by one or other of Eqs (8.57) or (8.58). Other possible assumptions involve the relative magnitudes of the inter-slice forces X and E. Thus, for example, Janbu (1954) assumed $X/E =$ constant, while Morgenstern and Price (1965) assumed $X/E = \lambda f(x)$, where λ is a constant which may be calculated as part of the solution and $f(x)$ is chosen so that the line of action $A(x)$ of the interslice forces is located in a reasonable position between the surface and the slip plane.

8.8 FACTOR OF SAFETY

Throughout this chapter, and indeed throughout the previous three chapters, we have been concerned with structures on the point of collapse for which the factor of safety discussed in Sec. 3.9 was $F_s = 1.0$ and for which stresses on certain planes through the soil were those corresponding to either the drained or the undrained failure criterion given by, for example Eqs (8.1) and (8.2). More often, however, we will be concerned with structures which do not collapse and for which $F_s > 1.0$ and we will seek to calculate the value of the factor of safety.

As discussed in Sec. 3.9, we estimate the factor of safety of a soil structure by carrying out an appropriate stability calculation, using one or other of the methods described in the previous chapters and using either an allowable undrained shear strength c_{ua} or an allowable angle of friction ϕ'_a given by

$$c_{ua} = \frac{c_u}{F_s} \tag{8.59}$$

$$\phi'_a = \tan^{-1}\left(\frac{\tan \phi'_{cs}}{F_s}\right) \tag{8.60}$$

In general, we will not be able to calculate a value for F_s for a soil structure directly. Instead, we must usually guess a value for F_s and then determine whether the reduced soil strength just causes collapse to occur. Thus, for the limit equilibrium method, the factor of safety of a soil structure is taken to be that value for F_s which will just cause collapse for the most critical mechanism. Thus a limit equilibrium calculation may be a lengthy process and, even at the end, there can be no certainty that the most critical mechanism has been found or that the solution is correct.

8.9 DISCUSSION

The limit equilibrium method is, in practice, the most widely used method for examining the stability of soil structures. We have seen, though, that the solutions may not be theoretically correct, since they do not always satisfy the requirements for upper bounds or for lower bounds. Nevertheless, experience has shown that limit equilibrium calculations often lead to very good estimates for the collapse of soil structures, even though in some cases it may be necessary to make simplifying assumptions in order to make the problem statically determinate.

The limit equilibrium method has a number of advantages. It is quite general and may be applied equally to walls, slopes, or foundations, and indeed to any combination of these. The method may easily be adapted for cases where the soil consists of layers, each of which may have different properties, and it is simple to include irregularly shaped boundaries. The calculations for determining the forces on slices and for seeking a critical mechanism are largely repetitive, and they are well suited to machine computation. Thus there exist a number of computer programs for the stability of soil structures which are based on the limit equilibrium method and which make use of one or other of the particular methods described in this chapter.

REFERENCES

Bishop, A. W. (1955), 'The use of the slip circle in the stability analysis of earth slopes', *Geotechnique*, 5, 7–17.

Coulomb, C. A. (1776), 'Essai sur une application des règles *des maximis et minimis* à quelques problèmes de statique, relatifs à l'architecture', *Mémoires de Mathématique de l'Académie Royale des Sciences*, 7, 343–392, Paris.

eyman, J. (1972), *Coulomb's memoir on statics*, Cambridge University Press.
anbu, N. (1954), 'Application of composite slip circles for stability analysis', *Proc. European Conf. on Stability of Earth Slopes*, 4, 43–49, Stockholm.
forgenstern, N. R. and V. E. Price (1965), 'The analysis of the stability of general slip surfaces', *Geotechnique*, 15, 79–93.

WORKED EXAMPLES

E8.1 Load on Trench Struts for Undrained Loading

A trench is excavated to a depth of 5 m through saturated soil, with undrained shear strength $c_u = 15 \, \text{kN/m}^2$ and unit weight $\gamma = 20 \, \text{kN/m}^3$. Strong rock occurs at the base of the trench and there is a uniform surcharge of $80 \, \text{kN/m}^2$ at the surface. The sides of the trench are stabilized by smooth, rigid sheet piles held apart by struts at intervals of 1 m, placed so that the sheet piles do not rotate. Taking a mechanism consisting of a wedge with a slip plane at an angle $45°$ to the vertical, and making use of a graphical method, calculate a limit equilibrium solution for the strut loads required to maintain the stability of the trench for undrained loading. (It may be assumed that the surcharge load is sufficiently large to prevent the formation of tension cracks.)

Figure E8.1(a) shows the mechanism with a single slip plane at an angle $45°$ to the vertical. The known forces acting on the wedge are its weight W, a force Q due to the surcharge, and T due to the shear stresses on the slip plane. For a slice 1 m thick we have

$$W = \tfrac{1}{2}\gamma H^2 = \tfrac{1}{2} \times 20 \times 5^2 = 250 \, \text{kN}$$

$$Q = qH = 80 \times 5 = 400 \, \text{kN}$$

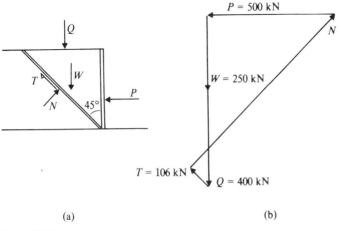

(a) (b)

Figure E8.1

$$T = c_u\sqrt{2}H = 15\sqrt{2} \times 5 = 106\,\text{kN}$$

The polygon of forces for the wedge in shown in Fig. E8.1(b) and, scaling from the diagram, we have

$$\underline{P = 500\,\text{kN}}$$

This equilibrium solution is the same as that found for the same problem in Example E5.1, for which the upper bound and lower bound solutions were equal.

E8.2 Loads on Trench Struts for Dry Soil

A trench is excavated to a depth of 5 m through dry soil with critical state angle of friction $\phi'_{cs} = 30°$ and unit weight $\gamma = 15\,\text{kN/m}^3$. Strong rock occurs at the base of the trench and there is a uniform surcharge of $80\,\text{kN/m}^2$ at the surface. The sides of the trench are stabilized by smooth, rigid sheet piles held apart by struts at intervals of 1 m normal to the page, placed so that the sheet piles do not rotate. Taking a mechanism consisting of a wedge with a slip plane at $(45° - \frac{1}{2}\phi'_{cs}) = 30°$ to the vertical and making use of a graphical method, calculate a limit equilibrium solution for the strut loads required to maintain the stability of the trench.

Figure E8.2(a) shows the mechanism with a single slip plane at an angle $30°$ to the vertical. The known forces acting on the wedge are its weight W and a force Q due to the surcharge and, from Eq. (8.12), for dry soil the shear and normal forces on the slip plane are related by

$$T = N \tan \phi'_{cs}$$

For a slice 1 m thick normal to the page we have

$$W = \tfrac{1}{2}\gamma H^2 \tan (45° - \tfrac{1}{2}\phi'_{cs}) = 108\,\text{kN}$$

$$Q = qH \tan (45° - \tfrac{1}{2}\phi'_{cs}) = 231\,\text{kN}$$

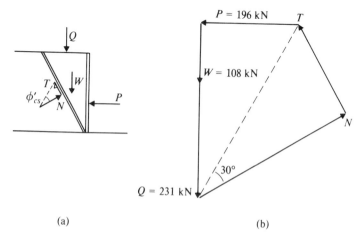

(a)   (b)

Figure E8.2

The polygon of forces for the wedge is shown in Fig. E8.2(b) and, scaling from the diagram, we have

$$P = 196\,\text{kN}$$

This equilibrium solution is the same as that found for the same problem in Example E6.1, for which the upper bound solutions were equal.

E8.3 Loads on Trench Struts with Steady State Seepage

Figure E8.3(a) shows a section through a trench excavated to a depth of 5 m through soil for which the water table before construction was at ground level. The critical state angle of friction for the soil is $\phi'_{cs} = 30°$, the unit weight of saturated soil is $\gamma = 20\,\text{kN/m}^3$, and the unit weight of dry soil is $\gamma_d = 15\,\text{kN/m}^3$. The sides of the trench are stabilized by smooth, rigid sheet piles held apart by struts at intervals of 1 m normal to the page, placed so that the piles do not rotate.

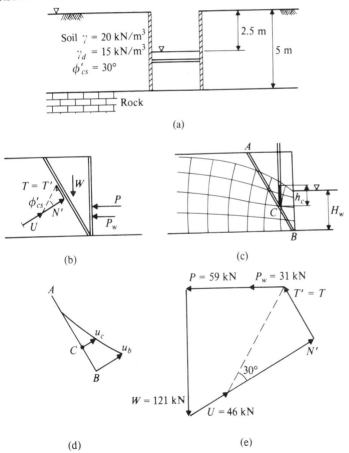

Soil $\gamma = 20\,\text{kN/m}^3$
$\gamma_d = 15\,\text{kN/m}^3$
$\phi'_{cs} = 30°$

2.5 m

5 m

Rock

(a)

$T = T'$
ϕ'_{cs}
N'
W
U
P
P_w

(b)

A
h_c
C
H_w
B

(c)

A
u_c
C
u_b
B

(d)

$P = 59\,\text{kN}$ $P_w = 31\,\text{kN}$
$T' = T$
N'
$30°$
$W = 121\,\text{kN}$
$U = 46\,\text{kN}$

(e)

Figure E8.3

Water is pumped steadily from the trench so that the water level in the trench 2.5 m below ground level and the sheet piles contain holes so that there is steady state seepage through the soil and into the trench. Taking a mechanism consisting of a wedge with a slip plane at $(45° - \frac{1}{2}\phi'_{cs}) = 30°$ to the vertical as before, and making use of a graphical method, calculate a limit equilibrium solution for the strut loads required to maintain the stability of the trench.

Figure E8.3(b) shows the mechanism with a single slip plane at an angle 30° to the vertical. The known forces acting on the wedge are its weight W, a force U due to the pore pressures along the slip plane, a force P_w due to the pressures of the water in the trench and the shear and normal forces on the slip plane which are related by

$$T = (N - U) \tan \phi'_{cs}$$

Figure E8.3(c) shows the slip plane AB and a sketched square flownet for steady state seepage flow into the trench. For a point such as C, water rises in a standpipe to a height h_c as shown, and hence, scaling from the diagram, the pore pressure at C is given by

$$u_c = \gamma_w h_c = 9.81 \times 1.3 = 12.8 \, \text{kN/m}^2$$

Figure E8.3(d) shows the pore pressures on the slip plane plotted normal to it and the force U is given by the area below the pore pressure curve. Hence, by making use of Simpson's rule, or otherwise, for a slice 1 m thick normal to the page, we have

$$U = 46 \, \text{kN}$$

The horizontal force P_w due to the free water pressures is given simply by

$$P_w = \frac{1}{2}\gamma_w H_w^2 = 31 \, \text{kN}$$

The unit weight of the soil above the top flowline is $\gamma_a = 15 \, \text{kN/m}^3$ and the unit weight of the soil below the top flowline is $\gamma = 20 \, \text{kN/m}^3$. Hence by making use of Simpson's rule, or otherwise, we find that the weight of the wedge for a slice 1 m thick normal to the page is given by

$$W = 2.6 \times 20 + 4.6 \times 15 = 121 \, \text{kN}$$

The polygon of forces for the wedge is shown in Fig. E8.3(e), and scaling from the diagram we have

$$P = 59 \, \text{kN}$$

E8.4 Stability of a Slope for Undrained Loading

Figure E8.4 shows a slope with angle 20° and depth 5 m cut into saturated soil with undrained shear strength $c_u = 20 \, \text{kN/m}^2$ and unit weight $\gamma = 20 \, \text{kN/m}^3$. Taking a slip circle with its centre at O above the midpoint of the slope and 5 m above the top of the slope, calculate the factor of safety for the slope for undrained loading.

Figure E8.4 shows the slip circle mechanism divided into a number of slices. Replacing c_u with c_u/F_s, where F_s is the factor of safety for the slope, and making use of Eq. (8.30), we have

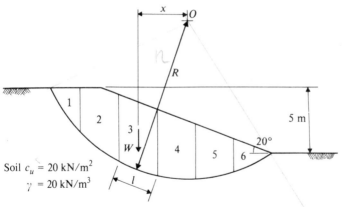

Figure E8.4

$W x = c_u R L$

$W_{1c} = \dfrac{c_u}{F_s} \cdot 2L$

$F_s = \dfrac{c_u R L}{W x}$

$$F_s = \frac{\sum c_u R l}{\sum W x}$$

where R is the radius of the circle, W the weight of a slice, and x and l are shown in Fig. E8.4. Scaling from the diagram, we obtain $R = 12$ m and the values for x and l and the area of each slice given in Table E8.1. Hence, for a slice 1 m thick normal to the page, we have

$$F_s = \frac{4824}{3239}$$

$$\underline{F_s = 1.49}$$

In practice, we should now change the position of the centre of the circle, and its radius, and seek the lowest value for F_s, which is then taken as the limit equilibrium factor of safety.

Table E8.1

Slice	Area m²	W kN	x m	Wx kN m	l m	$c_u R l$ kN m
1	3.8	76	9.2	699	4.0	960
2	14.4	288	6.8	1958	3.7	888
3	15.3	306	3.8	1163	3.2	768
4	13.8	276	0.8	221	3.0	720
5	10.2	204	−2.2	−449	3.0	720
6	3.8	75	−4.7	−353	3.2	768
Totals				3239		4824

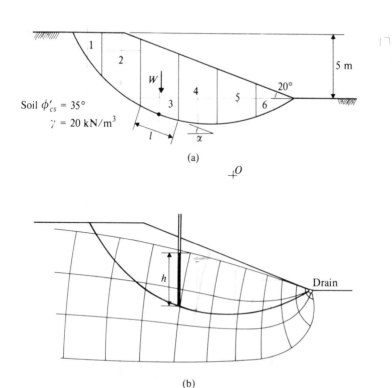

(a)

(b)

Figure E8.5

E8.5 Stability of a Slope for Drained Loading

Figure E8.5 shows a slope with angle $20°$ and depth 5 m cut into saturated soil with critical state angle of friction $\phi'_{cs} = 35°$ and unit weight $\gamma = 20\,\text{kN/m}^3$. A drain is placed at the toe of the slope and water seeps from the surrounding soil to the drain. Taking a slip circle with its centre at O above the midpoint of the slope and 5 m above the top of the slope and using the Swedish method of slices, calculate the factor of safety for the slope for drained loading with steady state seepage into the drain. (Assume that the unit weight of the soil is $\gamma = 20\,\text{kN/m}^3$ above and below the top flow line.)

Figure E8.5(a) shows the slip circle mechanism divided into a number of slices. Replacing $\tan \phi'_{cs}$ with $(\tan \phi'_{cs})/F_s$, where F_s is the factor of safety for the slope, and making use of Eq. (8.37), we have

Table E8.2 Slip circle analysis for the slope in Fig. E8.5

Slice	Area m²	W kN	α	$W \sin \alpha$ kN	$W \cos \alpha$ kN	h m	u kN/m²	l m	ul kN	$(W \cos \alpha - ul)$ kN
1	3.8	76	54°	61	45	1.4	13.7	4.0	55	−10
2	14.4	288	36°	169	233	3.0	29.4	3.7	109	124
3	15.3	306	20°	105	288	4.0	39.2	3.2	126	162
4	13.8	276	4°	19	275	3.8	37.3	3.0	112	163
5	10.2	204	−10°	−35	201	2.8	27.5	3.0	82	119
6	3.8	76	−25°	−32	69	1.4	13.7	3.2	44	25
Totals				287						583

(Note: values calculated for a strip 1.0 m thick normal to the page).

$$F_s = \frac{\sum (W \cos \alpha - ul) \tan \phi'_{cs}}{\sum W \sin \alpha}$$

where W is the weight of a slice, α and l are shown in Fig. E8.5(a), and u is the pore pressure at the base of a slice. Figure E8.5(b) shows a sketched square flownet for steady state seepage into the drain with a typical standpipe in which water rises to a height h. Values for the various parameters are obtained by scaling from the diagram and are given in Table E8.2. Hence, for a slice 1.0 m thick normal to the page, we have

$$F_s = \frac{583}{287} \tan 35°$$

$$\underline{F_s = 1.42}$$

In practice, we should now change the position of the centre of the circle, and its radius, and seek the lowest value for F_s and we should also examine other mechanisms.

At the toe of the slope, near the drain, the seepage flow is approximately parallel to the slope and we could consider a mechanism consisting of a single slip plane parallel with and close to the surface of the slope. This approximates to the case of an infinite slope with steady state seepage parallel with the slope as discussed in Sec. 6.6 for which an exact solution is given by Eq. (6.128). Hence, replacing $\tan \phi'_{cs}$ by $(\tan \phi'_{cs})/F_s$ we have

$$F_s = \frac{\tan \phi'_{cs}}{\tan i} \left(\frac{\gamma - \gamma_w}{\gamma} \right)$$

and, with $\gamma_w = 9.81$ kN/m³

$$F_s = 0.98$$

This factor of safety is slightly less than 1.0 and local failure will probably occur near the toe of the slope although there is an appreciable factor of safety against general failure.

NINE

ROUTINE METHODS FOR
STABILITY CALCULATIONS

9.1 INTRODUCTION

Many of the methods for determining the stability of soil structures discussed in the previous chapters involve tedious and repetitive calculation. While these calculations may be carried out by computer, standard solutions for relatively simple cases may be obtained as tables and charts.

Tables and charts of stability numbers, bearing capacity factors, and earth pressure coefficients are familiar to geotechnical engineers who use them as a matter of routine to estimate the stability of slopes, walls, and foundations. Many of these charts and tables are based on the limit equilibrium method, and consequently they involve the approximations and uncertainties implicit in that method. Some are based on other theories of stability which involve greater or lesser approximations and some are based on experience and experiment. In this chapter we will give some of the stability numbers, bearing capacity factors, and earth pressure coefficients commonly found in texts on soil mechanics and foundation engineering to illustrate the methods from which they were derived.

We should note at the outset that nearly all the common stability numbers, bearing capacity factors, and earth pressure coefficients given in tables and charts are based on a generalized Mohr–Coulomb failure criterion for soil given by

$$\tau_n = c + \sigma_n \tan \phi \qquad (9.1)$$

and appropriate parameters c', ϕ', or c_u, ϕ_u must be chosen for effective or total stresses. In this book we have been very careful always to distinguish clearly between analyses which are carried out in terms of effective stresses for drained loading and analyses which are carried out in terms of total stresses and which are valid only for the special case of undrained loading of saturated soil. Moreover we have argued, in Sec. 3.8, that the parameters appropriate for stability calculations are those which correspond to the ultimate or critical state strength of soil, rather than those which correspond to the peak or Hvorslev strength. Thus we have two quite separate failure criteria for soil given by

$$\tau'_n = \sigma'_n \tan \phi'_{cs} \tag{9.2}$$

$$\tau_n = c_u \tag{9.3}$$

for drained and for undrained loading respectively, and we will discuss separately stability numbers, bearing capacity factors, and earth pressure coefficients relevant to these two failure criteria.

In most texts on soil mechanics and foundation engineering, stability numbers, bearing capacity factors, and earth pressure coefficients are given for the general failure criterion given by Eq. (9.1) and it is left to the engineer to select values appropriate for drained or for undrained loading. While this approach is satisfactory for an experienced engineer, for the present, and for clarity, we will continue to consider drained and undrained loading quite separately.

9.2 BEARING CAPACITY FACTORS FOR UNDRAINED LOADING

Figure 9.1(a) shows a section of a long foundation, width B, at the surface of a soil with unit weight γ and undrained shear strength c_u. The foundation load at collapse is F_c per unit length normal to the page and a total stress $p^\dagger$ is applied to the surface outside the foundation. We have already obtained an exact solution for this problem from the slip line method and from equal upper and lower bounds as

$$F_c = c_u N B + p B \tag{9.4}$$

where N was called a *bearing capacity factor* and was given by

$$N = (2 + \pi) = 5.14 \tag{9.5}$$

Figure 9.1(b) shows a section of a long concrete foundation, width B and weight W_f per unit length, normal to the page at a depth D below the ground surface. For this case the total load is $F_c + W_f$ and the total vertical stress in the soil at the level of the foundation is $p = \gamma D$. Hence by analogy with Eq. (9.4) we have

$$F_c + W_f = c_u N_c B + \gamma D B \tag{9.6}$$

where N_c is the appropriate bearing capacity factor.

If we were to carry out upper bound, slip line, or limit equilibrium calculations for the foundation shown in Fig. 9.1(b) we would find that the value of the bearing capacity factor N_c in Eq. (9.6) would exceed the value of $N_c = 5.14$, because the collapse mechanisms would pass through the soil above foundation level. Thus we expect the bearing capacity factor N_c in Eq. (9.6) to depend on the ratio D/B and to be given by $N_c = 5.14$ when $D/B = 0$. In addition, the value $N_c = 5.14$ was obtained for the case of plane strain where mechanisms could occur to either side of the foundation but not out of the page. Thus for circular, square, or rectangular foundations, where mechanisms out of the page can occur, we expect

---

$\dagger$ See footnote on p. 164.

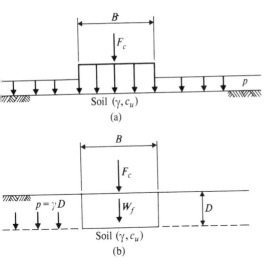

Figure 9.1 Bearing capacity of a foundation for undrained loading.

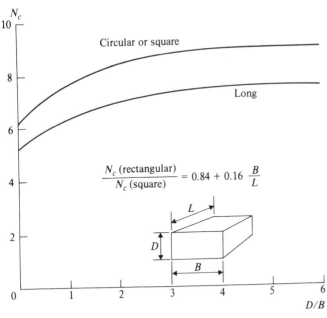

Figure 9.2 Bearing capacity factors for undrained loading of shallow foundations. (*After Skempton, 1951.*)

the value for the bearing capacity factor N_c to exceed that for the plane strain case.

Figure 9.2 shows the variation with depth of the bearing capacity factor N_c in Eq. (9.6) for circular, square, rectangular, and long foundations given by

Skempton (1951). These values were based on limit equilibrium calculation by Meyerhof (1951), on the results of model tests and on an analysis by Gibson (1950). The stability chart shown in Fig. 9.2 is the one most commonly used by engineers to estimate the collapse load of foundations for undrained loading. The allowable, or working, load F_a of a foundation for a factor of safety F_s is given by substituting c_u/F_s for c_u in Eq. (9.6) and hence

$$F_a + W_f = \frac{c_u}{F_s} N_c B + \gamma D B \tag{9.7}$$

It is usual to take the unit weights of soil and concrete as equal and hence, for a solid concrete foundation placed below ground level, $W_f = \gamma D B$. Occasionally the foundation is constructed as a hollow box or as a basement, in which case its weight W_f may be neglected.

9.3 STABILITY NUMBERS FOR UNDRAINED LOADING

Figure 9.3(a) shows a section of a vertical slope cut into soil with unit weight γ and undrained shear strength c_u. The height of the cut at collapse is H_c and from the upper and lower bounds given in Sec. 5.3

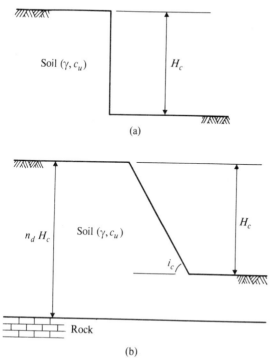

(a)

(b)

Figure 9.3 Stability of slopes for undrained loading.

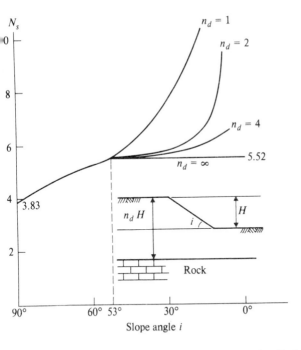

Figure 9.4 Stability numbers for undrained loading. (*After Taylor, 1948.*)

$$\frac{4c_u}{\gamma} \geqslant H_c \geqslant \frac{2c_u}{\gamma} \tag{9.8}$$

Equation (9.8) may be rewritten as

$$H_c = N_s \frac{c_u}{\gamma} \tag{9.9}$$

where N_s is known as a *stability number* and, for the vertical slope shown in Fig. 9.3(a),

$$4 \geqslant N_s \geqslant 2 \tag{9.10}$$

Figure 9.3(b) shows a more general case of a slope of angle i_c and height H_c where strong rock occurs at a depth $n_d H_c$ below the top ground level. For this case, the height of the slope at collapse is again given by Eq. (9.9)

$$H_c = N_s \frac{c_u}{\gamma} \tag{[9.9]}$$

but now the stability number N_s depends on the slope angle i_c and on the depth ratio n_d.

Figure 9.4 shows the variation of stability number N_s with slope angle and depth ratio for undrained loading. The data shown in Fig. 9.4 are taken from those given by Taylor (1948, pp. 459) and were obtained from the limit equilibrium slip circle method for undrained loading described in Sec. 8.5. For a vertical slope for which $i_c = 90°$, we have $N_s = 3.83$ from Fig. 9.4, which is close to the upper bound value $N_s = 4$ given by Eq. (9.10). The stability chart shown in Fig. 9.4 may be used to obtain quick estimates for the stability of slopes for undrained loading. To include a factor of safety F_s for the stability of a slope, we substitute c_u/F_s for c_u in Eq. (9.9), and hence we may determine allowable combinations of slope angle i_a and height H_a.

9.4 EARTH PRESSURE COEFFICIENTS FOR UNDRAINED LOADING

Figure 9.5 shows a section of a long wall, height H, retaining soil with unit weight γ and undrained shear strength c_u. The wall may be rough, in which case there is a uniform shear stress c_w between the soil and the wall, where $c_w \leqslant c_u$, and for a smooth wall $c_w = 0$. As the wall fails by moving towards the soil the passive force is P_p and it has a normal component N_p. We have already obtained upper and lower bounds and limit equilibrium solutions for N_p and these may be written

$$N_p = \tfrac{1}{2}\gamma H^2 + K_{pu}c_u H \tag{9.11}$$

where K_{pu} is a *passive earth pressure coefficient* and the subscript u is a reminder that K_{pu} applies only for undrained loading. Similar analyses apply for the active force P_a, for which the normal component N_a may be written

$$N_a = \tfrac{1}{2}\gamma H^2 - K_{au}c_u H \tag{9.12}$$

where K_{au} is an *active earth pressure coefficient*. Values for K_{au} and K_{pu} depend on the values of the ratio c_w/c_u as shown in Fig. 9.6, which is taken from the *Civil Engineering Code of Practice for Earth Retaining Structures* (CP2, 1951).

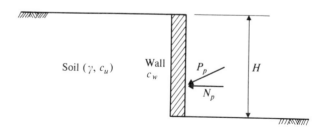

Figure 9.5 Passive force on a wall for undrained loading.

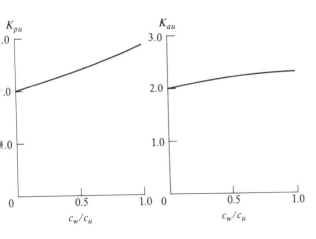

Figure 9.6 Active and passive earth pressure coefficients for undrained loading. (*After CP2, 1951.*)

9.5 BEARING CAPACITY FACTORS FOR DRAINED LOADING

Figure 9.7(a) shows a section of a long foundation, width B and weight W_f per unit length normal to the page, at the surface of a soil with unit weight γ and critical state angle of friction ϕ'_{cs}. The depth of the foundation is D and there is a depth H_w of water above ground level. The foundation load at collapse is F_c per unit length normal to the page and a *total* stress p is applied to the soil surface. We must be very careful to note here that p is the sum of any applied stress and the free water pressure, so that, if the applied stress is zero, we have $p = \gamma_w H_w$. We have already, in Sec. 6.6, obtained a solution for this problem in the form

$$F_c + W_f = \tfrac{1}{2}(\gamma - \gamma_w)B^2 G + (p - \gamma_w H_w)BJ + \gamma_w H_w B \qquad (9.13)$$

where G and J are bearing capacity factors and, from upper and lower bound calculations in Sec. 6.5, these were given by

$$J = \tan^2 (45° + \tfrac{1}{2}\phi'_{cs}) \exp (\pi \tan \phi'_{cs}) \qquad (9.14)$$

$$0 \leqslant G \leqslant \frac{4 \tan \phi'_{cs}}{1 + 9 \tan \phi'_{cs}} [1 + \exp (3\pi \tan \phi'_{cs})] \qquad (9.15)$$

The bearing capacity factors J and G depend only on the value of the critical state friction angle ϕ'_{cs}. Figure 9.7(b) shows a section of a long concrete foundation, width B and weight W_f per unit length, normal to the page founded at a depth D in saturated soil. The pore pressures in the soil are hydrostatic and the water table is at the ground surface. For this case the total vertical stress in the soil at the level of the foundation is $p = \gamma D$ and hence, by analogy with Eq. (9.13), we have

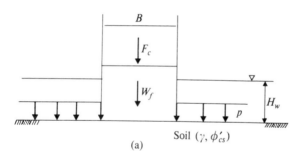

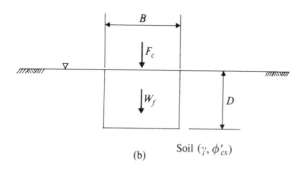

Figure 9.7 Bearing capacity of a foundation for drained loading.

$$F_c + W_f = \tfrac{1}{2}(\gamma - \gamma_w)B^2G + (\gamma - \gamma_w)JBD + \gamma_w BD \qquad (9.16)$$

where G and J are the appropriate bearing capacity factors. Equation (9.18) may be written in a slightly more convenient form as

$$F_c + W_f = \tfrac{1}{2}(\gamma - \gamma_w)B^2G + (\gamma - \gamma_w)(J - 1)BD + \gamma BD \qquad (9.17)$$

If we were to carry out upper bound, slip line, or limit equilibrium calculations for the foundation shown in Fig. 9.7(a), we would obtain values for the bearing capacity factors G and J greater than those given by Eqs (9.14) and (9.15) because the collapse mechanisms would pass through the soil above foundation level. In addition, for circular, square, or rectangular foundations, where mechanisms can occur out of the page we expect values for G and J greater than those given by Eqs (9.14) and (9.15). Thus, as was the case for undrained loading of a foundation discussed in Sec. 9.2, we have used the theory developed in earlier chapters to develop an appropriate form of the bearing capacity equation for drained loading. The bearing capacity factors in Eq. (9.17) are usually given the symbols N_γ and N_q and the bearing capacity equation for drained loading becomes

$$F_c + W_f = \beta(\gamma - \gamma_w)B^2N_\gamma + (\gamma - \gamma_w)(N_q - 1)BD + \gamma BD \qquad (9.18)$$

where the parameter β is included to account for the shape of the foundation. The values of N_γ and N_q, like J and G, will depend on the value of the critical state angle of friction ϕ'_{cs}.

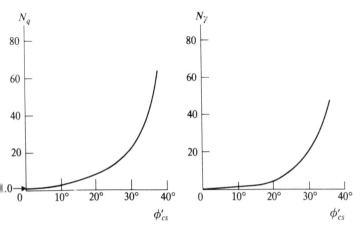

Figure 9.8 Bearing capacity factors for drained loading of shallow foundations. (*After Terzaghi, 1943.*)

Figure 9.8 shows the variation of the bearing capacity factors N_γ and N_q with ϕ'_{cs} given by Terzaghi (1943, p. 125) but these are not exact solutions. They were obtained from essentially limit equilibrium calculations using mechanisms consisting of straight lines and logarithmic spirals. For foundations with smooth bases we have already obtained the exact solution for $N_q = J$ given by Eq. (9.14). For the value of β in Eq. (9.18) Terzaghi (1943) gave $\beta = 0.5$ for long foundations, $\beta = 0.4$ for square foundations, and $\beta = 0.3$ for circular foundations based on the results of model tests. The bearing capacity factors shown in Fig. 9.8 are applicable for shallow foundations for which the depth D is not large compared to the breadth B. For deep foundations, other bearing capacity factors were given by Meyerhof (1951), who based them on a combination of limit equilibrium calculations and model tests.

The allowable, or working, load of a foundation F_a for drained loading is given by Eq. (9.18) with values of the bearing capacity factors $N_{\gamma a}$ and N_{qa} corresponding to an allowable angle of friction ϕ'_a given by

$$\tan \phi'_a = \frac{\tan \phi'_{cs}}{F_s} \tag{9.19}$$

where F_s is the required factor of safety. Alternatively, the factor of safety is often applied directly to the first two terms on the right hand side of Eq. (9.18), which give the contribution of the soil strength to the bearing capacity. Hence we have

$$F_a + W_f = 1/F_s [\beta(\gamma - \gamma_w)B^2 N_\gamma + (\gamma - \gamma_w)(N_q - 1)BD] + \gamma BD \tag{9.20}$$

which may be compared with Eq. (9.7) for undrained loading. As in the case of undrained loading, it is usual to take the unit weights of soil and concrete as equal and hence, for a solid concrete foundation placed below ground level, $W_f = \gamma D L$ For the case when the foundation is a hollow box or a basement, the weight W may be neglected.

9.6 STABILITY NUMBERS FOR DRAINED LOADING

Figure 9.9 shows a section of a slope for drained loading. As discussed in Sec. 8.6 the stability of the slope may be investigated by the method of slices and Fig. 9.9 shows the critical slip circle and a typical slice. The pore pressure u at the base of the slice should be found from a steady state seepage flownet, but it is convenient to define a pore pressure coefficient r_u as

$$r_u = \frac{u}{\sigma_v} = \frac{ub}{W} \tag{9.21}$$

where σ_v is the vertical total stress. If it is assumed that it is possible to take an average value for r_u for the whole slip surface the factor of safety may be written as

$$F_s = m - nr_u \tag{9.22}$$

where m and n are stability numbers. Equation (9.22) shows that as pore pressures rise, and r_u rises, the factor of safety diminishes.

Figure 9.10 shows values for the stability numbers m and n calculated by Bishop and Morgenstern (1960). These may be used to estimate the stability of slopes for drained loading by employing Eq. (9.22) with a suitable value for r_u.

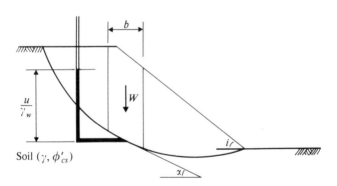

Figure 9.9 Stability of slope for drained loading.

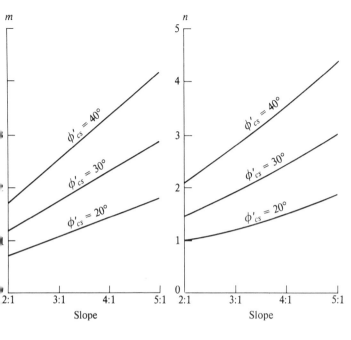

Figure 9.10 Stability numbers for drained loading. (*After Bishop and Morgenstern, 1960.*)

For an infinite slope where the slip surface is taken as a plane parallel with the surface rather than as a circular arc, the factor of safety is given by

$$F_s = \frac{\tan \phi'_{cs}}{\tan i}\,(1 - r_u \sec^2 i) \tag{9.23}$$

where i is the slope angle.

9.7 EARTH PRESSURE COEFFICIENTS FOR DRAINED LOADING

Figure 9.11 shows a section of a long wall, height H, retaining dry soil, with unit weight γ and critical state angle of friction ϕ'_{cs}. The wall may be rough with an angle of wall friction ϕ'_w where, clearly, $\phi'_w \leqslant \phi'_{cs}$ and for a smooth wall $\phi'_w = 0$. As the wall fails by moving away from the soil, the active force is P_a and has a normal component N_a. We have already obtained upper and lower bounds and limit equilibrium solutions for N_a and, for dry soils, these may be written

$$N_a = \tfrac{1}{2}K_a \gamma H^2 \tag{9.24}$$

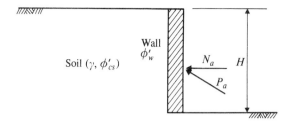

Figure 9.11 Active force on a wall for drained loading.

where K_a is an *active earth pressure coefficient*. Similar analyses apply for the passive force P_p for which the normal component N_p may be written

$$N_p = \tfrac{1}{2}K_p\gamma H^2 \tag{9.25}$$

where K_p is a *passive earth pressure coefficient*. Values for K_a and K_p depend on ϕ'_{cs} and ϕ'_w, as shown in Fig. 9.12, which is taken from the Civil Engineering Code of Practice for earth retaining structures (CP2, 1951). It should be noted that the earth pressure coefficients K_a and K_p shown in Fig. 9.12 are for effective stresses and apply only for *dry* soil. For cases where the soil is not dry, and where there is steady state seepage, these coefficients do not apply and analyses are best carried out using graphical methods of limit equilibrium described in Sec. 8.4.

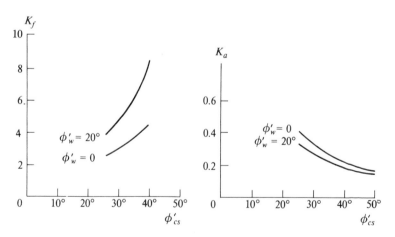

Figure 9.12 Active and passive earth pressure coefficients for drained loading of dry soil. (*After CP2, 1951.*)

9.8 DISCUSSION

The stability numbers, bearing capacity factors, and earth pressure coefficients given in this chapter apply for the relatively simple cases discussed. Although they may not apply strictly to more complex cases, they may often be used for preliminary design purposes before more detailed calculations are carried out. These stability numbers, bearing capacity factors, and earth pressure coefficients were mostly derived from limit equilibrium calculations and therefore contain the errors and assumptions of that method. They are, however, commonly used by engineers for the routine design of slopes, foundations, and walls and considerable experience has demonstrated their usefulness. Nevertheless, the stability of complex and important projects should always be investigated, using the methods described in previous chapters.

REFERENCES

Bishop, A. W. and N. Morgenstern (1960), 'Stability coefficients for earth slopes', *Geotechnique*, 10, 129–150.

Civil Engineering Code of Practice CP2 (1951), *Earth Retaining Structures*, Inst. Structural Engrs, London.

Gibson, R. E. (1950), 'Discussion on "The bearing capacity of screwed piles and screwcrete cylinders" by G. Wilson', *J. Instn. Civil Engrs*, 34, 382, London.

Meyerhof, G. G. (1951), 'The ultimate bearing capacity of foundations', *Geotechnique*, 2, 301–332.

Skempton, A. W. (1951), 'The bearing capacity of clays', *Proc. Building Research Congr.* 1, 180–189, Institution of Civil Engrs, London, 1951.

Taylor, D. W. (1948), *Fundamentals of Soil Mechanics*, Wiley, New York.

Terzaghi, K. (1943), *Theoretical Soil Mechanics*, Wiley, New York.

WORKED EXAMPLES

E9.1 Loads on a Bulldozer Blade for Undrained Loading

A bulldozer blade 1 m high and 3 m wide pushes saturated soil across the top of strong rock and the blade does not rotate. The soil has undrained shear strength $c_u = 40 \, \text{kN/m}^2$ and unit weight $\gamma = 20 \, \text{kN/m}^3$ and the shear stress between the soil and the blade is $c_w = 20 \, \text{kN/m}^2$. Making use of the earth pressure coefficients given in Fig. 9.6, calculate the force P which the bulldozer must apply to its blade.

From Eq. (9.11), the normal component N_p of the bulldozer force P is given by

$$N_p = \tfrac{1}{2}\gamma H^2 + K_{pu}c_u H$$

where K_{pu} is a passive earth pressure coefficient for undrained loading. From Fig. 9.6 with $c_w/c_u = 0.5$ we have

$$K_{pu} = 2.38$$

and
$$N_p = \tfrac{1}{2} \times 20 \times 1^2 + 2.38 \times 40 \times 1 = 105.2 \text{ kN}$$

The vertical component V_p is given by

$$V_p = c_w H = 20 \times 1 = 20 \text{ kN}$$

Hence, noting that the blade is 3 m wide normal to the page, we have

$$P = 3(V^2 + H^2)^{1/2} = 3(20^2 + 105.2^2)^{1/2}$$

$$\underline{P = 321 \text{ kN}}$$

E9.2 Loads on a Bulldozer Blade for Drained Loading

A bulldozer blade 1.0 m high and 3 m wide pushes dry soil across the top of strong rock and the blade does not rotate. The soil has a critical state angle of friction $\phi'_{cs} = 30°$ and unit weight $\gamma = 15 \text{ kN/m}^3$, and the friction angle between the soil and the blade is $\phi'_w = 15°$. Making use of the earth pressure coefficients given in Fig. 9.12, calculate the force P which the bulldozer must apply its its blade.

From Eq. (9.25) the normal component N_p of the bulldozer force P is given by

$$N_p = \tfrac{1}{2} K_p \gamma H^2$$

where K_p is a passive earth pressure coefficient for drained loading. From Fig. 9.12 interpolating for $\phi'_w = 15°$ we have, for $\phi'_{cs} = 30°$,

$$K_p = 4.3$$

and
$$N_p = \tfrac{1}{2} \times 4.3 \times 15 \times 1^2 = 32 \text{ kN}$$

The bulldozer force P is given by $P = N_p \sec \phi'_w$, and hence, noting that the blade is 3 m wide normal to the page, we have

$$P = 3 \times 32 \sec 15°$$

$$\underline{P = 100 \text{ kN}}$$

E9.3 Stability of a Slope

A slope with angle 20° and height 5 m is cut into saturated soil with unit weight $\gamma = 20 \text{ kN/m}^3$, undrained shear strength $c_u = 20 \text{ kN/m}^2$, and critical state angle of friction $\phi'_{cs} = 35°$. Making use of the stability charts given in Figs 9.4 and 9.10

calculate the factor of safety for the slope (1) immediately after excavation and (2) when there is steady state seepage taking $r_u = 0.3$.

1. From Eq. (9.9), replacing c_u with c_u/F_s, we have

$$F_s = N_s \frac{c_u}{\gamma H}$$

where N_s is a stability number for undrained loading. From Fig. 9.4, with $n_d = \infty$ for homogeneous soil and for $i = 20°$, we have

$$N_s = 5.52$$

Hence the factor of safety of the slope is

$$F_s = 5.52 \times \frac{20}{20 \times 5}$$

$$\underline{F_s = 1.10}$$

This result is rather lower than the value $F_s = 1.49$ obtained from a slip circle analysis of the same slope in Example E8.4, indicating that the slip circle analysed was not the critical mechanism.

2. From Eq. (9.22), the factor of safety of the slope for drained loading is given by

$$F_s = m - nr_u$$

where m and n are stability numbers and r_u is a pore pressure coefficient which will be taken as $r_u = 0.3$. From Fig. 9.10 for a slope of $20°$ (i.e. 2.75:1) and for $\phi'_{cs} = 35°$ we have

$$m = 2.0 \qquad n = 2.2$$

and hence

$$F_s = 2.0 - 0.3 \times 2.2$$

$$\underline{F_s = 1.34}$$

This result is slightly lower than the value $F_s = 1.42$ obtained from a slip circle analysis of the same slope in Example E8.4, indicating that the slip circle analysed was not the critical mechanism.

9.4 Stability of a Foundation

A long concrete foundation 2.5 m wide and 1.0 m deep is founded at a depth of 1.0 m in saturated soil. The soil has $\gamma = 20 \, \text{kN/m}^3$, $c_u = 20 \, \text{kN/m}^2$ and $\phi'_{cs} = 30°$, the foundation carries a load of 250 kN per metre of length, and the unit weight of concrete is $\gamma_c = 20 \, \text{kN/m}^3$. Making use of the bearing capacity factors given in Figs 9.2 and 9.8, calculate the factor of safety of the foundation (1) immediately after construction of the foundation assuming that the soil remains undrained, and (2) when the pore pressures are everywhere hydrostatic.

1. For undrained loading the foundation load is given by Eq. 9.7 as

$$F_a + W_f = \frac{c_u}{F_s} N_c B + \gamma DB$$

and, since the unit weights of soil and concrete are equal, $W_f = \gamma DB$. For the foundation, $D/B = 0.4$, and hence, from Fig. 9.2, for a long foundation, $N_c = 5.8$. Hence

$$250 = \frac{20}{F_s} \times 5.8 \times 2.5$$

$$\underline{F_s = 1.16}$$

2. For drained loading the allowable load on a foundation is given by

$$F_a + W_f = \beta(\gamma - \gamma_w)B^2 N_{\gamma a} + (\gamma - \gamma_w)(N_{qa} - 1)BD + \gamma BD$$

where $\beta = 0.5$ for a long foundation and $W_f = \gamma BD$ as before. The bearing capacity factors $N_{\gamma a}$ and N_{qa} are appropriate for an allowable friction angle ϕ'_a given by Eq. (9.19) as

$$\tan \phi'_a = \frac{\tan \phi'_{cs}}{F_s}$$

From Fig. 9.8, taking $\phi'_a = 18°$, we have

$$N_{\gamma a} = 3 \qquad N_{qa} = 7$$

and

$$F_a = \tfrac{1}{2}(20 - 9.81)2.5^2 \times 3 + (20 - 9.81)(7 - 1) \times 2.5$$

$$F_a = 248 \, \text{kN/m}$$

which is approximately the applied load. Hence we have

$$F_s = \frac{\tan 30°}{\tan 18°}$$

$$\underline{F_s = 1.78}$$

SETTLEMENT OF FOUNDATIONS

10.1 INTRODUCTION

In Chapters 5 to 9 we covered various calculations for the stability of foundations placed at, or just below, the surface of a soil, and we indicated how these could be applied to deep foundations. These calculations all seek to determine the load at which a foundation will collapse, and in practice this load should be reduced, or the foundation strengthened, until there is a suitable safety factor. Although foundations are designed and constructed so they do not collapse, still they will suffer displacements, and in this chapter we will examine simple methods for estimating the settlements of foundations.

Foundation settlements may be calculated by analyses such as the finite element method using soil models described in Chapter 2. We will not however discuss these calculations here and instead we will consider only a number of relatively simple but approximate methods.

10.2 DRAINED AND UNDRAINED LOADING OF FOUNDATIONS

In Sec. 3.5 we examined the approximate stress paths for an element of soil below a foundation for undrained and for drained loading, and we must now re-examine this analysis in slightly more detail. As we argued in Sec. 3.4, most natural soils are either lightly or heavily overconsolidated and their states will be below the state boundary surface and on an elastic wall. Thus, for most practical purposes we may make use of elastic theory to calculate the stresses and displacements in the soil, but as usual we must be very careful always to distinguish between drained loading, for which the elastic parameters in terms of effective stresses are E' and ν', and undrained loading, for which the elastic parameters in terms of total stresses are E_u and $\nu_u = \frac{1}{2}$, as discussed in Sec. 2.6.

Figure 10.1 shows a section of a long foundation carrying a load F, less than that which would cause failure, and typically the factor of safety of a foundation would be of the order of 2 to 3. Figure 10.2(a) shows approximate stress paths for an element of soil below the foundation where, before loading, $\sigma'_v = \sigma'_h$ and $K_0 = 1$. Fig. 10.2(a) corresponds to drained loading and Fig. 10.2(b) corresponds to undrained loading: these stress paths are similar to those shown in Figs. 3.7 and 3.8,

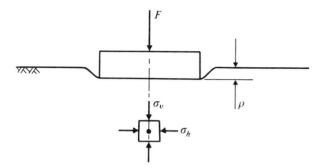

Figure 10.1 Loading and settlement of a foundation.

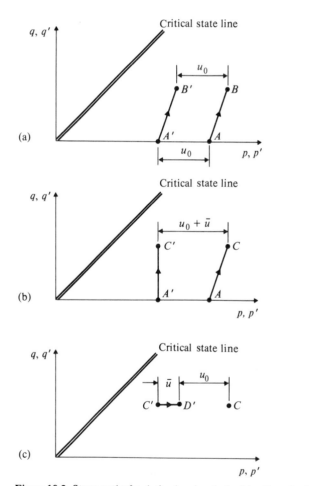

Figure 10.2 Stress paths for drained and undrained loading of a foundation.

except that those in Fig. 10.2 do not reach the critical state line, as the foundation in Fig. 10.1 remains stable. In Fig. 10.2(a), for drained loading, the pore pressure remains constant at u_0, which is the steady state pore pressure in the ground, and hence the total and effective stress paths are parallel. In Fig. 10.2(b), for undrained loading, the pore pressure increases as the effective stress path travels vertically up an elastic wall and the pore pressure is $u_0 + \bar{u}$, where $\bar{u}$ is an excess pore pressure. Excess pore pressures cannot remain indefinitely, since they are not in equilibrium with the hydraulic boundary conditions, which themselves are in equilibrium with the steady state pore pressure u_0. Thus, as time passes, the excess pore pressure will reduce. If the foundation load is unchanged then the total stress will remain approximately constant but the effective stresses will change as consolidation occurs. In Fig. 10.2(c), for consolidation, the total stresses are shown remaining constant at C and the effective stress path moves from C', where the excess pore pressure is $\bar{u}$, to D', where the excess pore pressure is zero.

For settlement calculations, we must distinguish two kinds of loading. For drained loading, represented by Fig. 10.2(a), excess pore pressures are zero and all settlements take place during the construction period. For the other kind of loading there are two stages; during the first, undrained loading stage, represented by Fig. 10.2(b), there are no volume changes but excess pore pressures are set up; during the second, consolidation stage, represented by Fig. 10.2(c), the total stresses remain constant but, as the excess pore pressures reduce, effective stresses change and settlements occur. In practice, none of these conditions is precisely satisfied; there is always some consolidation during construction and total stresses often change slightly during consolidation, but for most practical purposes it is usually possible to assume that one or other set of drainage conditions governs the loading and settlement. What is of critical importance, as always in geotechnical engineering, is not the absolute rate of loading but the rate of loading compared with the rate of consolidation; for drained loading the rate of loading is relatively slow, while for undrained loading it is relatively quick.

Figure 10.3(a) shows an arbitrary, but relatively slow, loading sequence in which the foundation load F is increased and which terminates after some time t_0 when construction is complete. It it is assumed that the loading is so slow that excess pore pressures may be taken as zero. The settlement shown in Fig. 10.3(b) follows the loading and so terminates at t_0 when the final settlement is ρ_f. For soil whose state is inside the state boundary surface and on an elastic wall, these settlements may be calculated from elastic theory with values of the elastic parameters E' and ν' for effective stresses.

Figure 10.4(a) shows an arbitary but relatively quick loading sequence in which the foundation load F is increased and which terminates after a short time t_0 when the excess pore pressure is $\bar{u}_i$ and the settlement ρ_i is known as the *initial settlement*. If the loading is sufficiently fast, volume changes during loading may be taken as zero. For soil whose state is inside the state boundary surface and on an elastic wall, the initial settlement may be calculated from elastic theory with values for the elastic parameters E_u and $\nu_u = \frac{1}{2}$ and the value of $\bar{u}_i$ in Fig. 10.4(b) may

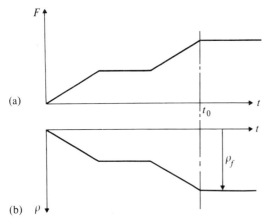

Figure 10.3 Loading and settlement of a foundation for drained loading.

also be calculated from elastic theory. Beyond the time t_0, the excess pore pressure dissipates steadily, but at a reducing rate, towards a value of $\bar{u}_\infty = 0$ after infinite time, as shown in Fig. 10.4(b), and after a time $(t_0 + t)$ from the start of loading the excess pore pressure is $\bar{u}_t$. The settlement curve beyond the time t_0, shown in Fig. 10.4(c), is similar to the excess pore pressure curve and approaches a value

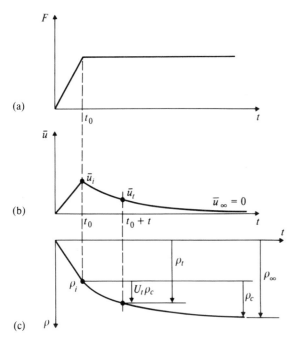

Figure 10.4 Loading and settlement of a foundation for undrained loading followed by consolidation.

ρ_∞ after infinite time. The settlement ρ_t after a time $(t_0 + t)$ from the start of loading is given by

$$\rho_t = \rho_i + U_t \rho_c \tag{10.1}$$

as shown in Fig. 10.4(c) where U_t is the *degree of consolidation* and ρ_c is the final *consolidation settlement*.

Figure 10.5 shows the stress paths in Fig. 10.2 superimposed, so that the total stress path AB for the drained loading is the same as the total stress path AC for undrained loading. The effective stress paths $A'B'$ and $A'C'D'$ are of course different, although they start and finish at the same points where $\bar{u} = 0$ in each case. Materials which are elastic are *path independent*, which means that the strains due to an increment of load depend on the initial and final states of stress and are independent of the stress path. Thus the final settlement ρ_f in Fig. 10.3(b), due to drained loading for the path $A'B'$, is the same as the final settlement ρ_∞ in Fig. 10.4(c), due to undrained loading along $A'C'$ followed by consolidation along $C'D'$. Since these settlements are the same, and are independent of the effective stress path for elastic soil, we may calculate a value for ρ_∞ for undrained loading, followed by consolidation, making use of the calculation for ρ_f for drained loading. For undrained loading, the initial settlement ρ_i is obtained from a total stress analysis, with values for the elastic parameters E_u and $\nu_u = \frac{1}{2}$. For any kind of loading, final settlements when all excess pore pressures are zero may be estimated from an effective stress analysis, with values for the elastic parameters E' and ν'. These elastic calculations may be used for soil whose state remains below the state boundary surface and on an elastic wall, and this will include many natural soils.

10.3 STATES OF STRESS IN ELASTIC SOIL

We have already seen in Chapter 1 that the stresses and strains in any loaded body must satisfy certain conditions of equilibrium and compatibility. For saturated soil the conditions of equilibrium in terms of effective stresses for plane strain are given by Eqs. (1.69) and (1.70) as

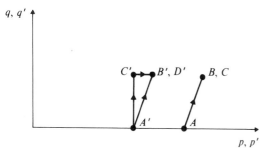

Figure 10.5 Stress paths for drained and undrained loading of a foundation (from Fig. 10.2).

$$\frac{\partial \sigma'_z}{\partial z} + \frac{\partial \tau'_{xz}}{\partial x} = \gamma - \frac{\partial u}{\partial z} \tag{10.2}$$

$$\frac{\partial \sigma'_x}{\partial x} + \frac{\partial \tau'_{zx}}{\partial z} = -\frac{\partial u}{\partial x} \tag{10.3}$$

where γ is the unit weight of the soil. The condition of compatibility for plane strain is given by Eq. (1.77) as

$$\frac{\partial^2 \epsilon_x}{\partial z^2} + \frac{\partial^2 \epsilon_z}{\partial x^2} - \frac{\partial^2 \gamma_{xz}}{\partial x \partial z} = 0 \tag{10.4}$$

In addition, stresses and strains at any point must satisfy the requirements of the particular material. For isotropic elastic soil and for plane strain, these are specified by the generalized form of Hooke's law for plane strain given by Eqs. (1.94) to (1.96) as

$$\delta\epsilon_x = \frac{1 + \nu'}{E'} [(1 - \nu')\delta\sigma'_x - \nu'\delta\sigma'_z] \tag{10.5}$$

$$\delta\epsilon_z = \frac{1 + \nu'}{E'} [(1 - \nu')\delta\sigma'_z - \nu'\delta\sigma'_x] \tag{10.6}$$

$$\delta\gamma_{xz} = \frac{2(1 + \nu')}{E'} \delta\tau'_{xz} \tag{10.7}$$

where E' and ν' are Young's modulus and Poisson's ratio, respectively, in terms of effective stress.

Equations (10.2) to (10.7) are a set of six partial differential equations with six unknowns (i.e., three components of stress increment and three components of strain increment). These govern the distribution of stress and strain throughout a loaded body for plane strain and they must also satisfy the load and displacement conditions at the boundaries. From Eqs (10.5) to (10.7), taking E' and ν' as constants, we have

$$\frac{\partial^2 \epsilon_x}{\partial z^2} = \frac{(1 + \nu')}{E'} \left[(1 - \nu')\frac{\partial^2 \sigma'_x}{\partial z^2} - \nu'\frac{\partial^2 \sigma'_z}{\partial z^2} \right] \tag{10.8}$$

$$\frac{\partial^2 \epsilon_z}{\partial x^2} = \frac{(1 + \nu')}{E'} \left[(1 - \nu')\frac{\partial^2 \sigma'_z}{\partial x^2} - \nu'\frac{\partial^2 \sigma'_x}{\partial x^2} \right] \tag{10.9}$$

$$\frac{\partial^2 \gamma_{xz}}{\partial x \partial z} = \frac{2(1 + \nu')}{E'} \frac{\partial^2 \tau'_{xz}}{\partial x \partial z} \tag{10.10}$$

and, from Eqs. (10.2) and (10.3), with $\partial u/\partial z = \gamma_w$ and $\partial u/\partial x = 0$, for the case when there is no seepage, and noting that γ and γ_w are constants, we have

$$\frac{\partial^2 \tau_{xz}}{\partial x \partial z} = -\frac{\partial^2 \sigma'_z}{\partial z^2} = \frac{\partial^2 \sigma'_x}{\partial x^2} \tag{10.11}$$

Hence, eliminating strain increments, we have

$$\frac{\partial^2 \sigma_x'}{\partial x^2} + \frac{\partial^2 \sigma_z'}{\partial x^2} + \frac{\partial^2 \sigma_x'}{\partial z^2} + \frac{\partial^2 \sigma_z'}{\partial z^2} = 0 \tag{10.12}$$

or

$$\frac{\partial^2 (\sigma_x' + \sigma_z')}{\partial x^2} + \frac{\partial^2 (\sigma_x' + \sigma_z')}{\partial z^2} = 0 \tag{10.13}$$

Equations (10.2), (10.3) and (10.13) are now three simultaneous partial differential equations which govern the distribution of effective stress throughout a loaded body of isotropic elastic soil for plane strain, and they must satisfy also the boundary loads and stresses. Having calculated the increments of stress at any point due to some change of loading, increments of strain may be calculated from Eqs. (10.5) to (10.7) and displacements from Eqs. (1.4) to (1.7).

For undrained loading of saturated soil, calculations may be carried out in terms of total stresses. The conditions of equilibrium for plane strain are

$$\frac{\partial \sigma_z}{\partial z} + \frac{\partial \tau_{xz}}{\partial x} = \gamma \tag{10.14}$$

$$\frac{\partial \sigma_x}{\partial x} + \frac{\partial \tau_{zx}}{\partial z} = 0 \tag{10.15}$$

and the conditions of compatibility are given, as before, by Eq. (10.4). For undrained loading of saturated isotropic elastic soil and for plane strain, increments of stress and strain are related by

$$\delta \epsilon_x = \frac{1 + \nu_u}{E_u} [(1 - \nu_u)\delta\sigma_x - \nu_u\delta\sigma_z] \tag{10.16}$$

$$\delta \epsilon_z = \frac{1 + \nu_u}{E_u} [(1 - \nu_u)\delta\sigma_z - \nu_u\delta\sigma_x] \tag{10.17}$$

$$\delta \gamma_{xz} = \frac{2(1 + \nu_u)}{E_u} \delta\tau_{xz} \tag{10.18}$$

where E_u is the undrained Young's modulus and $\nu_u = \frac{1}{2}$. Proceeding as before and eliminating strain increments, we have

$$\frac{\partial^2 (\sigma_x + \sigma_z)}{\partial x} + \frac{\partial^2 (\sigma_x + \sigma_z)}{\partial z} = 0 \tag{10.19}$$

Equations (10.14), (10.15), and (10.19) govern the distribution of total stress throughout a body of saturated isotropic elastic soil for undrained loading and for plane strain, and they must satisfy the boundary loads and stresses. Having calculated the increments of stress at any point, increments of strain may be calculated from Eqs. (10.16) to (10.18), and displacements from Eqs. (1.4) to (1.7).

The equations governing the distribution of effective stress through isotropic elastic soil for plane strain are very like those governing the distribution of total stress for undrained loading, the only differences being that effective stresses are replaced by total stresses and pore pressures are ignored. Moreover, in neither case do the Young's modulus and Poisson's ratio appear, so the analyses lead to the same kinds of distribution of effective and total stresses for drained and undrained loading, respectively, for *any* homogeneous isotropic linear elastic soil.[†] For calculation of strain, the condition $\nu_u = \frac{1}{2}$ for undrained loading automatically satisfies the condition of zero volumetric strain since, from Eqs. (10.16) and (10.17),

$$\delta\epsilon_x = \frac{3}{2E_u}[\tfrac{1}{2}\delta\sigma_x - \tfrac{1}{2}\delta\sigma_z] \tag{10.20}$$

$$\delta\epsilon_z = \frac{3}{2E_u}[\tfrac{1}{2}\delta\sigma_z - \tfrac{1}{2}\delta\sigma_x] \tag{10.21}$$

and

$$\delta\epsilon_v = \delta\epsilon_x + \delta\epsilon_z = 0 \tag{10.22}$$

The problem of calculating increments of stress and displacement in an elastic body due to increments of load and displacement applied at its boundaries is a familiar one in mechanics and a number of standard solutions are available which are applicable for the settlement of foundations and for stresses in soil below foundations. We will give some of the more useful of these solutions, but their derivations are beyond the scope of this book. A comprehensive catalogue of solutions for stresses and displacements in elastic bodies is given by Poulos and Davis (1974), and this includes some for anisotropic and non-homogeneous materials.

All these elastic solutions make use of the principle of superposition, and so they are applicable strictly only for *linear* elastic soils for which values of Young's modulus and Poisson's ratio remain constant. We have already seen, in Sec. 2.6, that the value of E' given by Eq. (2.55) depends on the current values of p' and v, and thus the drained Young's modulus is not a constant, although for undrained loading the value of E_u given by Eq. (2.67) remains constant, since neither p' nor v changes for undrained loading of isotropic elastic soil. Thus, for soil, elastic solutions are strictly valid only for undrained loading, but in practice they are used for drained loading as well.

In order to calculate the final stresses and displacements, we may make use of the principle of superposition and add the increments caused by the changes of the boundary loadings to any original stresses due to the self weight of the soil or to any pre-existing loads. The stresses due to the self weight of soil below a level ground surface are given by

$$\sigma_z' = \gamma z - u \qquad \text{or} \qquad \sigma_z = \gamma z \tag{10.23}$$

and the increments of stress due to boundary loadings may usually be found from a standard solution or from a summation of a number of standard solutions.

[†] This observation is valid only for plane strain; for other cases, stresses depend on Poisson's ratio, but they are still independent of Young's modulus.

Most of the standard solutions for stresses and displacements in elastic materials are given in terms of a Young's modulus E and a Poisson's ratio ν and, since it is usual to consider only single phase materials such as metals, no distinction is made between total and effective stresses. The standard solutions are, however, valid also when written in terms of E' and ν' or E_u and $\nu_u = \frac{1}{2}$. Thus, for drained loading we may use the standard solutions with values of E' and ν' for the soil and we will calculate effective stresses and drained deformations, while for undrained loading we may use the same standard solutions, but with values of E_u and $\nu_u = \frac{1}{2}$, and we will calculate total stresses and undrained deformations. In theory, values for E' and ν' for a soil may be found from the results of a drained triaxial compression test on an undisturbed sample. If the axial effective stress and strain are σ_a' and ϵ_a respectively, and the radial effective stress and strain are σ_r' and ϵ_r respectively, then, noting that $\Delta\sigma_r' = 0$ for drained triaxial compression, we have

$$E' = \frac{d\sigma_a'}{d\epsilon_a} \qquad \nu' = -\frac{d\epsilon_r}{d\epsilon_a} \qquad (10.24)$$

Similarly, values for E_u and ν_u for a soil may be found from the results of an undrained triaxial compression test with $\Delta\sigma_r = 0$. Thus, noting that $\Delta\epsilon_v = \Delta\epsilon_a + 2\Delta\epsilon_r = 0$ for undrained loading, we have

$$E_u = \frac{d\sigma_a}{d\epsilon_a} \qquad \nu_u = -\frac{d\epsilon_r}{d\epsilon_a} = \frac{1}{2} \qquad (10.25)$$

and, in addition, from Eqs. (2.55) and (2.67),

$$E_u = \frac{3E'}{2(1 + \nu')} \qquad (10.26)$$

It should be noted that both E' and E_u depend on the current state of the soil, and so values of v and p' in samples in triaxial tests should be chosen to correspond to those in the soil structure for which the calculations are required.

In Sec. 3.7 (p. 101), we remarked that it is doubtful whether any soil sample can be truly undisturbed, and it appears that sampling disturbance may have an appreciable influence on measured values of Young's modulus of soil. This is a subject of current research and, for the present, we simply assume that in some way it is possible to determine suitable values for E' and ν' for the soil in the ground, whether by careful laboratory testing, or by field testing, or by back analysis.

10.4 STANDARD SOLUTIONS FOR FOUNDATIONS ON ELASTIC SOIL

1. Vertical point load

The problem most simply stated is that for a single point load δQ acting vertically at the surface, as shown in Fig. 10.6. The soil is homogeneous, isotropic, and linear

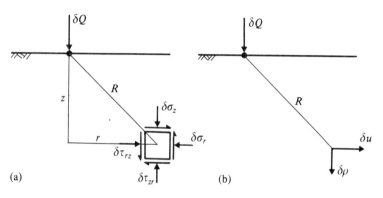

Figure 10.6 Stresses and displacements for a vertical point load.

elastic and it forms an infinite half space extending to infinity downwards and radially from the load. The solution to this problem was given by Boussinesq (1876) and now bears his name.

For a point load, stresses and displacements are axially symmetric and it is convenient to express the results in terms of the cylindrical stress system $\sigma_z : \sigma_r : \sigma_\theta$, as shown in Fig. 10.6(a), where σ_θ is the circumferential stress which, for the element in Fig. 10.6(a), is normal to the page. The shear stresses on the element in Fig. 10.6(a) are in the same directions as those shown in Fig. 1.10 and both diagrams show positive shearing. The Boussinesq solutions are conveniently given in terms of the coordinate system shown in Fig. 10.6(a) as

$$\delta\sigma_z = \frac{\delta Q}{2\pi R^2} \left[3\left(\frac{z}{R}\right)^3 \right] \tag{10.27}$$

$$\delta\sigma_r = \frac{\delta Q}{2\pi R^2} \left[\frac{3r^2 z}{R^3} - (1-2\nu)\frac{R}{(R+z)} \right] \tag{10.28}$$

$$\delta\sigma_\theta = -\frac{\delta Q}{2\pi R^2} \left[(1-2\nu)\left\{ \frac{z}{R} - \frac{R}{(R+z)} \right\} \right] \tag{10.29}$$

$$\delta\tau_{rz} = \frac{\delta Q}{2\pi R^2} \left[3\frac{rz^2}{R^3} \right] \tag{10.30}$$

and the corresponding displacements are given by

$$\delta\rho = \frac{\delta Q(1+\nu)}{2\pi E R} \left[\left(\frac{z}{R}\right)^2 + 2(1-\nu) \right] \tag{10.31}$$

$$\delta u = \frac{\delta Q(1+\nu)}{2\pi E R} \left[\frac{rz}{R^2} - (1-2\nu)\frac{r}{(R+z)} \right] \tag{10.32}$$

Stresses in planes in other directions may be found from those given in Eqs. (10.27) to (10.30), using a Mohr's circle construction, and displacements in any direction may be found by resolution of those given by Eqs. (10.31) and (10.32). Inspection shows that the stresses are independent of Young's modulus and σ_z and τ_{rz} are independent of Poisson's ratio, but displacements depend on both elastic parameters. Equations (10.27) to (10.32) show that at the point of application of the load, for which R is zero, stresses and settlements are infinite. This is clearly impossible, but so too is a point load and in practice loads will be applied over finite areas and so stresses and settlements will be finite also; the principle of St Venant holds that the stresses and settlements given by Eqs. (10.27) to (10.32) are valid for concentrated loads applied over infinitely small or finitely small areas, except in the immediate vicinity of the load.

2. Horizontal point load

A similar problem is that for a single point load δH acting horizontally at the surface in the direction of the x-axis, as shown in Fig. 10.7. The state of stress is neither plane strain nor axi-symmetric and, for simplicity, we will consider only the stresses in the plane containing the load; expressions for other stresses and for elements not in the plane of the load are given by Poulos and Davis (1974). The solutions are conveniently given in terms of the coordinate system shown in Fig. 10.7(a) as

$$\delta \sigma_z = \frac{\delta H}{2\pi R^2} \left[3 \frac{xz^2}{R^3} \right] \tag{10.33}$$

$$\delta \sigma_x = \frac{\delta H}{2\pi R^2} \left[3 \left(\frac{x}{R} \right)^3 - (1 - 2\nu) \frac{xR}{(R + z)^2} \right] \tag{10.34}$$

$$\delta \sigma_y = -\frac{\delta H}{2\pi R^2} \left[(1 - 2\nu) \frac{x}{R} \left\{ 1 - \frac{R^2}{(R + z)^2} \right\} \right] \tag{10.35}$$

$$\delta \tau_{xz} = \frac{\delta H}{2\pi R^2} \left[\frac{3x^2 z}{R^3} \right] \tag{10.36}$$

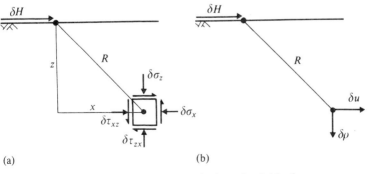

(a)   (b)

Figure 10.7 Stresses and displacements for a horizontal point load.

and the corresponding displacements are given by

$$\delta\rho = \frac{\delta H(1+\nu)}{2\pi ER}\left[\frac{xz}{R^2} + (1-2\nu)\frac{x}{(R+z)}\right] \tag{10.37}$$

$$\delta u = \frac{\delta H(1+\nu)}{2\pi ER}\left[1 + \left(\frac{x}{R}\right)^2 + (1-2\nu)\frac{z}{(R+z)}\right] \tag{10.38}$$

As before, stresses on other planes may be found using a Mohr's circle construction, while displacements in other directions may be found by resolution. Equations (10.33) to (10.38) are similar to Eqs. (10.27) to (10.32); the stresses are independent of Young's modulus and σ_z and τ_{xz} are independent of Poisson's ratio, but displacements depend on both elastic parameters. Any inclined point load may be resolved into horizontal and vertical components and, making use of the principle of superposition, Eqs. (10.27) to (10.38) employed to calculated stresses and displacements due to the inclined load. Solutions for uniformly distributed loadings may be obtained by integrating the point load solutions. It should be noted that such integration procedures are, in effect, summations and so depend on the principle of superposition, which is strictly valid only for linear materials.

3. Strip load with vertical normal stresses

Figure 10.8 shows part of a long strip load, width $B = 2a$, with a uniform vertical normal stress δq [†] where the direction of the strip coincides with the y-axis. The stresses correspond to a state of plane strain, and with reference to Fig. 10.8(a), are given by

$$\delta\sigma_z = \frac{\delta q}{\pi}\left[\beta + \sin\beta\cos 2\theta\right] \tag{10.39}$$

$$\delta\sigma_x = \frac{\delta q}{\pi}\left[\beta - \sin\beta\cos 2\theta\right] \tag{10.40}$$

$$\delta\sigma_y = \frac{\delta q}{\pi}\left[2\nu\beta\right] \tag{10.41}$$

$$\delta\tau_{xz} = \frac{\delta q}{\pi}\left[\sin\beta\sin 2\theta\right] \tag{10.42}$$

and the surface settlement $\delta\rho_x$ at a distance x from the centre of the load, as shown in Fig. 10.8(b), is given by

$$\delta\rho_x - \delta\rho_0 = \frac{\delta q\, 2a(1-\nu^2)}{\pi E}\left[2\ln a + \left(\frac{x}{a}-1\right)\ln\left(\frac{x}{a}-1\right) - \left(\frac{x}{a}+1\right)\ln\left(\frac{x}{a}+1\right)\right] \tag{10.43}$$

[†] See footnote on p. 164.

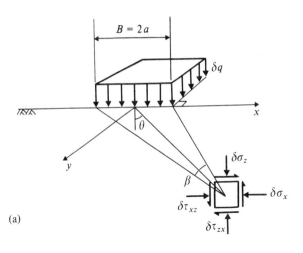

(a)

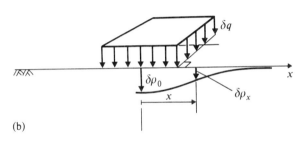

(b)

Figure 10.8 Stresses and displacements for a vertical strip load.

where $\delta\rho_0$ is the surface settlement at the centre of the load, as shown in Fig. 10.8(b). Inspection of Eqs, (10.39) to (10.43) shows that all the stresses, with the exception of σ_y, are independent of Young's modulus and Poisson's ratio, and σ_y is dependent only on Poisson's ratio; the settlements, however, are dependent on both elastic parameters.

4. Strip load with horizontal shear stresses

Figure 10.9 shows part of a long strip load, width $B = 2a$, with a uniform horizontal shear stress δh where the direction of the strip coincides with the y-axis. The stresses correspond to a state of plane strain and, with reference to Fig. 10.9(a), are given by

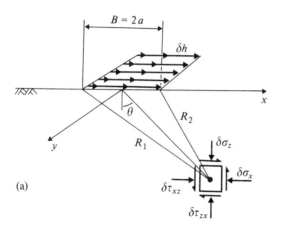

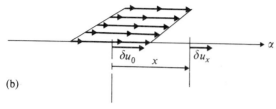

Figure 10.9 Stresses and displacements for a horizontal strip load.

$$\delta\sigma_z = \frac{\delta h}{\pi} \left[\sin \beta \sin 2\theta\right] \tag{10.44}$$

$$\delta\sigma_x = \frac{\delta h}{\pi} \left[2 \ln \left(\frac{R_1}{R_2}\right) - \sin \beta \sin 2\theta\right] \tag{10.45}$$

$$\delta\sigma_y = \frac{\delta h}{\pi} \left[2\nu \ln \left(\frac{R_1}{R_2}\right)\right] \tag{10.46}$$

$$\delta\tau_{xz} = \frac{\delta h}{\pi} \left[\beta - \sin \beta \cos 2\theta\right] \tag{10.47}$$

and the horizontal displacement δu_x at a distance x from the centre of the load as shown in Fig. 10.9(b) is given by

$$\delta u_x - \delta u_0 = \frac{\delta h \, 2a(1-\nu^2)}{\pi E} \left[2 \ln a + \left(\frac{x}{a} - 1\right) \ln \left(\frac{x}{a} - 1\right) - \left(\frac{x}{a} + 1\right) \ln \left(\frac{x}{a} + 1\right)\right]$$

$$\tag{10.48}$$

where δu_0 is the horizontal displacement of the surface at the centre of the load, as shown in Fig. 10.9(b).

The solutions for stresses and displacements for point loads and long strip loads are all relatively simple. Similar solutions may be written for circular loaded areas and rectangular loaded areas, but the corresponding expressions are rather complicated and will not be given here. Many of these more complicated expressions are given by Poulos and Davis (1974).

10.5 INFLUENCE FACTORS FOR STRESS AND DISPLACEMENT

From Eqs. (10.27) to (10.38), the stresses $\delta\sigma$ and displacements $\delta\rho$ due to a point load δF may be written generally as

$$\delta\sigma = \frac{\delta F}{2\pi R^2} I_\sigma \tag{10.49}$$

$$\delta\rho = \frac{\delta F(1+\nu)}{2\pi ER} I_\rho \tag{10.50}$$

Similarly, from Eqs. (10.39) to (10.48), the stresses and displacements due to a uniformly distributed load δq applied over a long strip of width $B = 2a$ may be written as

$$\delta\sigma = \frac{\delta q}{\pi} I_\sigma \tag{10.51}$$

$$\delta\rho = \frac{\delta q\, 2a(1-\nu^2)}{\pi E} I_\rho \tag{10.52}$$

For a rectangular area with breadth $b = 2a$ and a circular area with diameter $d = 2a$ with a uniformly distributed load δq, the stresses and displacements may be written as

$$\delta\sigma = \delta q\, I_\sigma \tag{10.53}$$

$$\delta\rho = \frac{\delta q\, 2a(1-\nu^2)}{E} I_\rho \tag{10.54}$$

In Eqs. (10.49) to (10.54) I_σ and I_ρ are known as *influence factors* for stress and displacement, respectively. Comparing Eqs. (10.27) to (10.48) with Eqs. (10.49) to (10.52), the influence factors are simply the expressions in the square brackets and are dimensionless.

The influence factors I_σ and I_ρ for stress and displacement respectively depend primarily on the geometry of the loading and on the position at which stresses and displacements are required, but some depend also on the value of Poisson's ratio. The standard solutions for stresses and displacements in elastic soil may be expressed in terms of appropriate influence factors, which may be given as equations, as tables, or as charts. For the relatively simple cases for point loads and long strip loads, there is little need to draw up tables or charts as the calculations are not lengthy, but for more complicated cases it is simplest to make use of suitable tables or charts of dimensionless influence factors. Thus, many of the solutions given by Poulos and Davis (1974) are given as tables or charts of influence factors for stress and displacement.

The cases of practical importance in geotechnical engineering are for loaded circular or rectangular areas placed at ground level, for which stresses and displacements are given by Eqs. (10.53) and (10.54). Tables 10.1 to 10.6 give values for influence factors for stresses and settlements below the centre of a circular area and below a corner of a rectangular area for isotropic and homogeneous elastic soil.

Table 10.1 Values of the influence factors $I_{\sigma z}$ and $I_{\sigma r}$ for stresses at a depth z below the centre of a uniformly stressed circular area of radius a

(a) Values of $I_{\sigma z}$

	z/a					
	0	0.2	0.5	1	2	5
All ν	1.00	0.99	0.91	0.65	0.28	0.06

(b) Values of $I_{\sigma r}$

ν	z/a					
	0	0.2	0.5	1	2	5
0	0.50	0.31	0.10	-0.03	-0.04	-0.01
0.25	0.75	0.51	0.24	0.04	-0.01	0.10
0.5	1.00	0.71	0.37	0.12	0.02	0

After Poulos and Davis (1974).

Table 10.2 Values of the influence factor $I_{\rho z}$ for the settlement at a depth z below the centre of a uniformly stressed circular area of radius a

ν	z/a					
	0	0.2	0.5	1	2	5
0	1.00	0.90	0.76	0.56	0.34	0.15
0.25	1.00	0.93	0.80	0.61	0.38	0.16
0.5	1.00	0.98	0.89	0.71	0.45	0.20

After Poulos and Davis (1974).

Table 10.3 Values of the influence factor $I_{\sigma z}$ for vertical stresses at a depth z below a corner of a uniformly stressed area length l and breadth b

l/b	z/b					
	0	0.2	0.5	1	2	5
1	0.25	0.25	0.23	0.18	0.08	0.02
2	0.25	0.25	0.24	0.20	0.12	0.03
5	0.25	0.25	0.24	0.20	0.14	0.06
10	0.25	0.25	0.24	0.21	0.14	0.06

For all values of ν.
After Poulos and Davis (1974).

Table 10.4 Values for the influence factor $I_{\sigma x}$ for horizontal stress at a depth z below a corner of a uniformly stressed area length l and breadth b

(a) $\nu = 0$

l/b	z/b					
	0	0.2	0.5	1	2	5
1	0.13	0.08	0.03	−0.01	−0.01	0
2	0.18	0.12	0.06	0	−0.01	−0.01
5	0.22	0.16	0.09	0.02	−0.01	−0.01
10	0.23	0.17	0.10	0.03	0	−0.01

(b) $\nu = 0.25$

l/b	z/b					
	0	0.2	0.5	1	2	5
1	0.19	0.13	0.07	0.02	0	0
2	0.21	0.15	0.08	0.02	0	0
5	0.24	0.17	0.10	0.03	0	0
10	0.24	0.18	0.11	0.04	0	0

(c) $\nu = 0.5$

l/b	z/b					
	0	0.2	0.5	1	2	5
1	0.25	0.18	0.11	0.04	0.01	0
2	0.25	0.19	0.11	0.04	0.01	0
5	0.25	0.19	0.11	0.05	0.01	0
10	0.25	0.19	0.11	0.05	0.01	0

After Poulos and Davis (1974).

Table 10.5 Values for the influence factor $I_{\sigma y}$ for horizontal stress at a depth z below a corner of a uniformly stressed rectangular area length l and breadth b

(a) $\nu = 0$

l/b	z/b					
	0	0.2	0.5	1	2	5
1	0.13	0.08	0.03	−0.01	−0.01	0
2	0.07	0.06	0.04	0.02	0	0
5	0.03	0.05	0.03	0.02	0.01	0
10	0.02	0.02	0.01	0.01	0.01	0

(b) $\nu = 0.25$

l/b	z/b					
	0	0.2	0.5	1	2	5
1	0.19	0.13	0.07	0.02	0	0
2	0.16	0.13	0.10	0.05	0.01	0
5	0.14	0.12	0.10	0.07	0.03	0
10	0.13	0.12	0.10	0.07	0.04	0.01

(c) $\nu = 0.5$

l/b	z/b					
	0	0.2	0.5	1	2	5
1	0.25	0.18	0.11	0.04	0.01	0
2	0.25	0.21	0.15	0.08	0.03	0
5	0.25	0.22	0.17	0.12	0.06	0.01
10	0.25	0.22	0.18	0.12	0.07	0.02

After Poulos and Davis (1974).

Table 10.6 Values for the influence factor $I_{\rho z}$ for the settlement of a corner of a uniformly stressed rectangular area length l and breadth b

l/b	$I_{\rho z}$
1	0.56
2	0.77
5	1.05
10	1.27

For all values of ν.

After Poulos and Davis (1974).

Building plans may often be subdivided into a number of rectangular areas and hence, making use of the principle of superposition, we may use Eqs. (10.53) and (10.54), together with the values of I_σ and I_ρ given in Tables 10.3 to 10.6, to calculate stresses and settlements below any point inside or outside the area. Thus, for example, Fig. 10.10(a) shows an L-shaped loaded area $ABCDEF$ and it is required to calculate the stresses and settlements at E. Noting that we can only calculate stresses and settlements at the *corner* of a rectangular area, we find those at E by considering the area $AJEF$ less the area $BJEH$ plus the area $CDEH$. Similarly, Fig. 10.10(b) shows a rectangular area $ABCG$ and it is required to calculate the stresses and settlements at the point E which is outside the area. These are found by considering the area $AJEF$, less the areas $BJEH$ and $GDEF$, plus the area $CDEH$.

From Eq. (10.52) with $v_u = \frac{1}{2}$ for undrained loading, the ratio of an undrained settlement ρ_u to a drained settlement ρ_d for a strip load is

$$\frac{\rho_u}{\rho_d} = \frac{3}{4(1 - v'^2)} \frac{E'}{E_u} \tag{10.55}$$

and the same result is obtained from Eq. (10.54) for uniformly stressed circular and rectangular areas. Making use of Eq. (10.26), we have

$$\frac{\rho_u}{\rho_d} = \frac{1}{2(1 - v')} \tag{10.56}$$

and, taking a typical value for Poisson's ratio for drained loading of $v' = 0.25$, we have

$$\rho_d = 1.5\,\rho_u \tag{10.57}$$

Thus, for foundations on elastic soil, the settlements for slow, drained loading are of the order of 1.5 times those for quick, undrained loading of the same foundation, but, of course, in the latter case there will be further settlements due to consolidation, as excess pore pressures developed during the undrained loading dissipate with the passage of time.

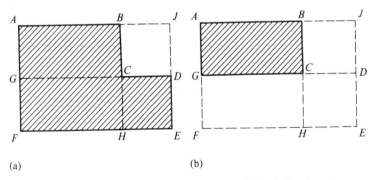

(a)   (b)

Figure 10.10 Calculation of stresses and settlements for loaded rectangular areas.

During undrained loading, pore pressures change as the total stresses change. For isotropic elastic soil, from Sec. 2.6, the change of pore pressure for undrained loading is given by

$$\delta u = \delta p \tag{10.58}$$

where δp is the change of the mean total stress given by

$$\delta p = \tfrac{1}{3}(\delta \sigma_1 + \delta \sigma_2 + \delta \sigma_3) = \tfrac{1}{3}(\delta \sigma_x + \delta \sigma_y + \delta \sigma_z) \tag{10.59}$$

and values for the changes of the total stresses may be found from the elastic calculations with $\nu_u = \tfrac{1}{2}$.

10.6 ONE-DIMENSIONAL LOADING OF ELASTIC SOIL

A special case of practical importance is that of a uniformly distributed load over an infinite area where strong and rigid rock occurs at a relatively shallow depth as shown in Fig. 10.11. In practice, of course, loads are not applied over infinite areas, but this case is often closely approximated by the wide load of an embankment or an oil storage tank where rock occurs at a relatively shallow depth. For an increment of surface stress δq, the vertical stress $\delta \sigma_z$ at any depth is given by

$$\delta \sigma_z = \delta q \tag{10.60}$$

and, assuming that there are no horizontal strains, and hence $\delta \epsilon_y = \delta \epsilon_z = 0$, we have, from Eqs. (1.43),

$$\delta \sigma_x = \delta \sigma_y = \left(\frac{\nu}{1-\nu}\right) \delta q \tag{10.61}$$

and hence

$$\delta \epsilon_z = \frac{\delta q}{E} \left[1 - \frac{2\nu^2}{1-\nu}\right] = -\frac{\delta z}{z} \tag{10.62}$$

Now, if the settlement $\delta \rho_z$ is measured positively, so that $\delta \rho_z = -\delta z$, where δz is the increase of thickness of the soil layer, we have

$$\delta \epsilon_z = -\frac{\delta z}{z} = \frac{\delta \rho_z}{z} \tag{10.63}$$

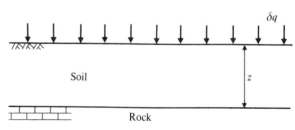

Figure 10.11 Distributed load over a very wide area at the surface of a thin soil layer.

and the surface settlement is given by

$$\delta\rho_z = z\,\delta q\,\frac{1}{E}\left[\frac{(1-2\nu)(1+\nu)}{(1-\nu)}\right] \tag{10.64}$$

For drained loading, we have $E = E'$ and $\nu = \nu'$ and $\delta u = 0$. Hence we have

$$\delta\sigma_z' = \delta q \tag{10.65}$$

$$\delta\sigma_x' = \delta\sigma_y' = \left(\frac{\nu'}{1-\nu'}\right)\delta q \tag{10.66}$$

and

$$\delta\rho_z = z\,\delta q\,\frac{1}{E'}\,\frac{(1-2\nu')(1+\nu')}{(1-\nu')} \tag{10.67}$$

For undrained loading, we have $E = E_u$ and $\nu = \nu_u = \frac{1}{2}$ and there will be changes of pore pressure. Hence we have, from Eqs. (10.60) and (10.61),

$$\delta\sigma_z = \delta\sigma_x = \delta\sigma_y = \delta q \tag{10.68}$$

from Eqs (10.58) and (10.59) with Eq. (10.68),

$$\delta u = \delta q \tag{10.69}$$

and, from Eq. (10.64),

$$\delta\rho_z = 0 \tag{10.70}$$

These results for undrained loading are, of course, applicable for all saturated soils, not just for isotropic elastic soils, since, for one-dimensional and undrained loading, both shear and volumetric strains are zero and, from the principle of effective stress, there are no changes of effective stress.

10.7 CONSOLIDATION SETTLEMENTS

After undrained loading, consolidation settlements occur as effective stresses increase, owing to dissipation of the excess pore pressures set up during the undrained loading. For soil which may be taken as elastic and so path-independent, these consolidation settlements are simply the difference between drained settlements and undrained settlements, both calculated from elastic theory using appropriate values for the elastic parameters, as described in the previous sections. Alternatively, consolidation settlements may be calculated from the results of oedometer tests on undisturbed samples and this method is widely used in geotechnical engineering.

The one-dimensional compression test is carried out in an oedometer described by Atkinson and Bransby (1978, pp. 80–81), and the conduct of the test is described in greater detail in the appropriate British Standard (BS 1377, 1975). In the oedometer, the sample is contained within a rigid and impermeable ring and hence

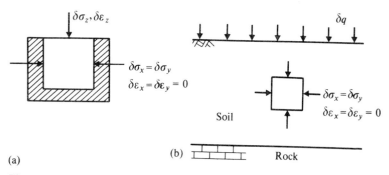

Figure 10.12 States of stress and strain in an oedometer sample and in soil below a very wide foundation. (a) Oedometer sample. (b) Wide foundation.

the essential feature of the one-dimensional compression test is that all components of strain and of pore water seepage are vertical, as indicated in Fig. 10.12(a). Figure 10.12(b) illustrates a section of a very wide foundation on a soil where strong rock occurs at a relatively shallow depth. The conditions of strain and seepage flow in any element of soil in the foundation, such as that shown, are the same as those in the oedometer sample and hence the one-dimensional compression test results may be used directly to estimate the vertical strains, and hence the settlements of the foundation.

In the one-dimensional compression test the vertical total stress σ_z is raised or lowered in increments $\Delta\sigma_z$ and, after each increment, sufficient time is allowed for consolidation to be complete and for excess pore pressures to become zero. The results are shown as change of thickness δz of the sample plotted against time for each increment, as shown in Fig. 10.13(a), and as specific volume plotted against effective vertical stress, as shown in Fig. 10.13(b).

For settlement calculations, it is convenient to define the coefficient of volume compressibility m_v for one-dimensional compression as

$$\delta\epsilon_v = m_v\,\delta\sigma_z' \tag{10.71}$$

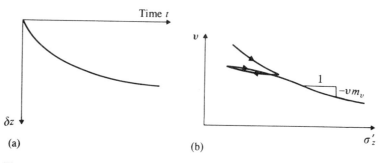

Figure 10.13 Behaviour of a sample in an oedometer test.

Now the volumetric strain is $\delta\epsilon_v = -\delta v/v$, and hence

$$\delta v = -vm_v\,\delta\sigma_z' \tag{10.72}$$

and $-vm_v$ is the slope of the compression curve shown in Fig. 10.13(b). From Eq. (2.116) in Sec. (2.10) we have, for one-dimensional loading,

$$\delta v = -\lambda\frac{\delta p'}{p'} \tag{10.73}$$

For normally consolidated soil K_0 has a constant value and $\delta\sigma_z'/\sigma_z' = \delta p'/p'$, and from Eqs. (10.72) and (10.73) we have

$$m_v = \frac{\lambda}{v\sigma_z'} \tag{10.74}$$

and, since λ is taken as a soil constant, the value of m_v is not a constant but depends on the current stress and specific volume.

For loading and reloading, the state of a sample is inside the state boundary surface, and its behaviour is taken as elastic. Hence, from Eqs. (1.43), with $\delta\epsilon_x = \delta\epsilon_y = 0$, and noting that $\delta\epsilon_v = \delta\epsilon_z$, we have

$$\delta\epsilon_v = \frac{1}{E'}\left[1 - \frac{2v'^2}{1-v'}\right]\delta\sigma_z' \tag{10.75}$$

and, making use of Eq. (2.55)

$$m_v = \frac{1}{E'}\left[\frac{(1-2v')(1+v')}{(1-v')}\right] = \frac{\kappa}{3vp'}\left[\frac{(1+v')}{(1-v')}\right] \tag{10.76}$$

Hence, since κ and v' are taken as soil constants, m_v is not a constant, even for elastic soil, but depends on the current values of stress and specific volume. If settlements are to be calculated using the parameter m_v, values must be selected which correspond to the state of the soil in the ground and to the particular increment of stress.

We have already seen that consolidation settlements are due to changes of effective stress caused by dissipation of excess pore pressures while the total stress may be assumed to be constant. Thus we wish to relate the settlement $\delta\rho_z$ to the initial excess pore pressure $\bar{u}_i$ and this should be related to the foundation load. From Eq. (10.71), noting that $\delta\epsilon_v = \delta\epsilon_z$ and $\delta\rho_z = -\delta z$ we have

$$\delta\rho_z = m_v z\,\delta\sigma_z' \tag{10.77}$$

From the principle of effective stress

$$\delta\sigma_z' = \delta\sigma_z - \delta u \tag{10.78}$$

and it is assumed that total stresses remain constant and $\delta\sigma_z = 0$. Now, during consolidation, the pore pressure changes from $(u_0 + \bar{u}_i)$, immediately after the undrained loading, to u_0 and hence

and hence
$$\delta u = u_0 - (u_0 + \bar{u}_i) = -\bar{u}_i \qquad (10.79)$$

$$\delta \rho_z = m_v z \bar{u}_i \qquad (10.80)$$

If the compressible soil is divided into a number of layers each of thickness h, so that values of m_v and $\bar{u}_i$ can be calculated for each layer, the consolidation settlement in Eq. (10.1) is given by

$$\rho_c = \sum m_v h \bar{u}_i \qquad (10.81)$$

and it remains only to calculate the value of $\bar{u}_i$, the initial pore pressure due to undrained loading δq at the surface. There are a number of separate methods of calculating $\bar{u}_i$ from δq.

For a very wide foundation, on a relatively thin layer of soil, as shown in Fig. 10.11, for which it may be assumed that the conditions are everywhere one-dimensional, we have, during the undrained loading,

$$\delta u = \bar{u}_i = \delta q \qquad (10.82)$$
and

Hence, from Eq. (10.81)
$$\rho_c = \sum m_v h \, \delta \sigma_z \qquad (10.83)$$

Alternatively, for foundations which are not very wide compared with the depth of compressive soil, it is sometimes assumed that although layers consolidate one-dimensionally the vertical stress decreases with depth and may be found from elastic theory. Thus, during the undrained loading we have

$$\delta u = \bar{u}_i = \delta \sigma_z \qquad (10.84)$$
and

$$\rho_c = \sum m_v h \, \delta \sigma_z \qquad (10.85)$$

In Eq. (10.85) the consolidation settlement is calculated directly from oedometer test results, making allowance for the decrease of total stress increment with depth, and ρ_c is known as the *oedometer settlement*.

Another method for calculating consolidation settlements was given by Skempton and Bjerrum (1957), This method makes some allowance for conditions below a foundation being not one-dimensional, and from Eq. (2.61) the initial excess pore pressure $\bar{u}_i = \delta u$ is given by

$$\bar{u}_i = \delta \sigma_x + A (\delta \sigma_z - \delta \sigma_x) \qquad (10.86)$$

where A is Skempton's pore pressure parameter. Thus, from Eq. (10.81), the consolidation settlement is given by

$$\delta \rho_c = \sum m_v h \, \delta \sigma_z \left[A + \frac{\delta \sigma_x}{\delta \sigma_z} (1 - A) \right] \qquad (10.87)$$
or

$$\delta \rho_c = \sum m_v h \, \delta \sigma_z [A + \alpha (1 - A)] \qquad (10.88)$$

Table 10.7 Values of α in Eq. (10.88)

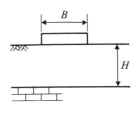

H/B	Values of α	
	◯ ↕B	⬡ ↕B
0	1.00	1.00
0.25	0.67	0.74
0.5	0.50	0.53
1	0.38	0.37
2	0.30	0.26
4	0.28	0.20
10	0.26	0.14
∞	0.25	0

After Skempton and Bjerrum (1957).

where α is a factor which depends on the geometry of the foundation and the depth of the compressible layer of soil. Values for α for strip and circular foundations were given by Skempton and Bjerrum (1957) and are shown in Table 10.7.

10.8 RATE OF CONSOLIDATION OF FOUNDATIONS

In Sec. 10.2 we discussed in general terms the various components of settlement, and, from Eq. (10.1) the time-dependent consolidation settlements ρ_t are given by

$$\rho_t - \rho_i = U_t \rho_c \tag{10.89}$$

where ρ_i is the initial settlement due to undrained loading, ρ_c is the consolidation settlement after infinite time due to dissipation of excess pore pressures, and U_t is the degree of consolidation. The value of U_t is related to time and depends on the boundary conditions of the consolidating soil and the initial distribution of excess pore pressure; the value of U_t runs from $U_t = 0$ at $t = 0$ to $U_t = 1.0$ after infinite time.

The relationship between degree of consolidation U_t and time for consolidating soil may be obtained for a number of cases and, although the governing partial differential equations are relatively simple, their solutions are not easy. For the present we will consider only the two special cases illustrated in Fig. 10.14. In both cases the loading is very wide compared with the depth of consolidating soil, so that all soil strains are one-dimensional and excess pore pressures are $\bar{u}_i = \delta q$, but the drainage conditions differ. In Fig. 10.14(a) the rock is impermeable, and at the soil surface $\bar{u} \equiv 0$; hence all seepage flows are vertical and one-dimensional, and the strain and drainage conditions in the ground are precisely the same as those in an oedometer test sample for which the base of the apparatus is impermeable, as

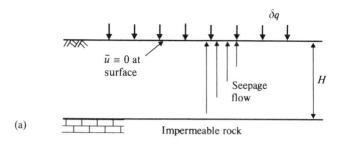

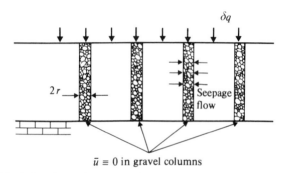

(a)

(b) $\bar{u} \equiv 0$ in gravel columns

Figure 10.14 One-dimensional and radial consolidation of a very wide foundation.

shown in Fig. 10.12(a). In Fig. 10.14(b) there are a number of vertical columns of very permeable sand or gravel and in these columns excess pore pressures are everywhere $\bar{u} \equiv 0$, and so seepage flows are horizontal towards the columns. For each case the relationships between U_t and time are different.

For one-dimensional consolidation corresponding to the case shown in Fig. 10.14(a), the equation governing the distribution of excess pore pressure is

$$c_v \frac{\partial^2 \bar{u}}{\partial x^2} = \frac{\partial \bar{u}}{\partial t} \tag{10.90}$$

where $\bar{u}(z, t)$ is a function of depth and time and c_v is the coefficient of consolidation given by

$$c_v = \frac{k_v}{m_v \gamma_w} \tag{10.91}$$

The theory and assumptions leading to Eq. (10.90), and its solution, are attributed to Terzaghi and are discussed by Atkinson and Bransby (1978, Chapter 8). Methods for determining values for c_v from the results of one-dimensional consolidation tests were discussed by Atkinson and Bransby (1978, pp. 160–164). In Eq. (10.91),

k_v is the coefficient of permeability of the soil and the subscript v is added to indicate that k_v is for vertical seepage. It should be noted that the expression for c_v in Eq. (10.91) contains m_v and k_v which both depend on the state of the soil and on the loading increment, but it turns out that c_v may often be taken as constant for modest changes of stress.

A complete solution of Eq. (10.90) obtains values for excess pore pressure at all depths, and at any time. For the present purpose, however, it is simplest to give the solution in terms of the average degree of consolidation U_t and the time factor T_v. The degree of consolidation is a measure of the average dissipation of excess pore pressure and, from Eq. (10.89),

$$U_t = \frac{\rho_t - \rho_i}{\rho_c} \tag{10.92}$$

The time factor T_v is given by

$$T_v = \frac{c_v t}{H^2} \tag{10.93}$$

where H is the maximum drainage path equal to the longest direct drainage path taken by an element of water as it is squeezed from the soil. For the case shown in Fig. 10.14(a), the maximum drainage path is equal to the depth of the soil, as an element of water initially at the level of the rock must eventually emerge at the surface. The relationship between U_t and T_v for one-dimensional consolidation for the case where $\bar{u}_i$ is the same at all depths is shown in Fig. 10.15. Hence, knowing values for c_v and H and making use of Eqs. (10.92) and (10.93), we may calculate the settlement ρ_t at any time t after the undrained loading.

For radial consolidation corresponding to the case shown in Fig. 10.14(b), the equation governing the distribution of excess pore pressure is

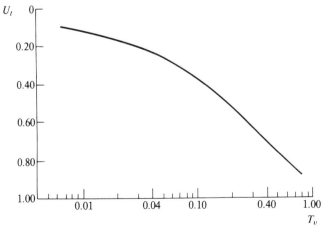

Figure 10.15 Relationship between degree of consolidation and time factor for one-dimensional consolidation. (*After Taylor, 1948.*)

$$c_h \left[\frac{\partial^2 \bar{u}}{\partial r^2} + \frac{1}{r} \frac{\partial \bar{u}}{\partial r} \right] = \frac{\partial \bar{u}}{\partial t} \tag{10.94}$$

where $\bar{u}(r, t)$ is a function of the radial distance from the centre of a column and time and c_h is the coefficient of consolidation for horizontal flow given by

$$c_h = \frac{k_h}{m_v \gamma_w} \tag{10.95}$$

where k_h is the coefficient of permeability for horizontal flow. For isotropic soil, of course, $k_h = k_v$ and $c_h = c_v$, but for layered soils k_h and k_v (and c_h and c_v) usually differ. As before, it is convenient to give the solution in terms of the degree of consolidation U_t given by Eq. (10.92) as

$$U_t = \frac{\rho_t - \rho_i}{\rho_c} \tag{10.92}$$

and the time factor for radial flow T_r given by

$$T_r = \frac{c_h t}{4R^2} \tag{10.96}$$

where R is the maximum drainage path which is approximately the radius of the cylinder of soil drained by each column. The relationship between U_t and T_r for radial consolidation for the case where $\bar{u}_i$ is the same at all depths is shown in Fig. 10.16, where n is given by

$$n = \frac{R}{r} \tag{10.97}$$

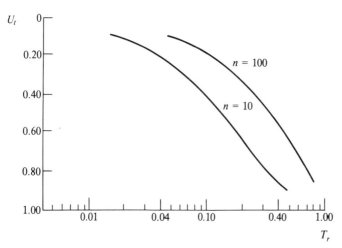

Figure 10.16 Relationship between degree of consolidation and time factor for radial consolidation. (*After Barron, 1948.*)

and r is the radius of a column as shown in Fig. 10.14(b). Hence, knowing values of c_h, r, and R, and making use of Eqs. (10.92) and (10.96), we may calculate the settlement ρ_t at any time t after the undrained loading.

The cases shown in Figs. 10.14(a) and (b) are similar, but for the presence of the vertical columns of sand or gravel in Fig. 10.14(b), which have the effect of changing the seepage flow from vertical to horizontal. Such columns are known as *sand drains* (or gravel drains) and are inserted to hasten the rate of consolidation and so shorten the time over which settlements occur. For a given degree of consolidation there is a particular value of T_v or T_r given by the curves in Figs. 10.15 and 10.16, and the time for this degree of consolidation depends on H^2 or on R^2 (i.e., on the square of the length of the drainage path). Thus by inserting drains we hasten the rate of consolidation by shortening the drainage paths. In addition, as discussed in Sec. 3.2, most soils are layered due to their method of deposition, with the result that the coefficient of permeability for horizontal seepage is greater than the coefficient of permeability for vertical seepage and so the coefficient of consolidation c_h is greater than c_v. Thus, even if the drainage paths are approximately the same, consolidation will occur most rapidly when the seepage is horizontal rather than vertical.

10.9 STRESS PATH METHODS

The settlement calculations discussed in previous sections depend to a large extent on accurate knowledge of various soil parameters, which are not soil constants but which depend on the current state of the soil, and a major difficulty in soil engineering is the determination of appropriate values for the parameters for settlement and deformation calculations. Part of this difficulty lies in obtaining representative undisturbed samples of soil from the ground, since the sampling process itself will probably alter the properties of the soil. Another difficulty is that tests to determine the soil parameters must be carried out at the states of stress, and for stress paths, corresponding to those in the ground for the loading being considered. The stress path method was developed to overcome these second difficulties, but problems of sample disturbance remain.

The basic idea of the stress path method is that elements of soil are removed from the ground and, in special laboratory tests, are subjected to the stress paths they would have experienced in the ground. The observed strains and deformations of the laboratory samples are then used to calculate the settlements of the structure. Thus, by subjecting samples to the appropriate state of stress and stress increment, it is supposed that their behaviour will correspond to that of the soil in the ground. There are two basic stress path methods, one proposed by Lambe (1964) and the other by Davis and Poulos (1968). These methods are similar and call for essentially the same laboratory testing procedures, but the methods of analysis differ.

For any stress path method, it is required to determine the initial state of stress and the changes of stress at several points in the soil. The initial vertical total and effective stresses may be calculated from knowledge of the unit weight of the soil and the pore pressures in the ground, as discussed in Sec. 3.3; the initial horizontal stresses require K_0, the coefficient of earth pressure at rest, which must be determined by special field tests or estimated from knowledge of the geological history of the site, as discussed in Sec. 3.4. For overconsolidated soils, the changes of stress in the ground during the various stages of loading and consolidation may be calculated from elastic theory. The important point is that changes of stress are independent of the values of the Young's moduli E_u or E', and depend only on the Poisson's ratios $\nu_u = \frac{1}{2}$ or ν' for undrained and drained loading, respectively; ν' may be taken as a constant for most soils and, in any case, has only a minor influence on the calculated stresses. Thus, for any overconsolidated soil, stress paths may be calculated without serious error.

Figure 10.17(b) shows a typical stress path for an element below the centre of a foundation, such as that shown in Fig. 10.17(a), for quick undrained loading followed by consolidation. For a circular foundation, the stresses and strains are axially symmetric, the axes used for plotting the stress path are q'' and p', and stress path tests may be carried out in a triaxial apparatus. For a long foundation,

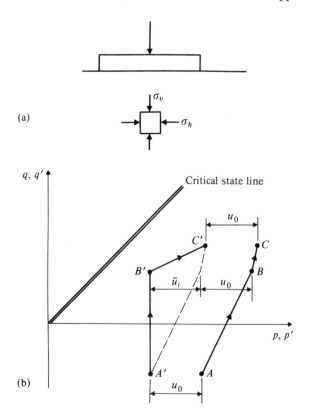

Figure 10.17 Stress path for an element below a circular foundation on overconsolidated soil.

however, the stresses and strains are plane strain, the axes used for plotting stress paths should be t' and s', and stress path tests should be carried out in a plane strain apparatus. Figure 10.17 shows the case for a circular foundation, but stress paths for long foundations are similar. The points A and A' correspond to the total and effective stresses in the ground for $K_0 > 1$ for a heavily overconsolidated soil, as discussed in Sec. 3.4. The paths AB and $A'B'$ correspond to undrained loading, for which $\delta p' = 0$ for isotropic elastic soil, and at B' there is a margin of safety indicated by the distance of B' from the critical state line. The paths BC and $B'C'$ correspond to consolidation as the initial excess pore pressures $\bar{u}_i$ dissipate; it may be noted that although the external load on the foundation remains constant during consolidation, the total stresses may change slightly along the path BC as the value of Poisson's ratio changes from $\nu_u = \frac{1}{2}$ to the drained value ν'.

For both the Lambe method and the Davis and Poulos method, the soil is divided into a number of layers and a sample taken to represent each layer. The layers may be chosen to correspond to different soil strata in the ground or different magnitudes of stress change caused by the foundation. Each element is then subjected to its appropriate stress path. For the Lambe stress path method, the change of thickness of each layer is calculated simply from the observed vertical strain of the appropriate sample when subjected to its particular stress path, and the settlement of the foundation found by addition of these changes of thickness. For the Davis and Poulos method, on the other hand, values of an elastic modulus, similar to Young's modulus, are found for each part of the stress path, and these moduli are then used to calculate the settlements from the elastic calculations described earlier.

REFERENCES

Atkinson, J. H. and P. L. Bransby (1978), *The Mechanics of Soils,* McGraw-Hill, London.

Barron, R. A. (1948), 'Consolidation of fine grained soils by drain wells', *Trans. Am. Soc. Civil Engrs,* 113, 718–754.

Boussinesq, J. V. (1876), 'Équilibre d'élasticité d'un sol isotropic sans pesanteur, supportant differents poids', *Comptes Rendus Hebdomadaires,* 16, 1260–1263, Paris.

BS 1377 : 1975, *Methods of Testing Soils for Civil Engineering Purposes,* British Standards Institution, London.

Davis, E. H. and H. G. Poulos (1968), 'The use of elastic theory for settlement prediction under three-dimensional conditions', *Geotechnique,* 18, 67–91.

Lambe, T. W. (1964), 'Methods of estimating settlement', *Proc. Am. Soc. Civil Engrs,* 90, (SM5), 43–67.

Poulos, H. G. and E. H. Davis (1974), *Elastic Solutions for Soil and Rock Mechanics,* Wiley, New York.

Skempton, A. W. and L. Bjerrum (1957), 'A contribution to the settlement analysis of foundations on clay', *Geotechnique,* 7, 168–178.

Taylor, D. W. (1948), *Fundamentals of Soil Mechanics,* Wiley, New York.

WORKED EXAMPLES

E10.1 Stresses below a Strip Foundation

A long strip foundation 2 m wide with a uniform stress $q = 50$ kN/m^2 is placed at the surface of isotropic and homogeneous elastic soil. The soil has Poisson's ratio $\nu' = 0.30$ and unit weight $\gamma = 20$ kN/m^3 and its Young's modulus may be taken as $E' = 10$ MN/m^2. Before construction, the coefficient of earth pressure at rest in the soil was $K_0 = 1.2$ and the pore pressures were hydrostatic with the water table at ground level. Assuming that the soil remains elastic, calculate the total and effective vertical and horizontal stresses at a depth of 2 m below the centre of the foundation (1) for drained loading and (2) for undrained loading.

Before construction the pore pressure and the stresses at a depth of 2 m were

$$u = \gamma_w z = 19.6 \text{ kN/m}^2$$

$$\sigma_v = \gamma z = 40.0 \text{ kN/m}^2 \qquad \sigma_v' = \sigma_v - u = 20.4 \text{ kN/m}^2$$

$$\sigma_h = \sigma_h' + u = 44.1 \text{ kN/m}^2 \qquad \sigma_h' = K_0 \sigma_v' = 24.5 \text{ kN/m}^2$$

1. From Eqs (10.39) and (10.40), with $\delta q = 50$ kN/m^2, $\theta = 0$, and $\beta = 53° = 0.93$, the changes of total stress are

$$\delta \sigma_v = \frac{\delta q}{\pi} [\beta + \sin \beta \cos 2\theta] = 27.5 \text{ kN/m}^2$$

$$\delta \sigma_h = \frac{\delta q}{\pi} [\beta - \sin \beta \cos 2\theta] = 2.0 \text{ kN/m}^2$$

and for drained loading $\delta u = 0$. Hence after construction we have

$$u = 19.6 \text{ kN/m}^2$$

$$\underline{\sigma_v = 67.5 \text{ kN/m}^2} \qquad \underline{\sigma_v' = 47.9 \text{ kN/m}^2}$$

$$\underline{\sigma_h = 46.1 \text{ kN/m}^2} \qquad \underline{\sigma_h' = 26.5 \text{ kN/m}^2}$$

2. For undrained loading there is no volume change, and from Eq. (10.58)

$$\delta u = \delta p = \tfrac{1}{3}(\delta \sigma_v + \delta \sigma_h + \delta \sigma_y)$$

Since Eqs. (10.39) and (10.40) do not contain the elastic parameters, we have $\delta \sigma_v$ and $\delta \sigma_h$ as before, and, from Eq. (10.41), with $\nu = \nu_u = \tfrac{1}{2}$ for undrained loading,

$$\delta \sigma_y = \frac{\delta q}{\pi} [\beta] = 14.7 \text{ kN/m}^2$$

Hence

$$\delta u = \tfrac{1}{3}(27.5 + 2.0 + 14.7) = 14.7 \text{ kN/m}^2$$

and

$$u = 34.3 \text{ kN/m}^2$$

Hence

$$\sigma_v = 67.5 \text{ kN/m}^2 \qquad \sigma'_v = 33.2 \text{ kN/m}^2$$

$$\sigma_h = 46.1 \text{ kN/m}^2 \qquad \sigma'_h = 11.8 \text{ kN/m}^2$$

E10.2 Stresses and Settlements Below a Loaded Circular Area

A loaded circular area, radius 2.5 m, is founded at the surface of isotropic and homogeneous elastic soil. The stress applied to the circular area is raised by $\delta q = 50 \text{ kN/m}^2$ and the soil has $E' = 10 \text{ MN/m}^2$ and $\nu' = 0.25$. Making use of influence factors, plot changes of vertical total stress and of settlement down the centreline below the foundation for undrained loading.

The changes of vertical stress and of displacement are given by Eqs. (10.53) and (10.54) as

$$\delta \sigma_z = \delta q \, I_{\sigma z}$$

$$\delta \rho_z = \delta q \, \frac{2a(1 - \nu^2)}{E} I_{\rho z}$$

where $I_{\sigma z}$ and $I_{\rho z}$ are influence factors given in Tables 10.1 and 10.2. For undrained loading, $\nu = \nu_u = 0.5$ and $E = E_u = 3E'/2(1 + \nu') = 1.2 \times 10^4 \text{ kN/m}^2$. The radius of the circular area is $a = 2.5$ m, the change of stress is $\delta q = 50 \text{ kN/m}^2$, and thus we have

$$\delta \sigma_z = 50 \, I_{\sigma z} \text{ kN/m}^2$$

$$\delta \rho_z = \frac{50 \times 5 \times (1 - 0.5^2)}{1.2 \times 10^4} I_{\rho z} \times 10^3 \text{ mm}$$

$$= 15.63 \, I_{\rho z} \text{ mm}$$

Hence, from Tables 10.1(a) and 10.2, we obtain the values listed in Table E10.1 and values of $\delta \sigma_z$ and $\delta \rho_z$ are shown plotted against depth in Fig. E10.1.

Table E10.1

Depth z m	z/a	$I_{\sigma z}$	$\delta \sigma_z$ kN/m²	$I_{\rho z}$	$\delta \rho_z$ mm
0	0	1.00	50.0	1.00	15.6
0.5	0.2	0.99	49.5	0.98	15.3
1.25	0.5	0.91	45.5	0.89	13.9
2.5	1.0	0.65	32.5	0.71	11.1
5	2.0	0.28	14.0	0.45	7.0
12.5	5.0	0.06	3.0	0.20	3.1

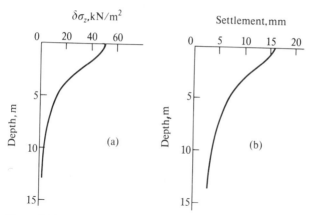

Figure E10.1

E10.3 Settlement of a loaded Area

A uniform vertical stress $q = 50 \text{ kN/m}^2$ is applied suddenly to the surface of a layer of saturated soil. The soil layer is 2.5 m thick and overlies strong, rigid, and impermeable rock. For the particular loading, and at any depth in the soil, the coefficient of volume compressibility is $m_v = 0.83 \times 10^{-4} \text{ m}^2/\text{kN}$ and the coefficient of consolidation is $c_v = 2 \text{ m}^2/\text{year}$. Calculate the magnitude of the final settlement and the time taken for the settlement to reach 50 per cent of this value.

For a very wide area of load the conditions in the soil are one-dimensional and, for saturated soil, initial settlements are zero. The consolidation settlement is given by Eq. (10.83) and, for one uniform layer

$$\delta \rho_c = m_v H \, \delta q = 0.83 \times 10^{-4} \times 2.5 \times 50 \times 10^3$$
$$\underline{\delta \rho_c = 10.4 \text{ mm}}$$

Since the rock is impermeable, the drainage path is the same as the thickness of the soil layer, and hence the time factor is given by

$$T_v = \frac{c_v t}{H^2} = \frac{2t}{2.5^2} = 0.32t$$

where t is the time. For 50 per cent consolidation, $U_t = 0.5$, and from Fig. 10.15 we have

$$T_v = 0.196 = 0.32t$$

Hence, the time for 50 per cent settlement is

$$t = \frac{0.196}{0.32}$$

$$\underline{t = 0.61 \text{ years}}$$

E10.4 Settlement of a Foundation

A circular foundation 2.5 m radius is placed at the surface of a layer of saturated soil 10 m thick over strong, rigid, and impermeable rock. The foundation is loaded quickly and applies a uniform vertical stress $q = 50$ kN/m^2 to the soil surface. At any depth in the soil, $m_v = 0.83 \times 10^{-4}$ m^2/kN, the elastic parameters are $E' = 10$ MN/m^2, $v' = 0.25$, and the pore pressure parameter is $A = \frac{1}{3}$. Calculate the initial undrained settlement of the foundation, and, dividing the soil into four equal layers, calculate the consolidation settlement using the Skempton and Bjerrum method.

The settlement of a circular foundation on isotropic and homogeneous linear elastic soil is given by Eq. (10.54) as

$$\delta\rho = \delta q \, \frac{2a(1-v^2)}{E} I_{\rho z}$$

where, from Table 10.2, with $z = 0$, the influence factor is $I_{\rho z} = 1.0$. For undrained loading, $E = E_u = 3E'/2(1+v') = 1.2 \times 10^4$ kN/m^2 and $v = v_u = 0.5$. Hence assuming that the presence of the strong rock at depth does not affect the result, the undrained settlement of the foundation is

$$\delta\rho_i = \frac{50 \times 2 \times 2.5 \times (1 - 0.5^2)}{1.2 \times 10^4} \times 10^3 \text{ mm}$$

$$\delta\rho_i = 15.6 \text{ mm}$$

Making use of the Skempton and Bjerrum method, the consolidation settlement is given by Eq. (10.88)

$$\delta\rho_c = \sum m_v h \, \delta\sigma_z \, [A + \alpha(1-A)]$$

where $A = \frac{1}{3}$ and, from Table 10.7, with $H/B = 2$, and for a circular foundation, $\alpha = 0.30$. Hence

$$\delta\rho_c = \sum m_v h \, \delta\sigma_z \, [\tfrac{1}{3} + 0.3 \, (1 - \tfrac{1}{3})]$$

or

$$\delta\rho_c = 0.53 \sum m_v h \, \delta\sigma_z$$

Figure E10.2 shows the soil layer divided into four layers each $h = 2.5$ m thick and the variation of $\delta\sigma_z$ with depth from Eq. (10.53), with influence factors from Table 10.1. Table E10.2 gives calculations for each layer with values for $\delta\sigma_z$ at the centre of each layer found by scaling from Fig. E10.2. Hence the consolidation settlement is

$$\delta\rho_c = 0.53 \times 27.0 = 14.3 \text{ mm}$$

E10.5 Settlement of a Drained Foundation

A soil layer 5 m thick over strong, rigid and impermeable rock contains sand drains 0.25 m diameter at 2.5 m spacing and has $m_v = 0.83 \times 10^{-4}$ m^2/kN and $c_v = c_h = 2$ m^2/year. A uniform vertical stress $q = 50$ kN/m^2 is applied suddenly to the

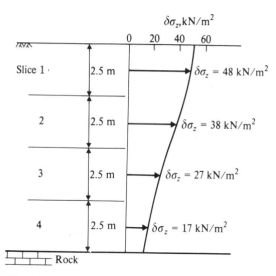

Figure E10.2

Table E10.2

Slice	m_v m²/kn	h m	Depth to centre of slice m	$\delta\sigma_z$ kN/m²	$m_vh\,\delta\sigma_z \times 10^3$ mm
1	0.83×10^{-4}	2.5	1.25	48	9.96
2	0.83×10^{-4}	2.5	3.75	38	7.89
3	0.83×10^{-4}	2.5	6.25	27	5.60
4	0.83×10^{-4}	2.5	8.75	17	3.53
Total					27.0 mm

surface over a very wide area. Calculate the magnitude of the final consolidation settlement and the time taken for the settlement to reach 50 per cent of this value (1) without the drains in place and (2) with the drains in place.

For a very wide area of load the conditions in the soil are one-dimensional and, for saturated soil, initial settlements are zero. The consolidation settlement is given by Eq. (10.83) and, for one uniform layer

$$\delta\rho_c = m_vH\,\delta q = 0.83 \times 10^{-4} \times 5 \times 50 \times 10^3$$

$$\underline{\delta\rho_c = 20.8 \text{ mm}}$$

1. without the sand drains, the consolidation seepage is one-dimensional and vertical and, since the rock is impermeable, the drainage path is the same as the thickness of the soil layer. Hence the time factor is given by Eq. (10.93) as

$$T_v = \frac{c_v t}{H^2} = \frac{2t}{5^2} = 0.08t$$

For 50 per cent consolidation $U_t = 0.5$ and, from Fig. 10.15, we have

$$T_v = 0.196 = 0.08t$$

and hence the time for 50 per cent settlement without drains is

$$t = \frac{0.196}{0.08}$$

$$\underline{t = 2.45 \text{ years}}$$

2. With sand drains the consolidation seepage is radial and the time factor is given by Eq. (10.96). Hence, taking the radius of one drained cylinder as $R = 1.25$ m, we have

$$T = \frac{c_h t}{4R^2} = \frac{2t}{4 \times 1.25^2} = 0.32t$$

If the radius of a drain is 0.125 m then from Eq. (10.97) we have

$$n = \frac{1.25}{0.125} = 10$$

For 50 per cent consolidation $U_t = 0.5$, and from Fig. 10.16 for $n = 10$ we have

$$T_r = 0.13 = 0.32t$$

and hence the time for 50 per cent settlement with drains is

$$t = \frac{0.13}{0.32}$$

$$\underline{t = 0.4 \text{ years}}$$

Thus the addition of the sand drains into the soil has increased the rate of consolidation by a factor of approximately six.

ELEVEN

CONCLUDING REMARKS

The aim of this book has been to describe, in a simple way, some of the methods which may be used to calculate the stability and deformations of soil structures. We have dealt principally with foundations, slopes, and retaining walls, as these are the soil structures most commonly found in geotechnical engineering practice, but many of the analyses described are applicable to other soil structures.

Throughout the book we have always distinguished carefully between undrained loading and drained loading, and this distinction is crucial in geotechnical engineering. For undrained loading of saturated soil, calculations may be carried out in terms of total stresses, but for drained loading it is essential always to work with effective, not total, stresses. For practical purposes, undrained loading is assumed when the rate of loading is so fast compared with the rate of consolidation that negligible volume changes occur, and drained loading is assumed when the rate of loading is so slow compared with the rate of consolidation that negligible excess pore pressures occur. For all calculations for stability or deformation of soil structures, it is essential to determine whether the loading should be taken to be drained or undrained.

As a first step in the analysis of a soil structure, an understanding of the fundamental behaviour of soil is required, and so the first part of the book deals with the loading of single elements of soil. This material follows closely the work on the fundamental behaviour of soil covered by Atkinson and Bransby in *The Mechanics of Soils* and makes use of the critical state approach to soil behaviour introduced by Schofield and Wroth in *Critical State Soil Mechanics*. Thus, after Chapter 1, which covers the basic ideas of stress and strain and stress–strain relationships, Chapter 2 deals with elastic behaviour, plastic yielding, hardening, and plastic failure of soils.

Although this book is concerned mainly with the theories of stability and deformation of soil structures, it is important to consider the application of these theories to real soils. Thus, Chapter 3 contains very brief descriptions of the occurrence and loading of soils in the ground and it covers *in situ* states of stress and overconsolidation of natural soils. Chapter 3 also discusses, again very briefly, some of the methods of site investigation, sampling, and testing of soils to determine their engineering properties.

Chapters 4 to 9 deal with analyses for the stability of soil structures and they contain the familiar limit equilibrium method and the less familiar, at least to geotechnical engineers, upper and lower bound and slip line methods. The upper and lower bound method is very powerful and the calculations are relatively simple; it leads on to the slip line method, which provides an approach for finding equal upper and lower bounds which must therefore be exact solutions. These plastic calculations are theoretically correct, but only for perfectly plastic materials, and they are well known in other branches of engineering. For undrained loading, the behaviour of soil at the critical state may be taken to be perfectly plastic and the bound and slip line methods may be used without difficulty. For drained loading, however, soil behaviour at the critical state is not perfectly plastic, but still the bound and slip line methods may be used to give meaningful results. In Chapters 5 to 7 we have taken the simple upper and lower bound and slip line methods and used these to calculate the stability of simple soil structures. For undrained loading, the analyses follow closely those given in books on metal plasticity such as *Engineering Plasticity* by Calladine, but for drained loading the calculations are rather different.

Chapters 8 and 9 deal with the limit equilibrium method and the use of bearing capacity factors, stability charts, and earth pressure coefficients. These are methods familiar to geotechnical engineers and are covered in most current texts on soil mechanics and foundation engineering. In our discussion of these calculations we have examined the theoretical basis of the limit equilibrium method and the origins of many of the common factors, charts, and coefficients.

Only Chapter 10 considers the settlements of foundations at their working loads. We have seen, in Chapter 3, that most natural soils are overconsolidated and so, in accordance with the ideas of critical state soil mechanics, their stress–strain behaviour may be taken as elastic. Thus in Chapter 10 we examined the applications of elastic theory, together with alternative methods for calculating the settlement of foundations from the results of oedometer tests. It will be noted that only a relatively small space is given to calculations of deformations in this book, and, indeed deformations of slopes and retaining walls have not been covered at all. This is deliberate, and reflects the difficulty in obtaining simple calculations for the deformations of soil structures compared with the several relatively simple methods for stability analysis. Other methods for calculating deformations of soil structures are considerably more complicated and they are beyond the scope of this book.

Most of the analyses described in this book are strictly valid only for isotropic and homogeneous soil for which the behaviour is elastic and plastic, as given by the simple critical state model. Real soils, however, are not simple materials; they are often non-homogeneous and anisotropic, and the behaviour of small samples may only approximate to that predicted by the simple model. For routine engineering design purposes, stability and deformation calculations should be relatively simple and so, often, considerable approximations and idealizations are required. Many of these approximations and idealizations are already familiar to geotechnical engineers, who commonly use the limit equilibrium method for stability analysis and elastic theory for deformation calculations. Many of the analyses described in this book involve similar approximations and idealizations for soil behaviour, and, for routine calculations, we must accept the errors which will result from these simplifications. For important projects, for which more accurate estimates of stability and deformation are required, more exact complex analyses will be used, but we have not dealt with these more advanced methods.

INDEX

Abbott, N. B., 255
α-Characteristic, 249, 260
   (*see also* Characteristic)
α-Discontinuity, 141
   (*see also* Discontinuity)
Active pressure, 159, 202
   coefficient of, 207, 324, 330
   for drained loading, 203–205,
     233–236, 289–291, 293,
     294–296
   for undrained loading, 162–163
Allowable:
   angle of friction, 105, 310, 327
   bearing capacity, 322, 327
   shear stress, 105
   slope angle, 324
   slope height, 324
   undrained shear strength, 105, 310
Analysis of strain, 4–10
Analysis of stress, 11–14
Angle between characteristics, 249
Angle between slip planes, 119, 263,
   269
Angle of dilation, 8–10, 40, 65,
   117–120, 127, 195, 249–252,
   258–261
Angle of friction (*see* Critical state
   angle of friction, Peak angle
   of friction, Residual angle of
   friction)
Angle of shearing resistance, 9, 11–13,
   38, 134, 138–140, 197
Angle of wall friction, 232–236, 276,
   294, 330
Anisotropic compression, 68–70
   (*see also* One-dimensional compression)
Anisotropic soil, 85, 342
Associated fields method, 261–262
Associated flow rule, 21, 24, 57, 63,
   111, 117, 147, 195, 233, 247,
   251–253, 261–262
   (*see also* Flow rule)
Atkinson, J. H., 2, 4, 8, 15, 16, 23, 24,
   39, 36, 38, 56, 101, 105, 194,
   262, 355, 360, 372

β-Characteristic, 249, 260
   (*see also* Characteristic)
β-Discontinuity, 141
   (*see also* Discontinuity)
Barron, R. A., 362
Bearing capacity, 164, 208, 266
   (*see also* Allowable bearing
   capacity, Bearing capacity factor)
Bearing capacity factor
   for drained loading, 219–220,
     223–225, 325–328
   for undrained loading, 175–176,
     320–322
Bearing pressure, 164, 208
Bishop, A. W., 39, 101, 304, 329
Bishop routine method, 304–307, 309
Bjerrum, L., 93, 95, 358, 359
Boulder clay, 84
Bounds, 109–115, 143, 247, 286 (*see
   also* Lower bound Upper
   bound)
   for drained loading, 197–236
   for foundations, 164–176,
     183–184, 208–226
   for infinite slopes, 155–158,
     199–202, 226–232
   for undrained loading, 149–184
   for vertical cuts, 149–155,
     197–198
   for walls, 158–163, 177–180,
     202–207, 232–236
Boussinesq, J. V., 344
Boundary conditions, 102, 341, 359
Bransby, P. L., 2, 4, 8, 15, 16, 23, 24,
   30, 36, 38, 56, 101, 105, 194,
   262, 355, 360, 372
British Standard 1377: 1975, 101,
   355
Bulk modulus, 22–25, 53–59, 71

Calladine, C. R., 373
Cam clay, 24, 36, 56, 71

Case, J., 114
Cementing, 50
Change of stress across a stress fan
  (*see* Stress fan)
Change of stress across a stress discontinuity (*see* Stress disconti-
  nuity)
Characteristics:
  coincidence of, 253
  mesh, 262
  method of, 255
  strain increment, 249–252,
    258–262
  stress, 248–258, 261–262
Chen, W. F., 219
Chilver, A. H., 114
Circular slip plane, 120, 127, 152, 165,
    171, 262–269
  (*see also* Slip circle method, Slip
    plane)
Circular foundation:
  bearing capacity factors for,
    320–322, 327
  stress and settlement below,
    349–353
Civil Engineering code of Practice,
  CP 2: 1951, 324, 330
  CP 2001: 1957, 101
Clay, 31, 84
Classification of soil, 30, 100
Coaxiality, 14, 251
Coefficient of active pressure (*see*
    Active pressure)
Coefficient of consolidation (*see*
    Consolidation)
Coefficient of earth pressure at rest,
    69, 85–89, 207, 364
Coefficient of passive pressure (*see*
    Passive pressure)
Coefficeint of permeability, 31,
    361–362
Coefficient of volume compressibility,
    356–359
Cohesion, 49–50
Collapse, 103, 105, 109
  of a beam, 114–116
  mechanisms, 118–121
  theorems, 111–113
  work during, 122–125
  (*see also* Bounds, Slip line
    method, Limit equilibrium
    method)
Collins, I. F., 233

Compacted soil, 83
Compatibility, 25–27, 101–103, 109,
    148, 195, 258, 262, 286,
    339–340
Compliance matrix, 15, 27–29, 102
Compressibility (*see* Coefficient of
    volume compressibility)
Concentrated load:
  stress and displacement below,
    343–346
  (*see also* Work done by external
    loads)
Conservative materials, 15
Consolidation, 31, 103, 181, 337, 353,
    365
  coefficient of, 360–362
  degree of, 339, 359–363
  settlement, 339, 355–363
Constant volume loading (*see*
    Undrained loading)
Constitutive relationships (*see*
    Stress–strain relationships)
Continuum, 30, 101, 111
Continuous straining, 4, 119, 262
Coulomb, C. A., 289
Critical mechanism, 286, 288–310
Critical state, 35, 67
  line, 32–41, 48–52, 57, 59–65, 70,
    89, 337
  model, 1, 30, 32
  strength, 49, 67, 104, 116, 195,
    286–7
Critical state angle of friction, 38–41,
    48–49, 64, 71, 104–105, 117,
    132, 139–141, 195–236,
    248–252, 256–258, 269–278,
    287, 289–294, 302–310, 320,
    325–330

Davis, E. H., 342, 345, 349, 350–352,
    363–365
Degree of consolidation (*see*
    Consolidation)
Deposited soil, 83
Depth of foundation, 320–322
Dilation (*see* Angle of dilation)
Discontinuity (*see* Slip plane, Stress
    discontinuity)
Discontinuous slipping, 4–11, 40,
    63–67, 118–129, 262
Discontinuous stress state, 130–143
Displacement 5, 258–261

diagram, 125–129
field calculations, 258–261
Displacements in elastic soil for
pant load, 343–346
strip load, 346–349
Dissipation:
of excess pore pressure (*see*
Consolidation)
Dissipative materials, 15
Disturbance (*see* Sample disturbance)
Drainage (*see* Consolidation, Drained
loading, Undrained loading)
Drainage path, 361–363
Drained loading, 31–32, 95–99,
102–105, 287, 319, 335–337
bearing capacity factor for, 325–328
bound calculations for, 118–143,
194–236
earth pressure coefficients for,
329–330
failure criteria for, 117
flow rule for, 62
of a foundation, 208–226
limit equilibrium calculations for,
289–297, 301–309
settlement of elastic soil for,
353–355
slip line sketching for, 269–278
of a slope, 197–202, 226–232
stability numbers for, 328–329
stress field calculations for, 256–258
of a wall, 202–207, 232–236
Drammen clay, 93, 95
Dry side of critical, 41–42, 87

Earth pressure (*see* Active pressure,
Coefficeint of earth pressure
at rest, Passive pressure)
Effective stress (See also Stress)
in the ground, 86
Mohr's circle of, 13–14
principle of, 3
Elastic;
material, 15
modulus (*see* Bulk modulus, Shear
modulus, Young's modulus)
settlements, 343–355
stresses in foundations 339–352
stresses in the ground, 88
stress–strain behaviour, 22–23,
53–56
theory, 16–17, 335
wall, 19, 33, 42, 57, 68, 86

Elasto-plastic behaviour, 23–25, 56–59
Equilibrium, 25–26, 101–103, 109,
261–262, 339–340 (*see also*
Limit equilibrium method)
Equilibrium stress state, 112, 130, 149,
196, 247
drained loading, 200, 204, 207, 211,
214, 218, 221, 227, 231, 235,
256–258
undrained loading, 151, 154, 157,
160, 163, 166, 170, 173, 176,
179, 183, 253–256
Equipotential, 228–229, 296
Erosion, 90, 93
Excess pore pressure, 31, 98, 103, 337,
353, 357, 365
calculation of, 358
External water pressures, 180–184,
225, 294, 300

Factor of safety, 105–106, 309–310,
322, 324, 327, 328–329, 335
Failure, 17, 32, 48–53, 59–67, 97,
104 (*see also* Critical state
strength Mohr–Coulomb
criterion of failure, Peak
strength, Residual strength,
Undrained shear strength)
criterion, 49, 62, 65, 116–117, 130,
147, 195, 319
envelope, 17, 49, 62, 65, 112, 117,
132–133, 147, 195, 248–250
plane, 49
Fan (See Slip fan, Stress fan)
Fan angle, 127, 136
Field tests, 343
Final settlement, 337
Finite element method, 29, 335
Flownet, 31, 194, 228, 294–296, 301,
328
Flow parameter, 24, 42
Flow rule, 21, 42,
(*see also* Associated flow rule)
Force polygon, 291–296, 304
Foundation, 95–99, 146, 319, 335
(*see also* Bearing capacity, Bounds,
Limit equilibrium method,
Settlement, Slip line method)
consolidation of, 355–363
drained loading of, 208–226, 274,
325–328, 353–355
undrained loading of, 164–176,
183–184, 264–266, 297–300,

324, 353–355
Friction (see Angle of friction)
Friction angle (see Angle of friction)
Funicular polygon, 291

Garabedian, P. R., 254
General limit equilibrium method,
    307–309
Gibson, R. E., 322
Glaciers, 84, 90
Graphical methods:
    for limit equilibrium calculations,
        291–297
Gravels, 84

Hardening, 17–19, 23, 42–48
    law, 17, 24, 42
    parameter, 24, 46
Heavily overconsolidated soil (see
    Overconsolidated soil)
Hencky's theorem, 264, 271
Henkel, D. J., 93, 95, 101
Heyman, J., 115, 233, 289
Holmes, A., 84
Hooke's law, 1, 22, 340
Horizontal stress in the ground,
    86–89
Hvorslev:
    angle of friction (see Peak angle of
        friction)
    strength (see Peak strength)
    surface, 32–42, 58, 71, 87–88
        (see also State boundary surface)
Hydraulic gradient, 195, 229
Hyperbolic equations, 254–260

Incremental model, 16, 59–62
Infinite half-space, 344
Infinite slope, 146
    drained loading of, 198–202,
        226–232, 329
    with steady state seepage, 231–232
    undrained loading of, 155–158
Influence factor:
    for stress and displacement,
        349–352
Initial:
    excess pore pressure (see Excess
        pore pressure)
    settlement, 337–339, 359
Interslice force, 297, 302, 303–309
    assumptions for, 309
Isotropic compression, 32–34

Keuper Marl, 90
Jaky, J., 89
Janbu, N., 309

Laboratory testing, 89, 101, 147, 195,
    343, 363
Lambe, T. W., 363–365
Layered soil, 362
Lias Clay, 90
Lightly overconsolidated soil (see
    Overconsolidated soil)
Limit equilibrium method, 286–310
    for foundations, 297–301, 320,
        327
    general, 307–309
    of slices, 301–309
    for slopes, 301–309, 323, 328
    for walls, 287–297
Linear elastic, 22, 342
    (see also Elastic)
Loaded area:
    stress and displacement below,
        346–349
    (see also Work done by external
        loads and stresses)
Loading (see Drained loading,
    Undrained loading)
Logarithmic spiral, 120, 127, 195, 212,
    217, 222, 262, 269, 274, (see
    also Slip plane)
London clay, 90, 93, 95
Lower bound (see also Bounds)
    for a foundation, 165–167,
        169–175, 183–184, 210–211,
        213–215, 217–222, 225–226
    for an infinite slope, 156–158,
        200–201, 227–228, 231–232
    for a river bank, 182–183
    for a rough wall, 178–180, 234–236
    for a smooth wall, 159–161,
        162–163, 204–205, 206–207
    theorem, 112, 117
    for a vertical cut, 151–152,
        154–155, 197–198

Material properties, 109, 262
Measurement of parameters, 99–101,
    147, 195, 343, 363
Mechanism, 112, 115, 118–129, 247,
    286
    for drained loading, 198, 199, 203,
        206, 209, 212, 217, 222, 230,
        234

for undrained loading, 150, 153, 156, 160, 161, 165, 168, 171, 175, 178, 182

Method (*see* Bounds, Characteristics, Limit equilibrium method, Slip circle method, Slip line method)

Method of slices, 301–309, 328

Meyerhof, G. G., 322, 327

Model, 1, 16, 62

Modulus (*see* Bulk modulus, Shear modulus, Young's modulus)

Mohr–Coulomb criterion of failure, 49–51, 65–67, 319

Mohr's circle:
    of strain, 6–10, 249–252
    of stress, 11–14, 38, 49–52, 130–143, 248–257, 344 (*see also* Lower bound, Slip line method)

Morgenstern, N. R., 307, 309, 329

Natural soils, 50, 83–106, 335

Naylor, D. J., 27, 56

Non-homogeneous soil, 342

Normal consolidation line, 32–34, 70, 91

Normal strain (*see* Strain)

Normal stress (*see* Stress)

Normality condition (*see* Associated flow rule)

Normally consolidated soil, 32, 84–89, 91–95, 357

No-tension surface, 32, 49

Oedometer settlement, 358

Oedometer test, 355–358

One dimensional compression, 69–70
    of elastic soil, 354–355
    in the ground, 85–89, 91

One dimensional consolidation, 355–361

Overconsolidated soil, 33, 66, 84, 86–93, 104, 335, 364–365

Overconsolidation ratio, 70, 87, 90

Oxford clay, 90

Palmer, A. C., 109, 117

Parameters for strain, 8

Parameters for stress, 12

Partial differential equations, 254

Particle size, 30, 84

Passive pressure, 159, 202

coefficient of, 207, 324, 330
    for drained loading, 205–207, 272–274, 276–278
    for undrained loading, 159–161, 177–180, 266–269, 287–289, 292

Path independent, 339

Peak (*see also* Hvorslev surface)
    angle of function, 49 104
    strength, 48, 66–67, 104–105, 116, 319

Permeability (*see* Coefficient of permeability, Seepage)

Physical geology, 84

Plane strain, 2, 22, 25, 27, 38, 48, 55, 58, 95, 102, 116, 130, 148, 196, 247, 339, 365

Plastic:
    collapse theorems, 111–114
    behaviour, 16–22, 23–25, 42–48, 88
    bending moment, 114
    flow (*see* Flow rule)
    hardening (*see* Hardening)
    material, 15
    mechanism, 118–121
    yield (See Yield)

Plastic flow, 59–65
    (*see also* Associated flow rule)
    Flow parameter, Flow rule)

Plastic potential, 21, 42, 62–65, 112, 116–117, 147, 195
    (*see also* Associated flow rule,

Plastic work dissipated in a slip plane:
    for drained loading, 123–124, 144
    for undrained loading, 123–124, 144

Pant load (*see* Concentrated load)

Passon's ratio, 22–23, 53–56, 340–357

Pole of Mohr's circle (*see* Mohr's circle)

Polygon (*see* Force polygon, Funicular polygon)

Pore pressure, 3, 13–14, 25–26, 30, 48, 51, 96–98, 122–124, 130, 181, 194, 226–232, 290, 294–296, 301–309, 337–339, 357–362
    coefficient r_u, 328–329
    excess, 31, 181, 194, 337–339, 357–365
    in the ground, 85

parameters A and B, 54, 358
parameters α and β, 54
steady state, 31, 337
Potential, 194, 226–229, 296, 307
    (see also Equipotential)
    Plastic potential)
Potts, D. M., 262
Paulos, H. G., 342, 345, 349, 350–352,
    363–365
Price, V. E., 307, 309
Principal:
    plane, 7–8, 11–14, 119, 131–141,
        249–260
    strain, 7–8, 119, 249–252, 258–260
    stress, 11–14, 68, 95, 131–141,
        249–258
Principle of effective stress, 3
Principle of virtual work, 109–111

Quaternary soils, 90
Quick loading (see Undrained loading)

Radial consolidation, 361–363
Rankine, W. J. M., 205, 289
Rate of consolidation, 359–363
    (see also Consolidation)
Rectangular foundation:
    bearing capacity factor for, 320,
        327
    elastic stress and settlement,
        349–353
Remoulded soils, 50
Residual:
    angle of friction, 67, 104
    slip plane, 63, 104–105
    strength, 66–67, 72, 104
    undrained shear strength, 104
Residual soil, 83
Retaining wall (see Active pressure,
    Passive pressure, Wall)
Ring shear test, 66–67
River bank
    undrained stability, 181–183
Rock, 83
Roscoe surface, 32–42, 56–59, 70–71,
    86
    (see also State boundary surface)
Rotation of the major principal stress:
    across a discontinuity (see Stress
        discontinuity)
    across a stress fan (see Stress fan)
Rough wall (see Wall)
St. Venant's principle, 345

Safety factor (see Factor of safety)
Sample, 99
    disturbance, 101, 343, 363
Sand:
    drain, 363
    soil, 31
Schofield, A. N., 2, 24, 35, 42, 372
Sea level rise, 91
Seepage, 31, 101, 356
    transient, 31
    (see also Consolidation)
    Steady state, 31, 194, 228–229,
        262, 294–296, 301, 328
    (see also Flownet)
    stress, 194, 228–229
Settlement, 164, 208, 335–365
Shear box test, 177, 232
Shear modulus, 22–25, 53–59, 71
Shear strength (see Failure, Strength,
    Undrained shear strength)
Shear stress (see Stress)
Shield, R. T., 261
Silt, 84
Simpson's rule, 296
Site investigation, 99–101, 104, 147,
    195
Skempton, A. W., 54, 67, 93, 95, 322,
    358, 359
Slices (see Method of slices)
Slip circle method (see also Method of
    slices)
    for drained loading, 301–307, 328
    for undrained loading, 297–301
Slip fan, 126–129
Slip line method, 158, 320
    for drained loading, 269–278
    for a foundation, 264–266,
        274–275
    for undrained loading, 262–269
    for a wall, 266–269, 272–274,
        276–278
Slip plane, 5, 9–11, 33, 63–64, 66,
    125–126, 286, (see also
    Limit equilibrium method,
    Upper band)
    residual, 63
    shape of, 118–120
    work done on, 123–125
Slope stability, 95–99, 146, 319 (see
    also Stability numbers)
    bounds for drained loading,
        197–202, 226–232
    by the limit equilibrium method,
        299–310

bounds for undrained loading, 149–158
Slow loading (*see* Drained loading)
Smooth wall (*see* Wall)
Soil profile, 83
Softening, 18–20, 46
Sokolovskii, V. V., 258
Sorting of soils, 83
Specific gravity, 93
Specific volume, 4, 30, 41, 91–92, 117, 356 (*see also* State boundary surface)
Square foundation:
  bearing capacity factor for, 320, 327
Stability:
  calculations (*see* Bounds, Limit equilibrium method, Slip line method)
  numbers, 322–324, 328–329
Standpipe, 85, 225–227, 296, 307
State boundary surface, 30, 32–48, 56–58, 68–70, 86–88, 90, 335
  for plane strain, 38–41
  for triaxial compression, 32–36
  for triaxial extension, 36–38
Steady state pore pressure (*see* Pore pressure)
Straight slip plane (*see* Slip plane)
Strain, 4–5
  in the ground, 88
  hardening (*see* Hardening)
  increment characteristic (*see* Characteristics)
  Mohr's circle of (*see* Mohr's circle)
  plane (*see* Plane strain)
  softening (*see* Softening)
Strength (*see* Failure)
  of natural soils, 91–95
  selection of parameters, 104–105
Stress, 2–3 (*see also* Effective stress, Stress discontinuity, Stress fan, Stress–strain relationships, Total stress)
  characteristic, 248–258
  equilibrium (*see* Equilibrium stress state)
  fields, 253–258
  in elastic soil, 339–355
  in the ground, 85–89
  Mohr's circle of (*see* Mohr's circle of stress)

path method, 363–365
principle of effective (*see* Principle of effective stress)
shear on a wall, 177–180, 232–236, 267–269, 276–278, 294–296
work done by (*see* Work done by stresses)
Stress discontinuity, 130
  for drained loading, 133–135, 144, 197
  for undrained loading, 130–133, 144, 149
Stress fan, 135–136
  for drained loading, 138–141, 145, 197
  for undrained loading, 136–138, 144, 149
Stress–strain relationships, 15–16, 102–103
  for elastic soil, 22–23, 53–56, 340–341
  for elasto-plastic soil, 23–25, 56–59, 60
  for plane strain, 27–29
Strip load:
  stress and settlement below, 346–349
Superposition:
  principle of 342, 346, 353
Swedish method of slices, 303–304, 309
Swelling line, 33–34, 91

Taylor, D. W., 323, 361
Tension crack, 161–163, 180
Tertiary soils, 90
Terzaghi, K., 3, 224, 327
Testing (*see* Field tests, Laboratory testing)
Theorems:
  of plastic collapse, 111–113
Topsoil, 85
Total differentials along characteristics, 255–261
Total stress, 3 (*see also* Stress, Undrained loading)
  in the ground, 86
  Mohr's circle of, 11–14
Transformation matrix, 28
Transported soils, 84
Triaxial:
  compression 36, 55

extension, 37
tests, 55, 343, 364
(*see also* Laboratory testing)

Ultimate:
   failure (*see* Critical state)
   strength (*see* Critical state strength)
Undisturbed sample, 101
Undrained loading, 31–32, 35, 46, 51,
      54, 95–99, 102–105, 287,
      319, 335–337, 365
   bearing capacity factors for,
      320–322
   bound calculations for, 118–143,
      146–184
   earth pressure coefficients for,
      324–325
   failure criteria for, 117
   flow rule for, 62–63
   of a foundation, 164–176,
      183–184
   limit equilibrium calculations for,
      287–301
   settlement of elastic soil for,
      353–355
   slip line sketching for, 262–269
   of a slope, 149–158,
   stability number for, 322–324
   stress field calculations for,
      253–25(
   of a wall, 158–163, 177–180
Undrained settlement, 353
Undrained shear strength, 51–53,
      62–65, 93–95, 104–105, 117,
      124, 147, 253–256, 287, 320,
   residual, 104
Undrained slip line solutions (*see* Slip
      line method for undrained
      loading)
Unit weight, 4, 25, 85, 102, 122, 130,
      148–149, 196, 253, 256–257,
      307, 340
Unsaturated soil, 85
Upper bound (*see also* Bounds)
   for a foundation, 164–165,
      167–175, 183–184, 209–210,
      211–213, 215–217, 222–223,
      225–226
   for an infinite slope, 155–156,
      199–200, 227–228, 229–231
   for a river bank, 181–182
   for a rough wall, 177–178, 233–234
   for a smooth wall, 159, 162,
      203–204, 205

theorem, 112, 117
   for a vertical cut, 149–150,
      152–154, 197

Velocity characteristic, 249
   (*see also* Characteristics)
Vertical cut slope, 146
   (*see also* Bounds, Stability numbers)
   drained loading of, 197–198
   undrained loading of, 149–155
Vertical stress in the ground, 85–89,
      342
Virtual work (Principle of virtual work)
Volumetric strain, 8–10, 22–25,
      44–48, 53–65, 356–357

Wall, 146, 319
   (*see also* Active pressure, Bounds,
      Limit equilibrium method,
      Passive pressure, Slip line
      method)
   drained loading of, 202–207,
      232–236, 272–274, 287–297,
      329–330
   undrained loading of, 158–163,
      177–180, 266–269, 287–297,
      324–325
Water content, 4
   of natural soils, 91–93
Weald clay, 90
Weathering, 83
Wet side of critical, 41, 86–87
Work done:
   by forces on an element, 14–15
   by external loads and stresses,
      122–123
   in a slip fan,
   by internal stresses on a slip plane,
      123–124
Wroth, C. P., 2, 24, 35, 42, 372

Yield, 17–22, 23–25, 42–48, 56–59
   curve, 17, 24, 42, 57
   point, 16
   surface, 17, 42, 56
Young's modulus, 22–23, 53–55,
      340–357, 365

Zero extension line, 249
   (*see also* Strain increment characteristic)
Zero strain:
   direction of, 9, 63
   plane of, 9, 40
Zienkiewicz, O. C., 23, 27, 56